W9-CBA-424

# STUDIES IN
# LOGIC AND PROBABILITY

GEORGE BOOLE

# Studies in
# Logic and Probability

BY

GEORGE BOOLE

THE OPEN COURT PUBLISHING COMPANY

LA SALLE, ILLINOIS

PUBLISHED 1952 BY THE OPEN COURT PUBLISHING COMPANY,
LA SALLE, ILLINOIS

*Printed in Great Britain by Richard Clay and Company, Ltd., Bungay, Suffolk.*

# CONTENTS

5

# PREFACE

GEORGE BOOLE's principal work was *The Laws of Thought*, published in 1854. In 1916 this was reprinted by The Open Court Publishing Company as Volume II of his Logical Works. Volume I was promised, and was to include Boole's miscellaneous writings on logical subjects, together with his papers on related questions of probability. The book which now appears, under the editorship, at my suggestion, of Mr. R. Rhees, is a delayed fulfilment of that promise. It may well be that the postponement has not been a bad thing because Boole's increasing influence can be seen in better perspective.

Among the notes passed on to me by the late P. E. B. Jourdain there were references to important Boole manuscripts in the Library of the Royal Society. Mr. Rhees has been given access to these. They include material, later than *The Laws of Thought* and contemporary with his last articles on probability, which shows interesting developments in Boole's views on the nature of logic. There are also earlier writings on the application of his logical calculus to the theory of probabilities. By permission of the Royal Society some of these papers, either in full or in abstract, are included.

The Royal Society manuscripts also contained Boole's own interleaved copy of his earlier book *The Mathematical Analysis of Logic*, with a number of hitherto unpublished notes and revisions. This work, with Boole's more significant emendations, is reproduced here.

The Open Court Publishing Company wish to thank Mrs. Ethel S. Dummer of Chicago for her help and interest in this publication. Mrs. Dummer was a great friend and admirer of George Boole's wife. She arranged for an edition of the *Collected Works* of Mary Everest Boole which was published in London by the C. W. Daniel Company in 1931, The Open Court Publishing Company now being distributors in the United States. Mrs. Boole had a very remarkable mind, her work covering a wide range. She believed that her husband's logical writings had a psychological bearing which was complementary to its strictly logical one, and that both should be studied if his work was to be fully appreciated. Those who are interested in this aspect of Boole's writings may be referred to the volumes mentioned above, together with a *Memoir with Some Letters* by E. M. Cobham (C. W. Daniel, 1951). There are also pertinent comments in the Rev. Robert Harley's Biography of Boole printed in Appendix A. Boole himself, in his later thought, seems to have been trying to show how the laws of symbolical reasoning were based on, or issue from, the laws of intellectual processes which were prior to any expression of them; and especially on the laws of the intellectual processes of conception.

In general this volume is designed to be an authoritative account of the development of Boole's ideas, both in logic and in the theory of probability, from the time of *The Mathematical Analysis of Logic* to shortly before his death in 1864.

A. E. HEATH.

# NOTE IN EDITING

THESE papers often refer to *The Laws of Thought*, and they would be best understood as a companion volume to it. *The Laws of Thought* appeared in 1854, and the dates of these papers may give a first indication of their bearing on it. They show at least that although *The Laws of Thought* was the most systematic statement of Boole's ideas on logic and probability, it was also one of a long series of inquiries which did not stop there; and the book can be better understood when that is recognized. Boole died ten years after *The Laws of Thought* was published. The manuscripts which he left * show that he had planned a sequel to it. And although it is impossible to tell just what the form and the scope of the sequel would have been, there is material enough to show that he had made important changes in his views, and to suggest something of the lines his interests were following.

What Boole actually published on these matters,† after the appearance of *The Laws of Thought*, was all of it on the theory of probabilities. In those papers he often raised fundamental logical difficulties,—especially in the Keith Prize essay "On the Application of the Theory of Probabilities to the Question of the Combination of Testimonies or Judgments." But he did not publish any further papers directly on logic,—on the questions of the nature of conception and symbolic expression and reasoning, which make up the first half of *The Laws of Thought*. This was presumably because he had not reached a satisfactory statement of the ideas which he was working out. For the manuscripts show that he was working over, and in some respects changing his views of logic, apparently at the

---

* Now in the library of the Royal Society, London.

† Leaving aside his publications in mathematics, especially the *Treatise on Differential Equations*, 1859, and the *Treatise on the Calculus of Finite Differences*, 1860. These should not be forgotten. Boole's work in mathematics always influenced the way in which he thought about logic, even when he came to look on logic as independent of mathematics and fundamental to it.

9

same time as he was making his most important revisions
and additions in his theory of probabilities.  The theory
of probabilities was the part of *The Laws of Thought* which
attracted the most attention at first, and the criticisms
often led Boole to new ideas—in logic, we may guess, as
well as in its application.  But it is likely that he would
have gone on with his logical investigations anyway.  These
had been the source of his theory of probabilities.  And if
in later years it was from there that he found a stimulus to
new developments in his logic, the principal developments
were still along the lines that had been his chief preoccupation
from the time of his earliest logical writing.  He was still
working on a general method in logic and on a theory of
the general nature of reasoning.  The theory of probabilities
was always subordinate to this.  (It is to mistake the whole
character of Boole's thinking to say, as Venn for instance
said, that " it was in fact largely for the purpose of improving
the calculus of probabilities that Boole devised his system."
See Harley's biographical sketch at the end of this volume.
Also Boole's own words in his first published essay of probabilities, below, pp. 250–255.  Compare also the " Sketch of a
Theory and Method of Probabilities founded upon the Calculus of Logic," included here.  Also Boole's manuscript
revisions of the *Mathematical Analysis of Logic*.)

He was trying in his later papers * to find a more general
and a simpler statement of the problem of formal logic and of
logical principles.  And since he wanted to give a " philosophical interpretation " of the methods and principles of
mathematical logic, he tried to state the matter for the most
part without using mathematical symbols.  This raised
problems and difficulties on its own account.  Boole was
convinced that the logical principles he was stating were
independent of mathematics; he may even have thought
that they could not be reached just by a generalization of
mathematical methods, but stood in some other relation to

* One of these, " Logic and Reasoning," is included here entire, and
another, " On the Mathematical Theory of Logic and on the Philosophical
Interpretation of its Methods and Processes," with considerable omissions.
Many of the later manuscripts are obviously different drafts to which he
never gave the final form.

it. At any rate, he thought that they could be presented without using mathematical conventions. But when he tried to do this, and especially when he tried to give examples of the application of those principles, his statement often became tiresomely elaborate and artificial. Boole had met this trouble before. In *The Laws of Thought*, for instance, at the end of a discussion of the probability of an hypothetical syllogism, he says, " The result is one which ordinary reasoning verifies, and which it does not indeed require a calculus to obtain. General methods are apt to appear most cumbrous when applied to cases in which their aid is least required." * That was a rather more special case,—the application of the methods of the probability calculus to ordinary reasonings. But in the later papers especially, he often finds the same trouble in showing how the formal laws of logic are illustrated in " ordinary reasoning." This may raise real difficulties about the nature of logic, and Boole seems to have thought it did. That is presumably why he went back again and again to an examination and re-statement of what he called the laws of the fundamental intellectual processes, and especially the " laws of Conception," and of their relation to symbolic or formal expression; or to the allied question of the interpretation, or conditions of interpretability, of formal principles. The main point is that the difficulty belonged to a matter which Boole thought was fundamental. The question of the extent to which the actual procedure of thought is governed by formal laws, and the extent to which it is governed by other relations of dependence,† the question of the nature of the " formal identity " which holds between different departments of reasoning, are all connected with it. And it would be wrong to think of it only as a difficulty in putting technical matters in popular language.

The difficulty of statement may have been one reason why Boole did not publish any of these later papers on logic. Perhaps he would have preferred that they should never be published in their present form. This is what De Morgan

---

\* *Laws of Thought*, p. (285) 301.
† See the paper on " Logic and Reasoning."

felt. He was asked to examine Boole's papers, and it was he, apparently, who deposited them with the Royal Society. In a note dated November 30th, 1867 (roughly three years after Boole's death), De Morgan said that most of the papers were " clearly incapable of use except for a supply of notes and comments for a second edition of *The Laws of Thought*," but that there was one group of " letters on logic intended for publication, and other matters which might go with them if they were published." He added, " But I cannot recommend the publication. After much consideration, I am satisfied with two things. First, the author himself would have objected to their publication as they stand. He would have introduced much change of expression, and allusion to his higher views; or rather, preparations without allusion. Secondly, a false impression would be produced. A posthumous work by George Boole on logic would be taken for his latest and highest view. Those who would know better, when they came to open the book, would have all the bias of disappointment; but those who did not find out how the matter stood, would really believe they were in possession of all Boole's intentions. And as a hundred copies would sell for one of the *Laws of Thought*, a very wide misapprehension of the contents of *The Laws of Thought* would get about."

The latter part of this objection will hardly apply today. And it is doubtful how far De Morgan really got a clear impression of what was in the papers which he had. The manuscripts seem to have been in a very disordered state. And it was only later, especially, it seems, through the work of someone signing " H. J. F.," that many of the different portions were fitted together into the coherent studies which they formed. De Morgan does not seem to have given much attention even to the different dates and periods to which the various manuscripts belonged. There is still much work that might be done on them, but as they stand now they present a different picture from any that could have been found when De Morgan looked them over. Some of the logical papers apparently were written before *The Mathematical Analysis of Logic*, others just afterwards, or later but before *The Laws of Thought*, and others still after that. And it is doubtful if De Morgan could see fully even what there was in these later papers. (The only paper which he himself sent for publication was the one " On Propositions Numerically Definite," which belongs, as he remarked, to the period between *The Mathematical Analysis of Logic* and *The Laws of Thought*.)

Boole would not have published the papers as they stand. But he evidently intended to publish something on the lines of these later papers, and there is nothing to show that he had changed his mind about that. And if they are taken for what they are, and not for his final statement, it is hard to see any disservice to him in making some of them known. It would be wrong to think that they supersede or replace *The Laws of Thought*. But they do give views which are important revisions of what he said there,—just as important as those changes in the theory of probabilities which Boole did publish. And it cannot really be said that the different form of statement here—the freedom from mathematical symbolism—gives only a misapprehenison of his " highest view." The symbolical calculus was always of first importance for what he had to say. He did not ever think, apparently, that logic could be properly understood without it, and he constantly refers to it here. But his attempt to discuss the principles in non-mathematical language, or to lay more emphasis on the " philosophical interpretation " of them, belonged to a change in his view of logic,—in certain respects, at least. It is hard to say how far he had gone with this, or how far he would have gone. He seems to have been coming on problems to which he did not find an answer. He would hardly have abandoned what he took to be fundamental in *The Laws of Thought*. And these papers help incidentally to show what that was. To that extent they help in understanding his highest intentions there.*

It should be remembered, too, that Boole was revising his views on probability at the time when these papers were

* Perhaps De Morgan's own views made him less apt to recognize some of the questions Boole was raising at the end. Cf. the quotation from De Morgan in Harley's article, p. 469.

written. We cannot say just how far it was the one or the other inquiry which led to the changes that he made in either. But the emphasis on certain matters in logic,—on the importance of the ideas of "existence" and "non-existence," in connexion both with concepts and with reasoning, for instance,—may have had a view to the theory of its application. At any rate, we may say that Boole's later publications on probability would also give a false impression of his higher intentions if they were left by themselves.

Boole made changes in his theory of probabilities, partly in his treatment of particular problems, but more especially in his account of the relation of the theory of probabilities to logic. In many ways he was changing his view of logic, and of the relation of logic to other formal sciences altogether. He now distinguished between a higher or more general meaning of "Logic," and the narrower or secondary sense in which it is commonly taken to mean the Logic of Class. The logical calculus is a part of the development of the Logic of Class. But there can be no special calculus of Logic in the higher sense. "In its highest conception . . . Logic might be said to be the Philosophy of *all* thought which is expressible by signs, whatever the object of that thought, whatever the nature of those signs may be. Nor is this conception either vague or unreal. There is a philosophy of signs which governs and explains all their particular uses and applications,—which is equally manifested in the forms of ordinary speech and in the symbolical language of mathematics. The perfect idea of Logic is not that of a mere system of rules, but of a philosophy from which, as from a common stem, all sciences whose method is deductive are developed, and with which they all stand in vital connexion." * The Logic of Class is the science of the Laws of Thought as expressed in ordinary language; it is not concerned with the thought which is expressed in mathematics. In mathematics "there are other conceptions and other

* This quotation, and those immediately following, are taken from a manuscript numbered "C.57" in the Royal Society collection. A large part of this manuscript is an earlier draft of the essay on "Logic and Reasoning."

lines of mental suggestion than those which are taken account of in the Logic of Class." (The " lines of mental suggestion " govern inferences that are made, and they may differ even in different branches of mathematics.) But the Logic of Class and the science of Algebra, for instance, both stand in vital connexion with, and depend on, Logic in the higher sense. The Logic of Class has a certain priority here, perhaps; because there is a sense in which all deductive sciences may be said to employ the notion of class. This may be a reason for saying that the Logic of Class stands " closer " to the more fundamental Logic than the other deductive sciences do. But it is not more general than they are, and the mathematical sciences cannot be reduced to it; nor vice versa.

Mathematics cannot be reduced to the higher Logic either; nor can the Logic of Class. It does not supply " the forms and laws of the intellectual procedure " in mathematical reasoning. But it is the condition under which they can be the forms and laws of a deductive system at all. And this is connected with the fact that the higher Logic cannot be developed independently, and we cannot begin with the study of it. " If it should seem to anyone that the preferable course would have been to investigate first and independently the principles of that higher Logic, it may be observed that it is from its very nature incapable of being developed *a priori.*" We can study it only by studying the special deductive sciences,—though by studying them " analytically " rather than directly. (The distinction between the analytic and the direct procedures is essential in Boole's later theory, and we shall return to it.) " For the most part we are only able to arrive at a knowledge of the universal by means of that of the individual and the particular. By studying particular manifestations of thought we ascend to its general laws; and this we do not so much by comparing particular forms and instances and selecting the truth which is common to them all, as by some deeper faculty of insight enabling us, when contemplating some general truth manifested under particular forms or conditions, to perceive how far such conditions are necessary and how far they are accidental. Thus the study of the intellectual procedure in a particular province of thought *may* lead us to some degree of acquaintance with its *general* philosophy. And it is only by the study of these special and external manifestations that it is possible for us to arrive at any adequate knowledge of that philosophy in itself."

For instance, " The method of Algebra involves the following elements :

A. A recognition of the fundamental operations to which the conception of Number is subject. . . .

B. A recognition of the *relations* to which the conception of Number is subject, and more particularly the relation of *equality*.

C. A recognition of the laws which determine the equivalent forms of expression arising from the performance of the operations referred to in A,—equivalent in the sense that the results which they express fall necessarily under the relation of equality B.

" And here we must distinguish between those elements of form which are arbitrary and those which are not arbitrary.

" The arbitrary elements are the signs by which we express the operations themselves. . . . The elements which are not arbitrary are those which do not depend upon the individual form or structure of the signs employed, but upon the laws of their combination. . . .

" Upon this basis of the expression of numbers, of the operations to which the numbers are subject and of the relations in which they stand, by signs, and upon the determination of the laws of these signs, the method of Algebra is founded. Now there is nothing in the *general* character of that method which in a peculiar sense restricts its application to the Science of Number. Wherever we have to do with the analysis of expressed thought, our object should be, first to determine the primary intellectual operations of which it consists, secondly to investigate the fundamental laws of these operations, thirdly to give formal expression to both in the signs by which the thought is expressed, and the laws by which the signs are governed.

" The procedure of the particular Science of Algebra serves to illustrate these principles which in reality belong to Logic itself in the higher sense of that term."

And the methods of Algebra illustrate another, and in some ways more important principle of the higher Logic. " Once the data of the process of reasoning within the province of Algebra are expressed by its symbols, the formal laws become everything. The result is always found to be the same as if the conditions of *material* realization had been attended to throughout. Now it is a very important question of general Logic, perhaps the deepest question of all Logic, whether this procedure is founded in the very constitution of the intellect, or to speak more precisely, in that part of the intellectual constitution in virtue of which we reason by the use of signs.

" I will say at once that I think it is thus founded, and I do this rather upon the ground of a large induction from the actual processes of mathematics than upon a perception of the truth as axiomatic. But quitting this somewhat conjectural reason . . . it is evidently possible that in the world of experience there may exist different systems of things, corresponding to which there may exist in the world of thought different systems of conceptions and ideas. And considering two such systems, it is possible that the formal laws may be the same, while the conditions of their realization in the world of experience may be different."

For instance, " the operation of subtracting one number from another is possible only on the supposition that the number to be subtracted is the smaller. But when we think of number not *simply*, but associated with the idea of linear extension in space, the condition above referred to ceases to be necessary. If we represent by $+x$, $+y$, etc., distances measured along a line in one direction from a given point, and by $-x$, $-y$, etc., distances measured in the opposite direction from the same point, then $x - y$ becomes interpretable whatever may be the absolute magnitudes of $x$ and $y$.

" At the same time, the formal laws of signs are the same in the one system as in the other,—in the system of simple

B

number as in that of other numbers affected with another attribute derived from our acquaintance with space and direction. There are indeed other affections of Number besides this one which would equally serve the same purpose of illustration, but all suppose equally an *extension of our powers of conception* through the means of larger experience, *without affecting the formal laws of thinking* * which govern thought as exercised in the domain of that lesser experience which presents Number only in its simple and unaffected essence. . . . It follows that in our reasonings about simple number we may proceed with the same freedom as if we were reasoning about number under affections which do not affect its formal laws but enlarge the conditions under which our processes founded upon those laws admit of interpretation.

" And generally, if any system of symbols subject to formal laws express thought under conditions of interpretation which are not *essential to all thought obeying the same formal laws,* * the conditions of interpretation do not impose any necessary restriction upon the processes which the formal laws sanction.

" In all this we have but an exemplification of one great truth, viz.: that the intellectual procedure as governed by formal laws, and the power of conception, whether as limited by its own constitution or by the constitution of the world of experience, are to a certain extent independent of each other."

These passages illustrate how we may pass to an understanding of the higher Logic by attending to the procedure of one of the deductive sciences. They have to do, in different ways, with " the philosophy of signs which governs and explains all their particular uses and applications." And the second of them emphasizes the formal conditions of interpretability of the symbolic expressions in any such science.

This is one of the most important ideas in Boole's conception of the higher Logic.

In one sense, Boole insisted, logic, like algebra, is inde-

* Not Boole's emphasis.

pendent of any interpretation which may be given to its symbols, and may develop its calculations in " freedom " from it. This is the reason for speaking of logic as a " noetic " rather than an " ostensive " science. It does not matter what the subject of its operations might be,—on what the operations of addition, subtraction or composition, for instance, may be performed. All that matters is the form of the operations and the relations we are led to recognize between them,—as we are led chiefly by recognizing that certain operations are equivalent.

On the other hand, there are certain conditions which must be satisfied if those operations are to have any meaning within the formal system. " The application of the formal laws as a completed system does implicitly and in a very remarkable manner supply the place of that direct consideration of the conditions of interpretability which the ostensive view of the subject would render necessary." But it does this partly because " the meaning of words is not always wholly independent of the expression in which they occur," and " the forms of language including symbolical language, which is but the outward expression of thought, impose conditions of *interpretability* upon the symbols which they connect." *

It is not only a question of the interpretability of the operations, then, but also of the expressions which are formed by them. And this is bound up with the formal laws of the symbols—$x$, $y$, etc.,—which appear in those operations. Unless these symbols themselves are understood to have certain formal properties, it may become meaningless to treat them as terms of a particular operation, such as addition, say. For " $x + y$ " is " strictly meaningless,"—i.e. it cannot belong to the system,—unless $x$ and $y$ are taken to be exclusive. This formal condition does not *depend* upon any meaning which may be given to $x$ and $y$; although to a certain extent it determines or restricts the meanings they can take if they are to be mutual subjects of that operation.

It is important to determine what *are* the formal conditions

* See the paper " On the Mathematical Theory of Logic and on the Philosophical Interpretation of its Methods and Processes," below, p. 233.

of interpretability, and not to confuse them with any material conditions under which the formulae may be applied.

If we do this, if from the study of a deductive system as a whole, and independently of any special application, we determine what are the formal laws or requirements to which the concepts employed in that system must always be subject, then we can see which systems are "formally identical" with one another, and which are formally different; and we can see in what the formal difference or the formal identity consists.

"The formal difference between Logic and Algebra consists in this, that the concepts with which the former science has to do are subject to a peculiar law symbolically expressed by the equation

$$xx = x." *$$

But if we consider an algebra which is restricted to the quantities 1 and 0,—an algebra in which, when $x, y$, etc., are general symbols, it shall be understood that $x$ means either 1 or 0 but it is undetermined which,—then we are considering a system whose concepts are subject to that same law, $xx = x$. "The formal laws of such an Algebra will be identical with those of Logic when expressed by symbols.

"And this agreement extends not only to the formal laws of operation in the systems compared, but also to the formal conditions of interpretability of expressions formed by those operations. . . .

"These conditions are capable of formal expression; and . . . they are when thus expressed common to the systems of Logic and Dual Algebra. The ground of this agreement will further be shewn to consist in the community of the formal laws of operation, and more especially of the distinguishing law $xx = x$.

"In fact, representing any combination of symbols by V, whether that combination express a logical concept or a concept in dual Algebra, i.e. one of the numbers 0 and 1, it must . . . equally satisfy the law

$$VV = V. \tag{1}$$

* From the paper "On the Mathematical Theory of Logic, etc." The passage is not included in the text printed below.

" First, then, suppose V to represent the combination $x + y$, wherein $x$ and $y$ obey the same law. . . . Now, writing $x + y$ for V, (1) becomes

$$(x + y)(x + y) = x + y.$$

Performing the operation indicated in the first member, and replacing in the result $xx$ by $x$ and $yy$ by $y$, we have

$$x + xy + yx + y = x + y;$$

whence $$xy + yx = 0,$$

an equation which in either system can only be satisfied by supposing

$$xy = 0, \qquad\qquad (2)$$

since in Logic the only class, and in dual Algebra the only number, which being added to itself produces Nothing, is Nothing. Hence the equation $xy = 0$ is the condition of interpretability of the operation of adding $y$ to $x$ in either system, and it is a condition formally expressed."

Boole then shows that when this formal expression is logically interpreted, it demands that the classes $x$ and $y$ shall be wholly distinct. And when it is interpreted in the system of dual algebra it demands that the values of $x$ and $y$ should be so chosen that their product should vanish; which excludes the combination " $x = 1$, $y = 1$,"—a combination which gives to the expression the value 2, which is not included in the system.

" If we apply the same analysis to the expression $x - y$ . . . we shall arrive at the formal condition of interpretability

$$y(1 - x) = 0,"$$

a formal expression which again may be interpreted either logically or algebraically (i.e. in the dual algebra).

" Applying the same analysis to the expression $xy$, formed by Composition, we find that no condition of interpretability is involved." (This may be important in the theory of probabilities.)

" To apply a similar principle of analysis to the expression $\frac{x}{y}$, formed by Abstraction, we must observe that, as Abstraction is only intelligible by reference to Composition, the expression $\frac{x}{y}$ only signifies a class which by Composition with $y$ gives $x$. Let us represent such a class by $w$. Then

$$x = yw.$$

Now if we compound both members with the class $(1 - y)$, attending to the condition $y(1 - y) = 0$, we have

$$x(1 - y) = 0.\text{''}$$

And again Boole shows how this expression may be interpreted both in logic and in the dual algebra. He adds, " The deduction of all three conditions is, however, more readily, and in the last case more directly performed by the process of Development . . . a process essentially founded on that peculiar law of thought which forms the basis of the previous deductions."

The formal conditions of interpretability, then, depend upon the formal laws.

They may be deduced from those formal laws; and that is why they are conditions essential to all thought which follows the same formal laws.

We may notice here that the emphasis upon the formal conditions of interpretability is something which has grown since the *Laws of Thought* was published. And so has the explanation of the *ground* of the formal identity between the two systems, by reference to it. The chapter on interpretation in the *Laws of Thought* (Chapter VI) is concerned with the possibility of reducing certain expressions " not directly interpretable in logic " to other expressions which are so, —and so with showing that the former may legitimately be used in the calculus. The question of the formal conditions of interpretability is different. He comes nearest to it in paragraph 13 of that chapter, where he says that " the condition $V(1 - V) = 0$ may be termed ' the condition of interpretability of logical functions.' " But he makes this statement in quite a different connexion from those we have been discussing. The interpretability is still the interpretability in *logic* only. And there is no suggestion of a general account of the formal conditions of interpretability, or of their importance.

For there are two different processes here, however closely they may be connected : one of determining the formal conditions of interpretability of the symbolic expressions, and one of showing that the formal expressions of these conditions themselves have one interpretation in logic and another in dual algebra. The latter is nothing so very new. Already in the *Mathematical Analysis of Logic* Boole had begun by saying that " the validity of the processes of analysis does not depend upon the interpretation of the symbols which are employed, but solely upon the laws of their combination. Every system of interpretation which does not affect the truth of the relations supposed, is equally admissible, and it is thus that the same process may, under one scheme of interpretation, represent the solution of a question on the properties of numbers, under another, that of a geometrical problem, under a third, that of a problem in dynamics or optics. . . . We might justly assign it as the definitive character of a true Calculus, that it is a method resting upon the employment of Symbols, whose laws of combination are known and general, and whose results admit of a consistent interpretation. . . . It is upon the foundation of this general principle, that I purpose to establish the Calculus of Logic, and that I claim for it a place among the acknowledged forms of Mathematical Analysis." But here again it is the interpretability of the *results* that is important. And although the calculus is said to depend solely upon the formal laws of combination of the symbols, the question of the formal conditions of interpretability of its expressions does not enter. The " different systems of interpretation " are, for instance, logic and algebra, or geometry and dynamics. But what he later called the formal conditions of interpretability would apply to the purely *formal* system, and they might be the *same* for *different* " systems of interpretation " in the sense in which the *Mathematical Analysis of Logic* is speaking of them.

And they have a special importance which was not considered there at all, or in the *Laws of Thought* either. This lies especially in the way in which they determine or limit the concepts which admit of that sort of formal expression. And further, and closely connected with that, they are important because they show the special rôle of certain formal laws which are fundamental to the system in question. They show that these are the " conditions of the possibility " of the symbolic procedures which are followed in the system. And they show the intimate connexion between the symbolical formulæ and their possible transformations, on the one hand, and the formal properties of the concepts of the system, on the other.

They bring out, in other words, at once the distinction and the relation between the formal processes of deduction in the system, and the fundamental laws which those processes exemplify. This is important, because those laws need not operate as principles of deduction themselves. The relation between them and the principles of deduction that are followed in the system, is one of a special sort of dependence. But it is different from the dependence of conclusion and premiss.

In other words, there is a difference between the formal laws of concepts and the formal laws of inference, although the latter are in a special way dependent upon the formal laws of concepts. And it will appear that the validity of any inference, in any system whatever, depends not simply upon the formal rules of inference in that system, but also on the relation which all its expressions have to the general laws of the concepts of which it can possibly treat.

That is why logic, as the study of these fundamental conditions, cannot be regarded just as a system or calculus which has " a place among the acknowledged forms of Mathematical Analysis." It is a study of the conditions on which any general algebra of symbols depends. And that is why Boole says, in " Logic and Reasoning," that " since the publication of the treatise (on the Laws of Thought), my attention has frequently turned to the question : What is the *logical* import of the processes there employed? Analogies, mathematical and otherwise, being cast aside, what doctrine of the intellectual operations lies concealed beneath the forms themselves ? "

The answer led him, for instance, to a somewhat different theory of the process of development, and of the coefficients that enter into it. His justification for introducing these had been by reference to the dual algebra, in which any symbol may take either the value 1 or 0. He had shown that they could have a logical interpretation also. But he had not tried to give a logical derivation of them, or to show, independently of the dual algebra, how and why they are necessary to logical reasoning. He does this in the later papers; and the description of reasoning which he emphasizes there,—that it "is always in the form of a necessary proposition modified by means of the premises,"—depends on what he says of those coefficients, or, as he there speaks of them, the "four categories of quantity."

Boole denied that the laws of identity, contradiction and excluded middle can be regarded as "the ultimate laws of all thought," because they cannot be regarded as principles of reasoning. They are rather what he calls formal laws of judgment, whose "real office is to determine the forms of necessary propositions." But although they "determine the forms of necessary propositions, it has never yet been shewn how they determine the forms of dependent propositions such as all propositions expressive of logical inference are. The conclusion of a syllogism is true, if true at all, in consequence of the assumed truth of the premises, not in virtue of its mere form. Whether the *dictum de omni et nullo* is the true, the only principle of syllogistic reasoning or not, it at least appears that it is a principle of reasoning, that it contains an element of formal truth different in *kind* from the elements which are contained in the principles of identity, contradiction and excluded middle. The logician who maintains that all *reasoning* is an application of the former, and they who hold that all *thought*, including reasoning, is governed by the latter, differ irreconcilably. And yet there are some who profess to hold both doctrines."

Boole notices a similar distinction in algebra, between the commutative, associative and distributive laws, on the one hand, and the "axioms of equality," on the other. The former "express the forms of what may be termed *necessary* equivalence," whereas the axioms of equality express the forms "of a dependent or inferred equivalence. The equality expressed by

$$x + y = y + x$$

depends not for its truth and validity upon what particular numbers are expressed by $x$ and $y$. But when from the given equations

$$x = y, \ w = z,$$

we infer the equation

$$x + w = y + z,$$

we arrive at a result which is true, not because $x$, $w$, $y$ and $z$ are numbers, but because they are numbers connected by given prior relations."

Perhaps the situation in logic is not in all respects the same. But Boole does formulate the principle of logical inference as a principle of substitution. And it is through substitution that the "modification" of the necessary proposition leads to a conclusion from the premises.

The necessary proposition is one that may be formed of the concepts employed in the reasoning, as it might be formed of any concepts whatever, simply in virtue of the law of excluded middle. Thus if we want a conclusion concerning the relation between sodium and the property "metallic", then we know at once that sodium is either metallic or not metallic. And generally, if $x$ and $y$ stand for any two concepts whatever, we know that $x$ is either $y$ or $1 - y$. Or if we want to know how $x$ should be described in terms of $y$ and $z$, we know that $x$ is either $yz$ or $y(1 - z)$ or $(1 - y)z$ or $(1 - y)(1 - z)$. And so on for any greater number of concepts we like. We do not have to have been given any information about sodium and metals,—we do not have to know even what sodium is or what metals are,—or to have any information about $x$ and $y$ and $z$, in order to make statements of this kind. But neither have we reached any definite conclusion.

Now in the simpler sorts of reasonings such necessary propositions do not enter, and they are not even formed.

In the ordinary examples of syllogisms the conclusion is reached by substitution alone from the premises assumed. But in more complicated forms, or in any reasoning of the form which Boole calls " analytic," we do have to refer to such propositions which are not given or assumed, but necessary. In such cases we cannot reach a conclusion by substitution alone. But neither can we conclude anything from the necessary proposition alone; for the reason just given,—that it is entirely indeterminate. We have, then, " to determine by means of the premises whatever is arbitrary in the general form, so far as such determination is possible. It is in this last step, chiefly, that the principle of substitution is employed." *

This is done by assigning the various constituents of the " general form," or necessary proposition, to coefficients in a development. From this we can see precisely which of them necessarily belong to the subject in question, in view of the premises given, and which are excluded, and which are still left indeterminate.

Boole takes a simple example in which we may want to determine $x$ in terms of $y$ and $z$, and which we are given as a premiss that $z = xy$. The equation might be the symbolic expression for " Men are rational animals "; and then the conclusion sought would be the relation of rational beings to men and animals. We can first solve this equation for $x$, giving $x = \dfrac{z}{y}$. Then, by developing the second member, we get

$$x = 1yz + 0y(1 - z) + \frac{1}{0}(1 - y)z + \frac{0}{0}(1 - y)(1 - z);$$

which shows that $x$ consists of everything that is both $y$ and $z$, and of an indefinite remainder (some, none or all) of things that are neither $y$ nor $z$; but that it does not consist of anything that is $y$ and not $z$, or of anything that is $z$ and not $y$.

Boole adds that although the " constituents " of this development,—the terms $yz$, $y(1 - z)$, etc.,—are quite independent of the manner in which $y$ and $z$ enter into the

* " On The Mathematical Theory of Logic etc.," below, p. 239.

original equation, the *coefficients* are " dependent upon the premiss. They shew under what logical categories the several terms of the necessary proposition must be thought in connexion with the premiss."

The development of the logical function $\frac{z}{y}$ is a necessary proposition. But it is a necessary proposition with regard to the terms of a particular logical *function*, and not just regarding any two terms whatever. Boole often speaks of development or expansion as the " inverse " of composition. And he says that it is " essentially dependent," for this reason; since it always presupposes some composition to start with. Perhaps in the present case one ought to say that the composition is not quite explicitly stated, since $\frac{z}{y}$ would seem itself to be the inverse of composition. But if we ask what such an expression signifies, the answer is that it only signifies a class which by composition with $y$ gives $z$. And the development is a formal analysis or expansion of this.

In the second place, the function $\frac{z}{y}$ was given in the conclusion from the premiss. The development is simply a restatement of that conclusion in a logically equivalent form. We said that we could give an indeterminate or trivial statement of the relation of $x$ to $y$ and $z$ without any given premiss at all. But what we have in the developed conclusion is a statement of the relation which they have to $x$ in consequence of the way in which they enter into a particular logical function; and that itself is a consequence of a given logical equation, stated as premiss.

It is in this way that the introduction of the coefficients is a modification of what could have been known by purely formal laws concerning the relation of $x$ to $y$ and $z$. And so we can see how the conclusion, when it is given the developed form, is a modification of the " general form " or necessary proposition by the premiss; and how the constituents themselves—which effect the modification—depend upon the premiss.

To show the way in which *substitution* enters to make the
general form determinate, we need perhaps a more elaborate
statement. Suppose we are ignorant of the premiss, and
know nothing about $y$ and $z$. Then the logically necessary
proposition could be put like this : $x$ (say rational beings)
$= yz$ in composition with some unknown concept A;
$z(1 - y)$ in composition with some unknown concept B;
$y(1 - z)$ in composition with some unknown concept C;
and $(1 - y)(1 - z)$ in composition with some unknown
concept D.

The premiss $z = xy$ tells us that $x$ is a class which by
composition with $y$ gives $z$; so we may substitute that
expression in the statement just given, writing it $\frac{z}{y}$. And we
have :

$\frac{z}{y} = yz$ in composition with some unknown concept A;
$z(1 - y)$ in composition with some unknown concept B; and
so on as above.

Now the determination of the categories, the assigning of
the various coefficients in place of the " unknown concepts,"
depends here upon this substitution,—on introducing the
idea of " the class which by composition with $y$ gives $z$."
But this can lead to a determination of the categories only
through certain further substitutions of a rather different
kind; the substitutions, namely, of 1 and of 0 in turn for
$x$, and similarly for $y$.

This is a familiar procedure in Boole's logical writings.
He used to justify it by saying that the formal laws which
must hold of any logical symbol, $x$, $y$, $z$ etc., as employed in
the logical calculus, are identical with the laws which will
hold for any symbol $x$ in algebra when $x = 1$ or $x = 0$. In
particular, when $x$ is given either of these values, it will
satisfy the fundamental law $x^2 = x$. And if we take $x = 1$,
then $1 - x = 0$, and vice versa. Since we get equivalent
results from the calculus, whether we are employing purely
logical conceptions, or whether we are operating with symbols
whose values are 1 or 0, we may always substitute the latter
procedure to reach a logical conclusion. If 1 or 0 appear

in the result, they can be given a logical interpretation as
"Universe" and "Nothing." In his earlier writings,
Boole does not go much further than this in justifying the
substitution of 1 or 0 for any elective symbol when it is
methodically convenient to do so. (There are, of course,
certain restrictions, as we have noticed. In an expression
like $x + y$, we cannot substitute 1 both for $x$ and for $y$;
although we may do so in an expression such as $xy$.)

In his later papers Boole does consider more fully the
ground of this substitution. And his account of the nature
of logic and of reasoning depends upon it. At the end he
speaks of 1 and 0 as standing for "existence" and "non-
existence." And the principle is that any symbol, $x$,
representing a general concept can be taken as representing
existence or non-existence. That was a late change, and
there may be important reasons for it. But it is better to
postpone them until we have completed the example to
show how the coefficients or categories are determined in
the general form.

We have given the equation,

$$\frac{z}{y} = Ayz + Bz(1 - y) + Cy(1 - z) + D(1 - y)(1 - z).$$

This expresses the fact that the class which in composition
with $y$ gives $z$ (" the class which in composition with animals
gives men "), in so far as it is determined as A, is $yz$; in
so far as it is determined as B, is $z(1 - y)$, and so on. And
A and B etc. are unknown.

Now throughout this equation we may take, first, $y = 1$,
$z = 1$. (Consider each term as representing existence.)
We then find that $\frac{1}{1} = A1$,—and all the other constituents
become 0 or nothing. For the same reason, however, " A1 "
is simply " A." (The product of any term, $x$, and 1, is
simply $x$. Any concept, as " men," in composition with
" existence," is just that concept " men.") And so we
have $A = 1$. $\frac{z}{y}$, or the class which in composition with $y$
gives $z$, is determined as $yz$ under those circumstances,—i.e.
*universally*.

Next, if we take $y = 0$, $z = 1$, then all the constituents become nothing, except the second one, $z(1 - y)$ (in which $1 - y$ becomes 1, on this substitution, as $z$ also does). $\frac{z}{y} =$ this constituent when it is in composition with B.

And since $B1 = B$, $B = \frac{z}{y}$; or, by the given substitution,

$B = \frac{1}{0}$,—or *impossibility*. In other words, when we make this substitution, we find that " the class which by composition with $y$ gives $z$ " becomes " the class which by composition with 0 gives 1,"—and that is impossible. (Just as there can be no class which, through composition with non-existence, —or through the non-existence of its members,—gives existence.) Yet it is only on this substitution that $\frac{z}{y}$ can be determined as $z(1 - y)$ at all. So B expresses the " condition " of impossibility. Or in other words, it is inconceivable that $\frac{z}{y}$ be so determined.

We said that it is only on this substitution that we can find any determination (even as impossible) of $\frac{z}{y}$ in terms of $z(1 - y)$. This appears in that for each of the two conceivable pairs of substitutions which remain ($y = 1$, $z = 0$, and $y = 0$, $z = 0$), this constituent becomes nothing, as it did for $y = 1$, $z = 1$. In fact, each of the four pairs of substitutions leaves us with one and only one of the constituents named. The substitutions express the conditions under which $\frac{z}{y}$ can be so described. And they show how it must be determined if it is so described.

By similar procedures we can show, by taking $y = 1$, $z = 0$, that the unknown concept $C = 0$, or that there are no circumstances under which the class can be described as $y(1 - z)$; and, by taking $y = 0$, $z = 0$, that the unknown concept $D = \frac{0}{0}$, or that the conditions under which the class might be described as $(1 - y)(1 - z)$ are entirely indeterminate. And the final statement of the development reads as given on page 27 above, viz.,

$$\frac{z}{y} = 1yz + \frac{1}{0}z(1 - y) + 0y(1 - z) + \frac{0}{0}(1 - y)(1 - z).$$

This is therefore also the expression for $x$, and that is how it was given in the earlier passage. What is important here is that in each case the coefficient is determined by reference to $\frac{z}{y}$, which we have from the *premiss*.

We know without the premiss, and simply from the law of excluded middle, that

$$x = yz + z(1 - y) + y(1 - z) + (1 - y)(1 - z);$$

and we make more precise what sort of statement this is, by placing the symbol, A, B etc., for an " unknown concept " before each of the constituents.

But if we had had a different premiss, perhaps one from which we learned that $x = \frac{1 - z}{y}$, then we should have

$$\frac{1 - z}{y} = 1y(1 - z) + \frac{1}{0}(1 - z)(1 - y) + 0yz + \frac{0}{0}(1 - y)z.$$

The *constituents* here are exactly the same as in the other case. And if we write them in the same order as before, but with their present coefficients, we have, for $x$ when this premiss is assumed,

$$x = 0yz + \frac{0}{0}z(1 - y) + 1y(1 - z) + \frac{1}{0}(1 - z)(1 - y).$$

This emphasizes the way in which it is the special character of the premiss which determines the coefficients, and modifies what we can know of the relation of $x$ to $y$ and $z$ from purely formal laws alone.

It may be felt that this is hardly " casting aside all analogies, mathematical and otherwise," and considering " what doctrine of the intellectual processes lies concealed beneath the forms themselves." But we cannot reach any such doctrine without some attention to the forms which lead to it. We said earlier that Logic, conceived as the philosophy of all thought which is expressible in signs, cannot

be studied independently. This is why it is difficult or
impossible to discuss it without seeming to have recourse to
the very formal or symbolic procedures which it is supposed
to explain. Perhaps it is putting the same point if we recall
that a part, at least, of any such study is the investigation
of the formal conditions of interpretability,—if that is not
in fact the whole of it. When Boole speaks of the " doctrine " which " lies concealed beneath the forms themselves,"
—or when he speaks, as he does elsewhere, of what " the
laws themselves, taken not individually but collectively and
as a system, reveal to us,"—he is referring to the formal
conditions of interpretability, and to the importance which
they have for an understanding of formal inference. They
show that in any symbolical procedure the formal laws
themselves are never used in perfect independence of what
the symbols may mean. They are independent of any
*particular* meanings. The formal validity of an inference
does not depend on whether animals or triangles are mentioned in it. But it does depend on the fact that its symbols
stand either for existence or non-existence. They do that,
whatever other meanings they may take; whatever else be
meant, it will always be thought of as something existing
or not existing. And without this the formal laws would
not be laws of a logical system at all. They would not be
laws of formal reasoning.

The point of the example just given was to illustrate this
sort of investigation and what is revealed by it. We can
see from it that formal reasoning consists partly in attention
to formal laws, and partly in attention to the ideas of
existence and non-existence (1 and 0) as they may be expressed by the symbols where these laws are applied. We
can see that this is so in cases like this one, anyway, and
there are reasons which show that it is general. This
is one of the most important of Boole's later views about
formal reasoning and the nature of a logical conclusion. And
he was led to it by thinking of the process of development
here in conjunction with the more general consideration of
the formal conditions of interpretability. We have said
that in the earlier writings Boole justified the substitution

c

of 1 and 0 for the logical symbols $x$, $y$ etc. simply by the formal analogy between them, or between the logical calculus and the dual algebra. When he did this, it still seemed that he was showing the dependence of the development or of the inference on the formal laws, and on nothing else. The substitution of 1 and 0 was simply a convenient way of showing how the formal laws were involved. But the formal conditions of interpretability were showing him that the processes of the calculus themselves, both in logic and in algebra, depended upon what the symbols could represent. It appeared that the relation between logical symbols and the symbols for existence and non-existence was not simply one of analogy of formal laws. Unless the logical symbols were thought of as capable of taking either of those meanings themselves, there could not even be the expressions between which this analogy should hold. Their relation to the ideas of existence and non-existence is prior to any relation they may have to expressions with other symbols. And we may say that the substitution depends upon it.

If the process of development be viewed in this light, we may say that it brings out the fundamental features that are involved in any inference. It shows that the formal laws of identity, contradiction and excluded middle cannot determine a conclusion; that the determination of the conclusion depends upon the relation of the terms to the ideas of existence and non-existence, and upon certain substitutions which these ideas, in conjunction with those formal laws, make possible. If we distinguish between the formal laws of judgment or conception, and formal laws of reasoning, then we may say that the development shows on what those formal laws of reasoning depend, or what it is that underlies them.

In introducing our example (p. 27 above), we said that when we are given $z = xy$, we might first solve the equation for $x$, to get $x = \dfrac{z}{y}$, and then develop the second member of this latter equation. But we need not have put it in just this way. We might consider the premiss by itself, and use development to determine the conclusion we want to draw.

This means that we know what sort of conclusion we are seeking, or that we have some problem in mind. We want to find how $x$, in that premiss, may be expressed in terms of $y$ and $z$ as they appear in that premiss. Put otherwise, we may regard $x$ as a function of $y$ and $z$ in that premiss, and we want to know how that function is to be expressed. $x$, we may say, $= f(y, z)$. If we do not know *what* function this is, we may still write

$$f(y, z) = Ayz + Bz(1 - y) + Cy(1 - z) + D(1 - y)(1 - z).$$

If in this development and also in the premiss we substitute for $y$ and $z$ respectively the values 1, 1; then 0, 1; 1, 0; 0, 0,—then we find that A becomes 1, B becomes inexpressible, C becomes 0 and D becomes indeterminate or is satisfied by anything whatever. This is identical with the developed solution which we reached before.

We have expressed the function which $x$, in that equation, is of $y$ and $z$ in that equation. If we solve the equation for $x$, and write $x = \dfrac{z}{y}$, we have done the same thing. But if we proceed by development, as we have just done, our procedure is "analytic." We consider the general form of conclusion which we are seeking, and we ask how that conclusion must be determined in order that the premiss should be true. In doing this,—in asking, "What function must $x$ be of $y$ and $z$ if that equation is to be true?",—we can show more explicitly how it is that the conclusion depends on the premiss.

This is the converse of what Boole sometimes called the "direct," sometimes the "synthetical" method of reasoning. When we reason synthetically or directly, we start with the premiss, and we apply the rules of solution or deduction directly to it, to get our result. In the analytic method we begin with the general form of conclusion which we want, and we may do this without regard to the special nature of the premiss,—i.e. without regard to the way in which $x$ and $y$ and $z$ are related in the premiss. (In the direct method we have to start with that.) When we ask how this general form of conclusion must be determined if the premiss is true, we answer by making certain substitutions in the general form and in the premiss. But at no point do we apply the laws of deduction directly to the premiss. On the other hand, we do show how the truth of the premiss makes the conclusion necessary; and so we show what the direct application of the law depends on.

It depends on the various " categories of quantity " in which the constituents must be thought in relation to the subject term, $x$. These are the categories of " the universal," " the impossible," " the non-existent," and " the indefinite," and they are expressed by the four coefficients in the development, $1, \frac{1}{0}, 0$ and $\frac{0}{0}$.* It is by showing under which of these categories the various constituents must be thought, in view of the premiss,—and the analytic method shows what governs this,—that we show what inference is possible. Certain conclusions are ruled out, and others are admitted.

It might at first seem that this scheme of the logical categories is just another way of *expressing* the distinction between valid and invalid inferences in any given case; but that it does not show us what the validity depends on, or show that the scheme of the categories is what governs all possible inference. But for Boole it does do that.

This is because the scheme of the categories is directly connected with those conditions which govern our use of signs. And these are the conditions on which the possibility of formal reasoning depends.

The formal laws of reasoning are laws which govern our use of signs, both in their special applications and independently of any application. But however independent, they are laws of certain processes, which we call formal processes. We call them that because they involve operations with signs. The laws of them are *laws* because they sanction certain formal processes and exclude others.

They do that, because they impose restrictions on the meanings, or formal interpretations, of the signs on which the operations are performed.

* Cf. " Logic and Reasoning," below, p. 220.

This is something different from imposing restrictions on the processes which are sanctioned or admitted in the system, and it is prior to that. And if we say the laws " impose " restrictions on the meanings of signs, we might have said equally that these are a condition of their being laws of reasoning processes.

We are speaking of " the formal conditions of interpretability." We are led to these, it was suggested, by applying one of the laws of thought, such as $xx = x$, to formal expressions. But this does not determine them unaided or directly, but only in connexion with other operations in the system. (In deducing the conditions of interpretability for $x + y$, for instance, we employed substitution,—and even addition. And in a way the procedure seemed circular.)

These conditions of interpretability admit of formal expression. This means that the way in which signs enter into one expression $(x + y)$ is dependent upon the way in which they enter into other expressions (such as $xy$; we must have $xy = 0$). More generally, we may say that the conditions of interpretability are determined by the relation of the expression to the formal system as a whole. It is the character of the system which restricts the interpretation of the signs in a given expression. The formal laws, such as $xx = x$, are needed to show this. But the consideration of the system as a whole is as important as they are.

We have quoted Boole's remark that the formal conditions of interpretability may be determined by the process of development " more readily " than in any other way. By giving the development of an expression, we may show which combinations of symbols are admitted and which are ruled out, if any are. We have seen of $\frac{z}{y}$, for instance, that it is not interpretable at all if $z = 1$ and $y = 0$. Whatever $z$ and $y$ may be, they cannot be such that $z(1 - y)$ would be interpretable also. (Similarly for the conditions of $x + y$, only there we have to show that a constituent with a coefficient such as 2, which does not obey $xx = x$, can be equated to 0. Boole has shown that this is a consequence of the same formal laws on which the rest of the development is founded.)

A development sets out the formal conditions of interpretability of any logical expression. It can be applied quite generally. This is a consequence of the law of excluded middle. But we have seen that the completed development depends also upon the substitutions of 1 and 0. This is essential to the statement of the formal conditions of interpretability by this method. But they or their equivalents also enter into the formal statements of these conditions which might be derived by any other method.

By the general application of development we see that the interpretability of logical expressions in general depends upon the relations which their signs bear to 1 and 0 (which in logic are the expressions for " existence " and " nonexistence," simply or absolutely). In other words, we arrive in this way at certain *general* conditions for the interpretability of logical expressions,—not simply for the particular expressions, such as $x + y$, from which we started.

We spoke of these just now as certain necessary relations which symbols employed in one expression have to their employment in others. And we say the same if we speak of necessary relations between one expression and another in which those symbols enter. These relations are expressed in the categories of quantity.

This is the reason for saying that the logical system rests on those categories, and that it is the scheme of the categories which governs what processes are possible within it.

It is hard to avoid the appearance of circularity in this. For it may be said that we are presupposing the relation of signs to 1 and 0 in the very process of development which we use to show it ; that the substitutions by which the development proceeds depend on that.

We are employing development merely as a formal process, in connexion with particular expressions. The important point is that the conditions of interpretability in these cases are what the development reveals. And this can be verified throughout the system. In this way we discover a feature of the system which is fundamental to it. But we do not discover anything which can be stated in independence of the system, or anything which *could* have been discovered without employing the very formal processes which we are investigating.

The validity of inference depends upon the conditions of interpretability. But we cannot *start* from them, to learn what inferences are valid. And although the system of logical inferences depends on the scheme of the categories, we cannot construct a system from them. We must know the principles of inference, and we must have the completed system. We can then ask what makes it possible that these should be principles of inference, and what makes possible a system of such principles. And our inquiry will be analytical.

It will not lead us to anything from which the principles could be derived, if we did not know them. Nor to anything which stands as a formal law to the processes which it governs. But nevertheless, by considering the system as a whole we can find certain conditions—certain relations among its expressions—without which its processes would be inexpressible. Which is to say : without which there would be no system at all.

We discover certain logical relations among signs, which are prior to the operations we perform upon them, and which underlie the connexions between one operation and another. That we have to use those operations to discover them, does not—or need not—cast suspicion on that priority. Though it would do so if we were not guided by the nature of the system as a whole.

This is part of the " general philosophy of signs which governs and explains all their particular uses and applications." As we have given it, it does not seem to be quite general, because the formal conditions we have studied, and the formal processes which rest on them, are those of the logic of class. But we have seen that the formal conditions of the interpretability of particular expressions may lead us to the conditions of interpretability—and here this means the possibility—of the system as a whole. It leads, that is, to a recognition of certain formal conditions for the interpretability of logical expressions in general. Boole thought, apparently, that this way might lead to a recognition of still more general conditions, which are the conditions of the possibility of any formal reasoning, and of any deductive system, whether its laws be those of the conception of class or of a different kind. All formal sciences, whatever their special laws, do operate with signs. All formal laws, and all reasonings governed by them, whatever their concepts, are independent of special applications. And in all there are formal conditions of interpretability. Otherwise there would not be formal laws. Formal laws and reasonings depend upon the " possibilities " of using signs. There seems to be something general in the formal character of reasoning, even if there is no general formal law.

The later account of formal reasoning influenced what he said, after the *Laws of Thought*, about the relation of the theory of probabilities to logic. Reasoning is always subject to "conditions of possibility." But there may be more general and more special conditions, peculiar to a particular deductive science. There are special conditions which make a calculus of probabilities possible, and which distinguish its processes from those of arithmetic in general. Perhaps the chief of these are " the conditions of possible experience." They must be observed if the statistical data of a problem in probabilities are to be consistent ; and otherwise it cannot be a problem in probabilities at all, or in other words, " the problem is not a real one." They must be observed also if the conclusion that is drawn from the data is to "represent a possible experience." They can be formally expressed, and there is a general method for determining them. The method was changed and simplified after the *Laws of Thought* was published. But it is an improvement in methods given there in the chapter " Of Statistical Conditions." And that chapter is partly a fuller treatment and application of the ideas in the paper " On Propositions Numerically Definite." (It is interesting to compare this paper with the chapter in De Morgan's *Formal Logic*, and to see how Boole's interest in finding perfectly general methods leads him to a different treatment of the question and a different view of its importance.) What is important in the later discussion of the conditions of possible

experience,—more important than the simpler method of
determining them, though the two are connected,—is the
rôle they play in the relation of the theory of probabilities
to logic.    They have now become a general feature of all
formal thinking about probabilities.    And it is by reference
to them that we can see how the statement of a problem in
logical terms can still be a statement about probabilities,
and can lead by the methods of the logical calculus to a
conclusion about probabilities.

This required a deeper study of the logical theory than
Boole had given in his earlier writings.    It required a fuller
discussion of the grounds which permit of different but
formally equivalent statements of the same problem,—
showing, for instance, how a statement in terms of simple
events and one in terms of compound events need make no
difference to the formal nature of the problem or to the
conclusion that is reached from it.    But especially it
required a fuller theory of the formal *analysis* of problems,
or the analysis into their " logical elements."    That was
part of the later theory of analytical reasoning, and of the
conditions of its possibility.    It was in this connexion that
Boole was led to emphasize, as he had not earlier, the distinction between the " ideal events " which appear in the logical
statement of the problem, and which are the subjects of a
purely formal treatment, and the actual events which this
logical statement " represents."

This development was not born of logical investigations
alone, but it did grow in connexion with them.    The correspondence with Bishop Terrot * apparently included discussions of " the principle of non-sufficient reason " (which
Keynes has called the Principle of Indifference).    Boole
was led to change his view of the importance of that principle
in the theory of probabilities.    And what he says of the
hypothesis of " ideal events " is partly a statement of that.
But for him it has become a question of the logical foundations of the subject; and without the further study of
logical problems he would hardly have answered it just as
he did.

* The letters were not preserved, apparently.

A proper discussion of Boole's views would go more fully into the changes in his later theory of probabilities. It would certainly consider the special problems which are treated in the paper on the combination of testimonies or judgments, and discuss their bearing on the general theory. But this note is already too long, and we cannot do that. The question we have referred to, regarding the hypothesis of ideal events, is more complicated and more interesting than the reference suggests, or than we can try to indicate.

We have printed all but two of Boole's published papers on probability. One of these—" On certain propositions in algebra connected with the theory of probabilities," *Philosophical Magazine*, 1855—is more of purely mathematical than of logical interest; and important parts of its substance are given again in papers which we print. The other—" On the theory of probabilities," *Philosophical Magazine*, 1863—is a report and summary of the paper which was published in the *Transactions of the Royal Society* (London) in 1862, which is included here.

Since the papers were written at various times, there is some repetition. But this generally means that Boole was treating the same question in a slightly different way. And the point of printing them all is to show the development of his thought.

One of the early papers, the " Sketch of a Theory and Method of Probabilities founded upon the Calculus of Logic," has not been published before. It is taken from Boole's notebooks, which are the property of the Royal Society, and which are together with his other manuscripts in the Royal Society Library. It was through the kindness of the Officers of the Society that we were able to consult them. And we are deeply grateful to the Officers of the Society for permission to quote and publish such portions of the manuscripts as we have. We should like especially to thank Mr. D. C. Martin, Assistant Secretary to the Society, for his help.

The editor's notes to the text are given in brackets. Where there are references to the *Laws of Thought*, the pages of the first edition are generally given in brackets, and these

are followed by the pages of the 1916 edition.    Boole's own
references, in the course of his papers, are to the pages of
the first edition; but these are given in the 1916 edition
as well.

R. RHEES.

# THE MATHEMATICAL ANALYSIS

# OF LOGIC,

## BEING AN ESSAY TOWARDS A CALCULUS
## OF DEDUCTIVE REASONING.

### BY GEORGE BOOLE.

Ἐπικοινωνοῦσι δὲ πᾶσαι αἱ ἐπιστῆμαι ἀλλήλαις κατὰ τὰ κοινά. Κοινὰ δὲ
λέγω, οἷς χρῶνται ὡς ἐκ τούτων ἀποδεικνύντες· ἀλλ' οὐ περὶ ὧν δεικνύουσιν,
οὐδὲ ὃ δεικνύουσι.

ARISTOTLE, Anal. Post., lib. I. cap. XI.

CAMBRIDGE:
MACMILLAN, BARCLAY, & MACMILLAN;
LONDON: GEORGE BELL.

1847

# PREFACE

In presenting this Work to public notice, I deem it not irrelevant to observe, that speculations similar to those which it records have, at different periods, occupied my thoughts. In the spring of the present year my attention was directed to the question then moved between Sir W. Hamilton and Professor De Morgan; and I was induced by the interest which it inspired, to resume the almost-forgotten thread of former inquiries. It appeared to me that, although Logic might be viewed with reference to the idea of quantity,* it had also another and a deeper system of relations. If it was lawful to regard it from *without*, as connecting itself through the medium of Number with the intuitions of Space and Time, it was lawful also to regard it from *within*, as based upon facts of another order which have their abode in the constitution of the Mind. The results of this view, and of the inquiries which it suggested, are embodied in the following Treatise.

It is not generally permitted to an Author to prescribe the mode in which his production shall be judged; but there are two conditions which I may venture to require of those who shall undertake to estimate the merits of this performance. The first is, that no preconceived notion of the impossibility of its objects shall be permitted to interfere with that candour and impartiality which the investigation of Truth demands; the second is, that their judgment of the system as a whole shall not be founded either upon the examination of only a part of it, or upon the measure of its conformity with any received system, considered as a standard of reference from which appeal is denied. It is in the general theorems which occupy the latter chapters of this work,—results to which there is no existing counterpart, —that the claims of the method, as a Calculus of Deductive Reasoning, are most fully set forth.

* See p. [42] 83.

What may be the final estimate of the value of the system, I have neither the wish nor the right to anticipate. The estimation of a theory is not simply determined by its truth. It also depends upon the importance of its subjects, and the extent of its applications; beyond which something must still be left to the arbitrariness of human Opinion. If the utility of the application of Mathematical forms to the science of Logic were solely a question of Notation, I should be content to rest the defence of this attempt upon a principle which has been stated by an able living writer : " Whenever the nature of the subject permits the reasoning process to be without danger carried on mechanically, the language should be constructed on as mechanical principles as possible ; while in the contrary case it should be so constructed, that there shall be the greatest possible obstacle to a mere mechanical use of it." * In one respect, the science of Logic differs from all others; the perfection of its method is chiefly valuable as an evidence of the speculative truth of its principles. To supersede the employment of common reason, or to subject it to the rigour of technical forms, would be the last desire of one who knows the value of that intellectual toil and warfare which imparts to the mind an athletic vigour, and teaches it to contend with difficulties and to rely upon itself in emergencies.

* Mill's *System of Logic, Ratiocinative and Inductive*, Vol. ii. p. 292.

Lincoln, *Oct.* 29, 1847.

# THE MATHEMATICAL ANALYSIS OF LOGIC

## INTRODUCTION

THEY who are acquainted with the present state of the theory of Symbolical Algebra, are aware, that the validity of the processes of analysis does not depend upon the interpretation of the symbols which are employed, but solely upon the laws of their combination. Every system of interpretation which does not affect the truth of the relations supposed, is equally admissible, and it is thus that the same process may, under one scheme of interpretation, represent the solution of a question on the properties of number, under another, that of a geometrical problem, and under a third, that of a problem of dynamics or optics. This principle is indeed of fundamental importance; and it may with safety be affirmed, that the recent advances of pure analysis have been much assisted by the influence which it has exerted in directing the current of investigation.

But the full recognition of the consequences of this important doctrine has been, in some measure, retarded by accidental circumstances. It has happened in every known form of analysis, that the elements to be determined have been conceived as measurable by comparison with some fixed standard. The predominant idea has been that of magnitude, or more strictly, of numerical ratio. The expression of magnitude, or [4] * of operations upon magnitude, has been the express object for which the symbols of Analysis have been invented, and for which their laws have been investigated. Thus the abstractions of the modern Analysis, not less than the ostensive diagrams of the ancient Geometry, have encouraged the notion, that Mathematics are essentially, as well as actually, the Science of Magnitude.

The consideration of that view which has already been stated, as embodying the true principle of the Algebra of

* [The numbers in square brackets show the paging of the original edition of this essay.]

Symbols, would, however, lead us to infer that this conclusion is by no means necessary. If every existing interpretation is shewn to involve the idea of magnitude, it is only by induction that we can assert that no other interpretation is possible. And it may be doubted whether our experience is sufficient to render such an induction legitimate. The history of pure Analysis is, it may be said, too recent to permit us to set limits to the extent of its applications. Should we grant to the inference a high degree of probability, we might still, and with reason, maintain the sufficiency of the definition to which the principle already stated would lead us. We might justly assign it as the definitive character of a true Calculus, that it is a method resting upon the employment of Symbols, whose laws of combination are known and general, and whose results admit of a consistent interpretation. That to the existing forms of Analysis a quantitative interpretation is assigned, is the result of the circumstances by which those forms were determined, and is not to be construed into a universal condition of Analysis. It is upon the foundation of this general principle, that I purpose to establish the Calculus of Logic, and that I claim for it a place among the acknowledged forms of Mathematical Analysis, regardless that in its object and in its instruments it must at present stand alone.

That which renders Logic possible, is the existence in our minds of general notions,—our ability to conceive of a class, and to designate its individual members by a common name. [5] The theory of Logic is thus intimately connected with that of Language. A successful attempt to express logical propositions by symbols, the laws of whose combinations should be founded upon the laws of the mental processes which they represent, would, so far, be a step toward a philosophical language. But this is a view which we need not here follow into detail.* Assuming the notion of a class, we are able,

---

* This view is well expressed in one of Blanco White's Letters :—" Logic is for the most part a collection of technical rules founded on classification. The Syllogism is nothing but a result of the classification of things, which the mind naturally and necessarily forms, in forming a language. All abstract terms are classifications; or rather the labels of the classes which the mind has settled."—*Memoirs of the Rev. Joseph Blanco White*, vol. II. p. 163. See also, for a very lucid introduction, Dr. Latham's *First Outlines of Logic*

from any conceivable collection of objects, to separate by
a mental act, those which belong to the given class, and to
contemplate them apart from the rest.   Such, or a similar
act of election, we may conceive to be repeated.   The group
of individuals left under consideration may be still further
limited, by mentally selecting those among them which belong
to some other recognised class, as well as to the one before
contemplated.   And this process may be repeated with
other elements of distinction, until we arrive at an individual
possessing all the distinctive characters which we have taken
into account, and a member, at the same time, of every
class which we have enumerated.   It is in fact a method
similar to this which we employ whenever, in common
language, we accumulate descriptive epithets for the sake
of more precise definition.

Now the several mental operations which in the above
case we have supposed to be performed, are subject to peculiar
laws.   It is possible to assign relations among them, whether
as respects the repetition of a given operation or the succession
of different ones, or some other particular, which are never
violated.   It is, for example, true that the result of two
successive acts is [6] unaffected by the order in which they
are performed; and there are at least two other laws which
will be pointed out in the proper place.   These will perhaps
to some appear so obvious as to be ranked among necessary
truths, and so little important as to be undeserving of special
notice.   And probably they are noticed for the first time in
this Essay.   Yet it may with confidence be asserted, that
if they were other than they are, the entire mechanism of
reasoning, nay the very laws and constitution of the human
intellect, would be vitally changed.   A Logic might indeed
exist, but it would no longer be the Logic we possess.

Such are the elementary laws upon the existence of which,
and upon their capability of exact symbolical expression, the
method of the following Essay is founded; and it is presumed
that the object which it seeks to attain will be thought to

---

*applied to Language*, Becker's *German Grammar*, &c.   Extreme Nominalists
make Logic entirely dependent upon language.   For the opposite view,
see Cudworth's *Eternal and Immutable Morality*, Book iv. Chap. III.

have been very fully accomplished. Every logical proposition, whether categorical or hypothetical, will be found to be capable of exact and rigorous expression, and not only will the laws of conversion and of syllogism be thence deducible, but the resolution of the most complex systems of propositions, the separation of any proposed element, and the expression of its value in terms of the remaining elements, with every subsidiary relation involved. Every process will represent deduction, every mathematical consequence will express a logical inference. The generality of the method will even permit us to express arbitrary operations of the intellect, and thus lead to the demonstration of general theorems in logic analogous, in no slight degree, to the general theorems of ordinary mathematics. No inconsiderable part of the pleasure which we derive from the application of analysis to the interpretation of external nature, arises from the conceptions which it enables us to form of the universality of the dominion of law. The general formulæ to which we are conducted seem to give to that element a visible presence, and the multitude of particular cases to which they apply, demonstrate the extent of its sway. Even the symmetry [7] of their analytical expression may in no fanciful sense be deemed indicative of its harmony and its consistency. Now I do not presume to say to what extent the same sources of pleasure are opened in the following Essay. The measure of that extent may be left to the estimate of those who shall think the subject worthy of their study. But I may venture to assert that such occasions of intellectual gratification are not here wanting. The laws we have to examine are the laws of one of the most important of our mental faculties. The mathematics we have to construct are the mathematics of the human intellect. Nor are the form and character of the method, apart from all regard to its interpretation, undeserving of notice. There is even a remarkable exemplification, in its general theorems, of that species of excellence which consists in freedom from exception. And this is observed where, in the corresponding cases of the received mathematics, such a character is by no means apparent. The few who think that there is that in analysis which renders it deserving of attention for its own sake, may find it worth while to study it under a form in which every equation can be solved and every solution interpreted.  Nor will it lessen the interest of this study to reflect that every peculiarity which they will notice in the form of the Calculus represents a corresponding feature in the constitution of their own minds.

It would be premature to speak of the value which this method may possess as an instrument of scientific investigation.  I speak here with reference to the theory of reasoning, and to the principle of a true classification of the forms and cases of Logic considered as a Science.*  The aim of these investigations was in the first instance confined to the expression of the received logic, and to the forms of the Aristotelian arrangement, [8] but it soon became apparent that restrictions were thus introduced, which were purely arbitrary and had no foundation in the nature of things.  These were noted as they occurred, and will be discussed in the proper place.  When it became necessary to consider the subject of hypothetical propositions (in which comparatively less has been done), and still more, when an interpretation was demanded for the general theorems of the Calculus, it was found to be imperative to dismiss all regard for precedent and authority, and to interrogate the method itself for an expression of the just limits of its application.  Still, however, there was no special effort to arrive at novel results.  But among those which at the time of their discovery appeared to be such, it may be proper to notice the following.

A logical proposition is, according to the method of this Essay, expressible by an equation the form of which determines the rules of conversion and of transformation, to which the given proposition is subject.  Thus the law of what logicians term simple conversion, is determined by the fact, that the corresponding equations are symmetrical, that they are unaffected by a mutual change of place, in those symbols which correspond to the convertible classes.  The received

---

* " Strictly a Science "; also " an Art."—*Whately's Elements of Logic.*
Indeed, ought we not to regard all Art as applied Science; unless we are willing, with " the multitude," to consider Art as " guessing and aiming well " ?—*Plato, Philebus.*

laws of conversion were thus determined, and afterwards another system, which is thought to be more elementary, and more general. See Chapter, *On the Conversion of Propositions*.

The premises of a syllogism being expressed by equations, the elimination of a common symbol between them leads to a third equation which expresses the conclusion, this conclusion being always the most general possible, whether Aristotelian or not. Among the cases in which no inference was possible, it was found, that there were two distinct forms of the final equation. It was a considerable time before the explanation of this fact was discovered, but it was at length seen to depend upon the presence or absence of a true medium of comparison between the premises. The distinction which is thought to be new is illustrated in the Chapter, *On Syllogisms*.

[9] The nonexclusive character of the disjunctive conclusion of a hypothetical syllogism, is very clearly pointed out in the examples of this species of argument.

The class of logical problems illustrated in the Chapter, *On the Solution of Elective Equations*, is conceived to be new : and it is believed that the method of that chapter affords the means of a perfect analysis of any conceivable system of propositions, an end toward which the rules for the conversion of a single categorical proposition are but the first step.

However, upon the originality of these or any of these views, I am conscious that I possess too slight an acquaintance with the literature of logical science, and especially with its older literature, to permit me to speak with confidence.

It may not be inappropriate, before concluding these observations, to offer a few remarks upon the general question of the use of symbolical language in the mathematics. Objections have lately been very strongly urged against this practice, on the ground, that by obviating the necessity of thought, and substituting a reference to general formulæ in the room of personal effort, it tends to weaken the reasoning faculties.

Now the question of the use of symbols may be considered in two distinct points of view. First, it may be considered with reference to the progress of scientific discovery, and secondly, with reference to its bearing upon the discipline of the intellect.

And with respect to the first view, it may be observed that as it is one fruit of an accomplished labour, that it sets us at liberty to engage in more arduous toils, so it is a necessary result of an advanced state of science, that we are permitted, and even called upon, to proceed to higher problems, than those which we before contemplated. The practical inference is obvious. If through the advancing power of scientific methods, we find that the pursuits on which we were once engaged, afford no longer a sufficiently ample field for intellectual effort, the remedy is, to proceed to higher inquiries, and, in new tracks, to seek for difficulties yet unsubdued. And such is, [10] indeed, the actual law of scientific progress. We must be content, either to abandon the hope of further conquest, or to employ such aids of symbolical language, as are proper to the stage of progress, at which we have arrived. Nor need we fear to commit ourselves to such a course. We have not yet arrived so near to the boundaries of possible knowledge, as to suggest the apprehension, that scope will fail for the exercise of the inventive faculties.

In discussing the second, and scarcely less momentous question of the influence of the use of symbols upon the discipline of the intellect, an important distinction ought to be made. It is of most material consequence, whether those symbols are used with a full understanding of their meaning, with a perfect comprehension of that which renders their use lawful, and an ability to expand the abbreviated forms of reasoning which they induce, into their full syllogistic development; or whether they are mere unsuggestive characters, the use of which is suffered to rest upon authority.

The answer which must be given to the question proposed, will differ according as the one or the other of these suppositions is admitted. In the former case an intellectual discipline of a high order is provided, an exercise not only of reason, but of the faculty of generalization. In the latter case there is no mental discipline whatever. It were perhaps the best security against the danger of an unreasoning reliance upon symbols, on the one hand, and a neglect of their just claims on the other, that each subject of applied mathematics should be treated in the spirit of the methods which were known at the time when the application was made, but in the best form which those methods have assumed. The order of attainment in the individual mind would thus bear some relation to the actual order of scientific discovery, and the more abstract methods of the higher analysis would be offered to such minds only, as were prepared to receive them.

The relation in which this Essay stands at once to Logic and [11] to Mathematics, may further justify some notice of the question which has lately been revived, as to the relative value of the two studies in a liberal education. One of the chief objections which have been urged against the study of Mathematics in general, is but another form of that which has been already considered with respect to the use of symbols in particular. And it need not here be further dwelt upon, than to notice, that if it avails anything, it applies with an equal force against the study of Logic. The canonical forms of the Aristotelian syllogism are really symbolical; only the symbols are less perfect of their kind than those of mathematics. If they are employed to test the validity of an argument, they as truly supersede the exercise of reason, as does a reference to a formula of analysis. Whether men do, in the present day, make this use of the Aristotelian canons, except as a special illustration of the rules of Logic, may be doubted; yet it cannot be questioned that when the authority of Aristotle was dominant in the schools of Europe, such applications were habitually made. And our argument only requires the admission, that the case is possible.

But the question before us has been argued upon higher grounds. Regarding Logic as a branch of Philosophy, and defining Philosophy as the " science of a real existence," and " the research of causes," and assigning as its *main* business the investigation of the " why, (τὸ διότι)," while

Mathematics display only the "that, (τὸ ὅτι)," Sir W. Hamilton has contended, not simply, that the superiority rests with the study of Logic, but that the study of Mathematics is at once dangerous and useless.* The pursuits of the mathematician " have not only not trained him to that acute scent, to that delicate, almost instinctive, tact which, in the twilight of probability, the search and discrimination of its finer facts demand; they have gone to cloud his vision, to indurate his touch, to all but the blazing light, the iron chain of demonstration, and left him out of the narrow confines of his science, to a passive *credulity* in any premises, or to [12] an absolute *incredulity* in all." In support of these and of other charges, both argument and copious authority are adduced.† I shall not attempt a complete discussion of the topics which are suggested by these remarks. My object is not controversy, and the observations which follow are offered not in the spirit of antagonism, but in the hope of contributing to the formation of just views upon an important subject. Of Sir W. Hamilton it is impossible to speak otherwise than with that respect which is due to genius and learning.

Philosophy is then described as the *science of a real existence* and *the research of causes*. And that no doubt may rest upon the meaning of the word *cause*, it is further said, that philosophy " mainly investigates the *why*." These definitions are common among the ancient writers. Thus Seneca, one of Sir W. Hamilton's authorities, *Epistle* LXXXVIII., " The philosopher seeks and knows the *causes* of natural things, of which the mathematician searches out and computes the numbers and the measures." It may be remarked, in passing, that in whatever degree the belief has prevailed, that the business of philosophy is immediately with *causes*, in the same degree has every science whose object is the investigation of *laws*, been lightly esteemed. Thus the Epistle to

---

* *Edinburgh Review*, vol. LXII. p. 409, and *Letter to A. De Morgan, Esq.*
† The arguments are in general better than the authorities. Many writers quoted in condemnation of mathematics (Aristo, Seneca, Jerome, Augustine, Cornelius Agrippa, &c.) have borne a no less explicit testimony against other sciences, nor least of all, against that of logic. The treatise of the last named writer *De Vanitate Scientiarum*, must surely have been referred to by mistake.—*Vide* cap. CII.

which we have referred, bestows, by contrast with Philosophy, a separate condemnation on Music and Grammar, on Mathematics and Astronomy, although it is that of Mathematics only that Sir W. Hamilton has quoted.

Now we might take our stand upon the conviction of many thoughtful and reflective minds, that in the extent of the meaning above stated, Philosophy is impossible. The business of true Science, they conclude, is with laws and phenomena. The nature of Being, the mode of the operation of Cause, the *why*, [13] they hold to be beyond the reach of our intelligence. But we do not require the vantage-ground of this position; nor is it doubted that whether the aim of Philosophy is attainable or not, the desire which impels us to the attempt is an instinct of our higher nature. Let it be granted that the problem which has baffled the efforts of ages is not a hopeless one; that the " science of a real existence," and " the research of causes," " that kernel " for which " Philosophy is still militant," do not transcend the limits of the human intellect. I am then compelled to assert, that, according to this view of the nature of Philosophy, *Logic forms no part of it.* On the principle of a true classification, we ought no longer to associate Logic and Metaphysics, but Logic and Mathematics.

Should any one after what has been said, entertain a doubt upon this point, I must refer him to the evidence which will be afforded in the following Essay. He will there see Logic resting like Geometry upon axiomatic truths, and its theorems constructed upon that general doctrine of symbols, which constitutes the foundation of the recognised Analysis. In the Logic of Aristotle he will be led to view a collection of the formulæ of the science, expressed by another, but, (it is thought) less perfect scheme of symbols. I feel bound to contend for the absolute exactness of this parallel. It is no escape from the conclusion to which it points to assert, that Logic not only constructs a science, but also inquires into the origin and the nature of its own principles,—a distinction which is denied to Mathematics. " It is wholly beyond the domain of mathematicians," it is said, " to inquire into the origin and nature of their principles."—

*Review*, page 415. But upon what ground can such a distinction be maintained? What definition of the term Science will be found sufficiently arbitrary to allow such differences?

The application of this conclusion to the question before us is clear and decisive. The mental discipline which is afforded by the study of Logic, *as an exact science*, is, in species, the same as that afforded by the study of Analysis.

[14] Is it then contended that either Logic or Mathematics can supply a perfect discipline to the Intellect? The most careful and unprejudiced examination of this question leads me to doubt whether such a position can be maintained. The exclusive claims of either must, I believe, be abandoned, nor can any others, partaking of a like exclusive character, be admitted in their room. It is an important observation, which has more than once been made, that it is one thing to arrive at correct premises, and another thing to deduce logical conclusions, and that the business of life depends more upon the former than upon the latter. The study of the exact sciences may teach us the one, and it may give us some general preparation of knowledge and of practice for the attainment of the other, but it is to the union of thought with action, in the field of Practical Logic, the arena of Human Life, that we are to look for its fuller and more perfect accomplishment.

I desire here to express my conviction, that with the advance of our knowledge of all true science, an ever-increasing harmony will be found to prevail among its separate branches. The view which leads to the rejection of one, ought, if consistent, to lead to the rejection of others. And indeed many of the authorities which have been quoted against the study of Mathematics, are even more explicit in their condemnation of Logic. "Natural science," says the Chian Aristo, "is above us, Logical science does not concern us." When such conclusions are founded (as they often are) upon a deep conviction of the preeminent value and importance of the study of Morals, we admit the premises, but must demur to the inference. For it has been well said by an ancient writer, that it is the "characteristic of the liberal sciences, not that they conduct us to Virtue, but that they prepare us for Virtue;" and Melancthon's sentiment, " abeunt studia in mores," has passed into a proverb. Moreover, there is a common ground upon which all sincere votaries of truth may meet, exchanging with each other the language of Flamsteeds' appeal to Newton, " The works of the Eternal Providence will be better understood through your labors and mine."

[15]    FIRST PRINCIPLES

LET us employ the symbol 1, or unity, to represent the Universe, and let us understand it as comprehending every conceivable class of objects whether actually existing or not, it being premised that the same individual may be found in more than one class, inasmuch as it may possess more than one quality in common with other individuals. Let us employ the letters X, Y, Z, to represent the individual members of classes, X applying to every member of one class, as members of that particular class, and Y to every member of another class as members of such class, and so on, according to the received language of treatises on Logic.

Further let us conceive a class of symbols $x$, $y$, $z$, possessed of the following character.

The symbol $x$ operating upon any subject comprehending individuals or classes, shall be supposed to select from that subject all the Xs which it contains. In like manner the symbol $y$, operating upon any subject, shall be supposed to select from it all individuals of the class Y which are comprised in it, and so on.

When no subject is expressed, we shall suppose 1 (the Universe) to be the subject understood, so that we shall have

$$x = x \quad (1),$$

the meaning of either term being the selection from the Universe of all the Xs which it contains, and the result of the operation [16] being in common language, the class X, *i.e.* the class of which each member is an X.

From these premises it will follow, that the product $xy$

will represent, in succession, the selection of the class Y, and the selection from the class Y of such individuals of the class X as are contained in it, the result being the class whose members are both Xs and Ys. And in like manner the product *xyz* will represent a compound operation of which the successive elements are the selection of the class Z, the selection from it of such individuals of the class Y as are contained in it, and the selection from the result thus obtained of all the individuals of the class X which it contains, the final result being the class common to X, Y, and Z.

From the nature of the operation which the symbols *x*, *y*, *z*, are conceived to represent, we shall designate them as elective symbols. An expression in which they are involved will be called an elective function, and an equation of which the members are elective functions, will be termed an elective equation.

It will not be necessary that we should here enter into the analysis of that mental operation which we have represented by the elective symbol. It is not an act of Abstraction according to the common acceptation of that term, because we never lose sight of the concrete, but it may probably be referred to an exercise of the faculties of Comparison and Attention. Our present concern is rather with the laws of combination and of succession, by which its results are governed, and of these it will suffice to notice the following.

1st. The result of an act of election is independent of the grouping or classification of the subject.

Thus it is indifferent whether from a group of objects considered as a whole, we select the class X, or whether we divide the group into two parts, select the Xs from them separately, and then connect the results in one aggregate conception.

We may express this law mathematically by the equation

$$x(u + v) = xu + xv,$$

[17] $u + v$ representing the undivided subject, and $u$ and $v$ the component parts of it.

2nd. It is indifferent in what order two successive acts of election are performed.

Whether from the class of animals we select sheep, and from the sheep those which are horned, or whether from the class of animals we select the horned, and from these such as are sheep, the result is unaffected. In either case we arrive at the class *horned sheep.*

The symbolical expression of this law is

$$xy = yx.$$

3rd.  The result of a given act of election performed twice, or any number of times in succession, is the result of the same act performed once.

If from a group of objects we select the Xs, we obtain a class of which all the members are Xs.  If we repeat the operation on this class no further change will ensue : in selecting the Xs we take the whole.   Thus we have

$$xx = x,$$
or
$$x^2 = x;$$

and supposing the same operation to be $n$ times performed, we have

$$x^n = x,$$

which is the mathematical expression of the law above stated.*

The laws we have established under the symbolical forms

$$x(u + v) = xu + xv \dots\dots\dots\dots \quad (1),$$
$$xy = yx \dots\dots\dots\dots\dots \quad (2),$$
$$x^n = x \dots\dots\dots\dots\dots \quad (3),$$

[18] are sufficient for the basis of a Calculus.   From the first of these, it appears that elective symbols are *distributive*, from the second that they are *commutative*;  properties which they possess in common with symbols of *quantity*, and in virtue of which, all the direct processes of common algebra are applicable to the present system.   The one and sufficient

---

* The office of the elective symbol $x$, is to select individuals comprehended in the class X.  Let the class X be supposed to embrace the universe; then, whatever the class Y may be, we have

$$xy = y.$$

The office which $x$ performs is now equivalent to the symbol $+$, in one at least of its interpretations, and the index law (3) gives

$$+^n = +,$$

which is the known property of that symbol.

axiom involved in this application is that equivalent operations performed upon equivalent subjects produce equivalent
results.*

The third law (3) we shall denominate the index law. It
is peculiar to elective symbols, and will be found of great
importance in enabling us to reduce our results to forms
meet for interpretation.

From the circumstance that the processes of algebra may
be applied to the present system, it is not to be inferred that
the interpretation of an elective equation will be unaffected
by such processes. The expression of a truth cannot be nega-
tived by [19] a legitimate operation, but it may be limited.
The equation $y = z$ implies that the classes Y and Z are
equivalent, member for member. Multiply it by a factor
$x$, and we have

$$xy = xz,$$

which expresses that the individuals which are common to
the classes X and Y are also common to X and Z, and *vice
versâ*. This is a perfectly legitimate inference, but the fact
which it declares is a less general one than was asserted in
the original proposition.

* It is generally asserted by writers on Logic, that all reasoning ultimately depends on an application of the dictum of Aristotle, *de omni et
nullo*. " Whatever is predicated universally of any class of things, may be
predicated in like manner of any thing comprehended in that class." But
it is agreed that this dictum is not immediately applicable in all cases, and
that in a majority of instances, a certain previous process of reduction is
necessary. What are the elements involved in that process of reduction?
Clearly they are as much a part of general reasoning as the dictum itself.

Another mode of considering the subject resolves all reasoning into an
application of one or other of the following canons, viz.

1. If two terms agree with one and the same third, they agree with each
other.

2. If one term agrees, and another disagrees, with one and the same third,
these two disagree with each other.

But the application of these canons depends on mental acts equivalent
to those which are involved in the before-named process of reduction. We
have to select individuals from classes, to convert propositions, &c., before
we can avail ourselves of their guidance. Any account of the process of
reasoning is insufficient, which does not represent, as well the laws of the
operation which the mind performs in that process, as the primary truths
which it recognises and applies.

It is presumed that the laws in question are adequately represented by
the fundamental equations of the present Calculus. The proof of this will
be found in its capability of expressing propositions, and of exhibiting in
the results of its processes, every result that may be arrived at by ordinary
reasoning.

[20]    OF EXPRESSION AND INTERPRETATION.

A Proposition is a sentence which either affirms or denies, as, All men are mortal, No creature is independent.

A Proposition has necessarily two terns, as *men, mortal;* the former of which, or the one spoken of, is called the subject; the latter, or that which is affirmed or denied of the subject, the predicate. These are connected together by the copula *is*, or *is not*, or by some other modification of the substantive verb.

The substantive verb is the only verb recognised in Logic; all others are resolvable by means of the verb *to be* and a participle or adjective, *e.g.* " The Romans conquered "; the word conquered is both copula and predicate, being equivalent to " were (copula) victorious " (predicate).

A Proposition must either be affirmative or negative, and must be also either universal or particular. Thus we reckon in all, four kinds of pure categorical Propositions :

1st.    Universal-affirmative, usually represented by A,
            Ex.    All Xs are Ys.

2nd.    Universal-negative, usually represented by E,
            Ex.    No Xs are Ys.

3rd.    Particular-affirmative, usually represented by I,
            Ex.    Some Xs are Ys.

4th.    Particular-negative, usually represented by O,*
            Ex.    Some Xs are not Ys.

1. To express the class, not-X, that is, the class including all individuals that are not Xs.

The class X and the class not-X together make the Universe. But the Universe is 1, and the class X is determined by the symbol $x$, therefore the class not-X will be determined by the symbol $1 - x$.

[21] Hence the office of the symbol $1 - x$ attached to a given subject will be, to select from it all the not-Xs which it contains.

And in like manner, as the product $xy$ expresses the entire class whose members are both Xs and Ys, the symbol $y(1 - x)$ will represent the class whose members are Ys but not Xs, and the symbol $(1 - x) (1 - y)$ the entire class whose members are neither Xs nor Ys.

2. To express the Proposition, All Xs are Ys.

As all the Xs which exist are found in the class Y, it is obvious that to select out of the Universe all Ys, and from

* The above is taken, with little variation, from the Treatises of Aldrich and Whately.

these to select all Xs, is the same as to select at once from the Universe all Xs.

Hence $$xy = x,$$

or $$x(1 - y) = 0, \quad (4).$$

3. To express the Proposition, No Xs are Ys.

To assert that no Xs are Ys, is the same as to assert that there are no terms common to the classes X and Y. Now all individuals common to those classes are represented by $xy$. Hence the Proposition that No Xs are Ys, is represented by the equation

$$xy = 0, \quad (5).$$

4. To express the Proposition, Some Xs are Ys.

If some Xs are Ys, there are some terms common to the classes X and Y. Let those terms constitute a separate class V, to which there shall correspond a separate elective symbol $v$, then

$$v = xy, \quad (6).$$

And as $v$ includes all terms common to the classes X and Y, we can indifferently interpret it, as Some Xs, or Some Ys.

[22] 5. To express the Proposition, Some Xs are not Ys.

In the last equation write $1 - y$ for $y$, and we have

$$v = x(1 - y), \quad (7),$$

the interpretation of $v$ being indifferently Some Xs or Some not-Ys.

The above equations involve the complete theory of categorical Propositions, and so far as respects the employment of analysis for the deduction of logical inferences, nothing more can be desired. But it may be satisfactory to notice some particular forms deducible from the third and fourth equations, and susceptible of similar application.

If we multiply the equation (6) by $x$, we have

$$vx = x^2 y = xy \text{ by (3).}$$

E

Comparing with (6), we find

$$v = vx,$$

or
$$v(1 - x) = 0, \quad (8).$$

And multiplying (6) by $y$, and reducing in a similar manner, we have

$$v = vy,$$

or
$$v(1 - y) = 0, \quad (9).$$

Comparing (8) and (9),

$$vx = vy = v, \quad (10).$$

And further comparing (8) and (9) with (4), we have as the equivalent of this system of equations the Propositions

$$\left.\begin{array}{l}\text{All Vs are Xs} \\ \text{All Vs are Ys}\end{array}\right\} .$$

The system (10) might be used to replace (6), or the single equation

$$vx = vy, \quad (11),$$

might be used, assigning to $vx$ the interpretation, Some Xs, and to $vy$ the interpretation, Some Ys. But it will be observed that [23] this system does not express quite so much as the single equation (6), from which it is derived. Both, indeed, express the Proposition, Some Xs are Ys, but the system (10) does not imply that the class V includes *all* the terms that are common to X and Y.

In like manner, from the equation (7), which expresses the Proposition Some Xs are not Ys, we may deduce the system

$$vx = v(1 - y) = v, \quad (12),$$

in which the interpretation of $v(1 - y)$ is Some not-Ys. Since in this case $vy = 0$, we must of course be careful not to interpret $vy$ as Some Ys.

If we multiply the first equation of the system (12), viz.

$$vx = v(1 - y),$$

by $y$, we have

$$vxy = vy(1 - y);$$

$$\therefore \quad vxy = 0, \quad (13),$$

which is a form that will occasionally present itself. It is not necessary to revert to the primitive equation in order to interpret this, for the condition that $vx$ represents Some Xs, shews us, by virtue of (5), that its import will be

$$\text{Some Xs are not Ys,}$$

the subject comprising *all* the Xs that are found in the class V.

Universally in these cases, difference of form implies a difference of interpretation with respect to the auxiliary symbol $v$, and each form is interpretable by itself.

Further, these differences do not introduce into the Calculus a needless perplexity. It will hereafter be seen that they give a precision and a definiteness to its conclusions, which could not otherwise be secured.

Finally, we may remark that all the equations by which particular truths are expressed, are deducible from any one general equation, expressing any one general Proposition, from which those particular Propositions are necessary deductions. [24] This has been partially shewn already, but it is much more fully exemplified in the following scheme.

The general equation    $x = y$,
implies that the classes X and Y are equivalent, member for member; that every individual belonging to the one, belongs to the other also. Multiply the equation by $x$, and we have

$$x^2 = xy,$$
$$\therefore \quad x = xy,$$

which implies, by (4), that all Xs are Ys. Multiply the same equation by $y$, and we have in like manner

$$y = xy,$$

the import of which is, that all Ys are Xs. Take either of these equations, the latter for instance, and writing it under the form

$$(1 - x)y = 0,$$

we may regard it as an equation in which $y$, an unknown quantity, is sought to be expressed in terms of $x$. Now it will be shewn when we come to treat of the Solution of Elective

Equations (and the result may here be verified by substitution) that the most general solution of this equation is

$$y = vx,$$

which implies that All Ys are Xs, and that Some Xs are Ys. Multiply by $v$, and we have

$$vy = vx,$$

which indifferently implies that some Ys are Xs and some Xs are Ys, being the particular form at which we before arrived.

For convenience of reference the above and some other results have been classified in the annexed Table, the first column of which contains propositions, the second equations, and the third the conditions of final interpretation. It is to be observed, that the auxiliary equations which are given in this column are not independent : they are implied either in the equations of the second column, or in the condition for [25] the interpretation of $v$. But it has been thought better to write them separately, for greater ease and convenience. And it is further to be borne in mind that although three different forms are given for the expression of each of the *particular* propositions, everything is really included in the first form.

TABLE

| | | |
|---|---|---|
| The class X | $x$ | |
| The class not-X | $1 - x$ | |
| All Xs are Ys<br>All Ys are Xs } | $x = y$ | |
| All Xs are Ys | $x(1 - y) = 0$ | |
| No Xs are Ys | $xy = 0$ | |
| All Ys are Xs<br>Some Xs are Ys } | $y = vx$ | $vx =$ some Xs<br>$v(1 - x) = 0.$ |
| No Ys are Xs<br>Some not-Xs are Ys } | $y = v(1 - x)$ | $v(1 - x) =$ some not-Xs<br>$vx = 0.$ |
| Some Xs are Ys | $\begin{cases} v = xy \\ \text{or } vx = vy \\ \text{or } vx(1 - y) = 0 \end{cases}$ | $v =$ some Xs or some Ys<br>$vx =$ some Xs, $vy =$ some Ys<br>$v(1 - x) = 0, v(1 - y) = 0.$ |

$$\text{Some Xs are not Ys}\begin{cases} v = x(1 - y) & v = \text{some Xs, or some not-Ys} \\ \text{or } vx = v(1 - y) & vx = \text{some Xs, } v(1 - y) = \text{some} \\ & \text{not-Ys} \\ \text{or } vxy = 0 & v(1 - x) = 0,\ vy = 0. \end{cases}$$

## [26]  OF THE CONVERSION OF PROPOSITIONS

A Proposition is said to be converted when its terms are transposed; when nothing more is done, this is called simple conversions; *e.g.*

> No virtuous man is a tyrant, *is converted into*
> No tyrant is a virtuous man.

Logicians also recognise conversion *per accidens*, or by limitation, *e.g.*

> All birds are animals, *is converted into*
> Some animals are birds.

And conversion by *contraposition* or *negation*, as

> Every poet is a man of genius, *converted into*
> He who is not a man of genius is not a poet.

In one of these three ways every Proposition may be illatively converted, viz. E and I simply, A and O by negation, A and E by limitation.

THE primary canonical forms already determined for the expression of Propositions, are

| | | |
|---|---|---|
| All Xs are Ys, | $x(1 - y) = 0,$ | ......A. |
| No Xs are Ys, | $xy = 0,$ | ......E. |
| Some Xs are Ys, | $v = xy,$ | ......I. |
| Some Xs are not Ys, | $v = x(1 - y)$ | ......O. |

On examining these, we perceive that E and I are symmetrical with respect to $x$ and $y$, so that $x$ being changed into $y$, and $y$ into $x$, the equations remain unchanged. Hence E and I may be interpreted into

> No Ys are Xs,
> Some Ys are Xs,

respectively. Thus we have the known rule of the Logicians, that particular affirmative and universal negative Propositions admit of simple conversion.

[27] The equations A and O may be written in the forms

$$(1 - y)\{1 - (1 - x)\} = 0,$$
$$v = (1 - y)\{1 - (1 - x)\}.$$

Now these are precisely the forms which we should have obtained if we had in those equations changed $x$ into $1 - y$, and $y$ into $1 - x$, which would have represented the changing in the original Propositions of the Xs into not-Ys, and the Ys into not-Xs, the resulting Propositions being

All not-Ys are not-Xs,

Some not-Ys are not not-Xs     (a).

Or we may, by simply inverting the order of the factors in the second member of O, and writing it in the form

$$v = (1 - y)x,$$

interpret it by I into

Some not-Ys are Xs

which is really another form of (a).   Hence follows the rule, that universal affirmative and particular negative Propositions admit of negative conversion, or, as it is also termed, conversion by contraposition.

The equations A and E, written in the forms

$$(1 - y)x = 0,$$
$$yx = 0,$$

give on solution the respective forms

$$x = vy,$$
$$x = v(1 - y),$$

the correctness of which may be shewn by substituting these values of $x$ in the equations to which they belong, and observing that those equations are satisfied quite independently of the nature of the symbol $v$.   The first solution may be interpreted into

Some Ys are Xs,

and the second into

Some not-Ys are Xs.

[28] From which it appears that universal-affirmative, and universal-negative Propositions are convertible by limitation, or, as it has been termed, *per accidens*.

The above are the laws of Conversion recognised by Abp. Whately.   Writers differ however as to the admissibility of negative conversion.   The question depends on whether we will consent to use such terms as not-X, not-Y. Agreeing with those who think that such terms ought to be admitted, even although they change the *kind* of the Proposition, I am constrained to observe that the present classification of them is faulty and defective. Thus the conversion of No Xs are Ys, into All Ys are not-Xs, though perfectly legitimate, is not recognised in the above scheme. It may therefore be proper to examine the subject somewhat more fully.

Should we endeavour, from the system of equations we have obtained, to deduce the laws not only of the conversion, but also of the general transformation of propositions, we should be led to recognise the following distinct elements, each connected with a distinct mathematical process.

1st. The negation of a term, *i.e.* the changing of X into not-X, or not-X into X.

2nd. The translation of a Proposition from one *kind* to another, as if we should change

All Xs are Ys into Some Xs are Ys.  A into I,

which would be lawful; or

All Xs are Ys into No Xs are Y.  A into E,

which would be unlawful.

3rd.  The simple conversion of a Proposition.

The conditions in obedience to which these processes may lawfully be performed, may be deduced from the equations by which Propositions are expressed.

We have

All Xs are Ys . . . . . . . . $x(1 - y) = 0$.  A,
No Xs are Ys . . . . . . . . . . . . . $xy = 0$.  E.

[29] Write E in the form

$$x\{1 - (1 - y)\} = 0,$$

and it is interpretable by A into

All Xs are not-Ys,

so that we may change

No Xs are Ys into All Xs are not-Ys.

In like manner A interpreted by E gives

No Xs are not-Ys,

so that we may change

All Xs are Ys into No Xs are not-Ys.

From these cases we have the following Rule : A universal-affirmative Proposition is convertible into a universal-negative, and, *vice versâ*, by negation of the predicate.

Again, we have

$$\text{Some Xs are Ys} \ldots\ldots\ldots\, v = xy,$$
$$\text{Some Xs are not Ys} \ldots\ldots v = x(1 - y).$$

These equations only differ from those last considered by the presence of the term $v$. The same reasoning therefore applies, and we have the Rule—

A particular-affirmative proposition is convertible into a particular-negative, and *vice versâ*, by negation of the predicate.

Assuming the universal Propositions

$$\text{All Xs are Ys} \ldots\ldots\ldots x(1 - y) = 0,$$
$$\text{No Xs are Ys} \ldots\ldots\ldots\ldots xy = 0.$$

Multiplying by $v$, we find

$$vx(1 - y) = 0,$$
$$vxy = 0,$$

which are interpretable into

$$\text{Some Xs are Ys} \ldots\ldots\ldots\ldots \text{I},$$
$$\text{Some Xs are not Ys} \ldots\ldots\ldots \text{O}.$$

[30] Hence a universal-affirmative is convertible into a particular-affirmative, and a universal-negative into a particular-negative without negation of subject or predicate.

Combining the above with the already proved rule of simple conversion, we arrive at the following system of independent laws of transformation.

1st. An affirmative Proposition may be changed into its corresponding negative (A into E, or I into O), and *vice versâ*, by negation of the predicate.

2nd. A universal Proposition may be changed into its corresponding particular Proposition (A into I, or E into O).

3rd. In a particular-affirmative, or universal-negative Proposition, the terms may be mutually converted.

Wherein negation of a term is the changing of X into not-X, and *vice versâ*, and is not to be understood as affecting the *kind* of the Proposition.

Every lawful transformation is reducible to the above rules.  Thus we have

> All Xs are Ys,
> No Xs are not-Ys        by 1st rule,
> No not-Ys are Xs        by 3rd rule,
> All not-Ys are not-Xs by 1st rule,

which is an example of *negative conversion*.  Again,

> No Xs are Ys,
> No Ys are Xs          3rd rule,
> All Ys are not-Xs     1st rule,

which is the case already deduced.

## [31]                    OF SYLLOGISMS.

A Syllogism consists of three Propositions, the last of which, called the conclusion, is a logical consequence of the two former, called the premises; e.g.

$$\textit{Premises}, \begin{cases} \text{All Ys are Xs.} \\ \text{All Zs are Ys.} \end{cases}$$
$$\textit{Conclusion}, \text{ All Zs are Xs.}$$

Every syllogism has three and only three terms, whereof that which is the subject of the conclusion is called the *minor* term, the predicate of the conclusion, the *major* term, and the remaining term common to both premises, the middle term.  Thus, in the above formula, Z is the minor term, X the major term, Y the middle term.

The figure of a syllogism consists in the situation of the middle term with respect to the terms of the conclusion.  The varieties of figure are exhibited in the annexed scheme.

| 1st Fig. | 2nd Fig. | 3rd Fig. | 4th Fig. |
|---|---|---|---|
| YX | XY | YX | XY |
| ZY | ZY | YZ | YZ |
| ZX | ZX | ZX | ZX |

When we designate the three propositions of a syllogism by their usual symbols (A, E, I, O), and in their actual order, we are said to determine the mood of the syllogism.  Thus the syllogism given above, by way of illustration, belongs to the mood AAA in the first figure.

The moods of all syllogisms commonly received as valid, are represented by the vowels in the following mnemonic verses.

Fig. 1.—bArbArA, cElArEnt, dArII, fErIO que prioris.
Fig. 2.—cEsArE, cAmEstrEs, fEstIno, bArOkO, secundæ.
Fig. 3.—Tertia dArAptI, dIsAmIs, dAtIsI, fElAptOn,
        bOkArdO, fErIsO, habet : quarta insuper addit.
Fig. 4.—brAmAntIp, cAmEnEs, dImArIs, fEsapO, frEsIsOn.

THE equation by which we express any Proposition concerning the classes X and Y, is an equation between the symbols $x$ and $y$, and the equation by which we express any [32] Proposition concerning the classes Y and Z, is an equation between the symbols $y$ and $z$. If from two such equations we eliminate $y$, the result, if it do not vanish, will be an equation between $x$ and $z$, and will be interpretable into a Proposition concerning the classes X and Z. And it will then constitute the third member, or Conclusion, of a Syllogism, of which the two given Propositions are the premises.

The result of the elimination of $y$ from the equations

$$ay + b = 0,$$
$$a'y + b' = 0, \quad (14),$$

is the equation     $ab' - a'b = 0, \quad (15).$

Now the equations of Propositions being of the first order with reference to each of the variables involved, all the cases of elimination which we shall have to consider, will be reducible to the above case, the constants $a$, $b$, $a'$, $b'$, being replaced by functions of $x$, $z$, and the auxiliary symbol $v$.

As to the choice of equations for the expression of our premises, the only restriction is, that the equations must not *both* be of the form $ay = 0$, for in such cases elimination would be impossible. When both equations are of this form, it is necessary to solve one of them, and it is indifferent which we choose for this purpose. If that which we select is of the form $xy = 0$, its solution is

$$y = v(1 - x), \quad (16),$$

if of the form $(1 - x)y = 0$, the solution will be

$$y = vx, \quad (17),$$

and these are the only cases which can arise. The reason of this exception will appear in the sequel.

For the sake of uniformity we shall, in the expression of particular propositions, confine ourselves to the forms

$$vx = vy, \qquad \text{Some Xs are Ys,}$$
$$vx = v(1 - y), \quad \text{Some Xs are not Ys.}$$

[33] These have a closer analogy with (16) and (17), than the other forms which might be used.

Between the forms about to be developed, and the Aristotelian canons, some points of difference will occasionally be observed, of which it may be proper to forewarn the reader.

To the right understanding of these it is proper to remark, that the essential structure of a Syllogism is, in some measure, arbitrary. Supposing the order of the premises to be fixed, and the distinction of the major and the minor term to be thereby determined, it is purely a matter of choice which of the two shall have precedence in the Conclusion. Logicians have settled this question in favour of the minor term, but it is clear, that this is a convention. Had it been agreed that the major term should have the first place in the conclusion, a logical scheme might have been constructed, less convenient in some cases than the existing one, but superior in others. What it lost in *barbara*, it would gain in *bramantip*. Convenience is *perhaps* in favour of the adopted arrangement,* but it is to be remembered that it is *merely* an arrangement.

Now the method we shall exhibit, not having reference to one scheme of arrangement more than to another, will always give the more general conclusion, regard being paid only to its abstract lawfulness, considered as a result of pure reasoning. And therefore we shall sometimes have presented to us the spectacle of conclusions, which a logician would pronounce informal, but never of such as a reasoning being would account false.

The Aristotelian canons, however, beside restricting the *order* of the terms of a conclusion, limit their nature also;— and this limitation is of more consequence than the former.

* The contrary view was maintained by Hobbes. The question is very fairly discussed in Hallam's *Introduction to the Literature of Europe*, vol. III, p. 309. In the rhetorical use of Syllogism, the advantage appears to rest with the rejected form.

We may, by a change of figure, replace the particular conclusion [34] of *bramantip*, by the general conclusion of *barbara*; but we cannot thus reduce to rule such inferences, as

Some not-Xs are not Ys.

Yet there are cases in which such inferences may lawfully be drawn, and in unrestricted argument they are of frequent occurrence. Now if an inference of this, or of any other kind, is lawful in itself, it will be exhibited in the results of our method.

We may by restricting the canon of interpretation confine our expressed results within the limits of the scholastic logic; but this would only be to restrict ourselves to the use of a part of the conclusions to which our analysis entitles us.

The classification we shall adopt will be purely mathematical, and we shall afterwards consider the logical arrangement to which it corresponds. It will be sufficient, for reference, to name the premises and the Figure in which they are found.

CLASS 1st.—Forms in which $v$ does not enter.

Those which admit of an inference are AA, EA, Fig. 1; AE, EA, Fig. 2; AA, AE, Fig. 4.

Ex. AA, Fig. 1, and, by mutation of premises (change of order), AA, Fig. 4.

| All Ys are Xs, | $y(1 - x) = 0,$ | or $(1 - x)y = 0.$ |
|---|---|---|
| All Zs are Ys, | $z(1 - y) = 0,$ | or $zy - z = 0.$ |

Eliminating $y$ by (15) we have

$$z(1 - x) = 0,$$
$$\therefore \quad \text{All Zs are Xs.}$$

A convenient mode of effecting the elimination, is to write the equation of the premises, so that $y$ shall appear only as a factor of one member in the first equation, and only as a factor of the opposite member in the second equation, and then to multiply the equations, omitting the $y$. This method we shall adopt.

[35] Ex. AE, Fig. 2, and, by mutation of premises, EA, Fig. 2.

| All Xs are Ys, | $x(1 - y) = 0,$ | or $x = xy$ |
|---|---|---|
| No Zs are Ys, | $zy = 0,$ | $zy = 0$ |

$$zx = 0$$

$$\therefore \text{ No Zs are Xs.}$$

The only case in which there is no inference is AA, Fig. 2,

| All Xs are Ys, | $x(1 - y) = 0,$ | $x = xy$ |
|---|---|---|
| All Zs are Ys, | $z(1 - y) = 0,$ | $zy = z$ |

$$xz = xz$$

$$\therefore \quad 0 = 0.$$

CLASS 2nd.—When $v$ is introduced by the solution of an equation.

The lawful cases directly or indirectly * determinable by the Aristotelian Rules are AE, Fig. 1; AA, AE, EA, Fig. 3; EA, Fig. 4.

The lawful cases not so determinable are EE, Fig. 1; EE, Fig. 2; EE, Fig. 3; EE, Fig. 4.

Ex. AE, Fig. 1, and, by mutation of premises, EA, Fig. 4.

| All Ys are Xs, | $y(1 - x) = 0,$ | $y = vx$ $(a)$ |
|---|---|---|
| No Zs are Ys, | $zy = 0,$ | $0 = zy$ |

$$0 = vzx$$

$$\therefore \text{ Some Xs are not Zs.}$$

The reason why we cannot interpret $vzx = 0$ into Some Zs are not-Xs, is that by the very terms of the first equation (a) the interpretation of $vx$ is fixed, as Some Xs; $v$ is regarded as the representative of Some, only with reference to the class X.

[36] For the reason of our employing a solution of one of the primitive equations, see the remarks on (16) and (17). Had

---

* We say *directly* or *indirectly*, mutation or conversion of premises being in some instances required. Thus, AE (fig. 1) is resolvable by Fesapo (fig. 4), or by Ferio (fig. 1). Aristotle and his followers rejected the fourth figure as only a modification of the first, but this being a mere question of form, either scheme may be termed Aristotelian.

we solved the second equation instead of the first, we should have had

$$(1 - x)y = 0,$$
$$v(1 - z) = y, \quad (a),$$
$$v(1 - z)(1 - x) = 0, \quad (b),$$
$$\therefore \quad \text{Some not-Zs are Xs.}$$

Here it is to be observed, that the second equation $(a)$ fixes the meaning of $v(1 - z)$, as Some not-Zs. The full meaning of the result $(b)$ is, that all the not-Zs which are found in the class Y are found in the class X, and it is evident that this could not have been expressed in any other way.

Ex. 2. AA, Fig. 3.

| | | |
|---|---|---|
| All Ys are Xs, | $y(1 - x) = 0,$ | $y = vx$ |
| All Ys are Zs, | $y(1 - z) = 0,$ | $0 = y(1 - z)$ |

$$0 = vx(1 - z)$$
$$\therefore \quad \text{Some Xs are Zs.}$$

Had we solved the second equation, we should have had as our result, Some Zs are Xs. The form of the final equation particularizes what Xs or what Zs are referred to, and this remark is general.

The following, EE, Fig. 1, and, by mutation, EE, Fig. 4, is an example of a lawful case not determinable by the Aristotelian Rules.

| | | |
|---|---|---|
| No Ys are Xs, | $xy = 0,$ | $0 = xy$ |
| No Zs are Ys, | $zy = 0,$ | $y = v(1 - z)$ |

$$0 = v(1 - z)x$$
$$\therefore \quad \text{Some not-Zs are not Xs.}$$

CLASS 3rd.—When $v$ is met with in one of the equations, but not introduced by solution.

[37] The lawful cases determinable *directly* or *indirectly* by the Aristotelian Rules, are AI, EI, Fig. 1; AO, EI, OA, IE, Fig. 2; AI, AO, EI, EO, IA, IE, OA, OE, Fig. 3; IA, IE, Fig. 4.

Those not so determinable are OE, Fig. 1; EO, Fig. 4.

The cases in which no inference is possible, are AO, EO,

IA, IE, OA, Fig. 1; AI, EO, IA, OE, Fig. 2; OA, OE, AI, EI, AO, Fig. 4.

Ex. 1. AI, Fig. 1, and, by mutation, IA, Fig. 4.

All Ys are Xs,   $y(1-x)=0$
Some Zs are Ys,       $vz=vy$

$$vz(1-x)=0$$

$\therefore$   Some Zs are Xs.

Ex. 2. AO, Fig. 2, and, by mutation, OA, Fig. 2.

All Xs are Ys,      $x(1-y)=0,$           $x=xy$
Some Zs are not Ys,     $vz=v(1-y),$   $vy=v(1-z)$

$$vz=vx(1-z)$$
$$vxz=0$$

$\therefore$   Some Zs are not Xs.

The interpretation of $vz$ as Some Zs, is implied, it will be observed, in the equation $vz=v(1-y)$ considered as representing the proposition Some Zs are not Ys.

The cases not determinable by the Aristotelian Rules are OE, Fig. 1, and, by mutation, EO, Fig. 4.

Some Ys are not Xs,   $vy=v(1-x)$
No Zs are Ys,       $0=zy$

$$0=v(1-x)z$$

$\therefore$   Some not-Xs are not Zs.

The equation of the first premiss here permits us to interpret $v(1-x)$, but it does not enable us to interpret $vz$.

[38] Of cases in which no inference is possible we take as examples—

AO, Fig. 1, and, by mutation, OA, Fig. 4,

All Ys are Xs,  $y(1-x)=0,$                $y(1-x)=0$
Some Zs are not
Ys,              $vz=v(1-y)$   $(a)$   $v(1-z)=vy$

$$v(1-z)(1-x)=0 \ (b)$$
$$0=0$$

since the auxiliary equation in this case is $v(1-z)=0$.

Practically it is not necessary to perform this reduction, but it is satisfactory to do so. The equation $(a)$, it is seen, defines $vz$ as Some Zs, but it does not define $v(1 - z)$, so that we might stop at the result of elimination $(b)$, and content ourselves with saying, that it is not interpretable into a relation between the classes X and Z.

Take as a second example AI, Fig. 2, and, by mutation, IA, Fig. 2,

$$\text{All Xs are Ys,} \qquad x(1 - y) = 0, \qquad\qquad x = xy$$
$$\text{Some Zs are Ys,} \qquad vz = vy, \qquad\qquad vy = vz$$

$$vx = vxz$$
$$v(1 - z)x = 0$$
$$0 = 0,$$

the auxiliary equation in this case being $v(1 - z) = 0$.

Indeed, in every case in this class, in which no inference is possible, the result of elimination is reducible to the form $0 = 0$. Examples therefore need not be multiplied.

CLASS 4th.—When $v$ enters into both equations.

No inference is possible in any case, but there exists a distinction among the unlawful cases which is peculiar to this class. The two divisions are,

1st. When the result of elimination is reducible by the auxiliary equations to the form $0 = 0$. The cases are II, OI, [39] Fig. 1; II, OO, Fig. 2; II, IO, OI, OO, Fig. 3; II, IO, Fig. 4.

2nd. When the result of elimination is not reducible by the auxiliary equations to the form $0 = 0$.

The cases are IO, OO, Fig. 1; IO, OI, Fig. 2; OI, OO, Fig. 4.

Let us take as an example of the former case, II, Fig. 3.

$$\text{Some Xs are Ys,} \qquad vx = vy, \qquad vx = vy$$
$$\text{Some Zs are Ys,} \qquad v'z = v'y, \qquad v'y = v'z$$

$$vv'x = vv'z$$

Now the auxiliary equations $v(1 - x) = 0$, $v'(1 - z) = 0$,
give $vx = v$, $v'z = v'$.

Substituting we have   $vv' = vv'$,

$$\therefore 0 = 0.$$

As an example of the latter case, let us take IO, Fig. 1,

| Some Ys are Xs, | $vy = vx$, | $vy = vx$ |
| Some Zs are not Ys, | $v'z = v'(1 - y)$, | $v'(1 - z) = v'y$ |

$$vv'(1 - z) = vv'x$$

Now the auxiliary equations being

$$v(1 - x) = 0, \; v'(1 - z) = 0,$$

the above reduces to $vv' = 0$.   It is to this form that all similar cases are reducible.   Its interpretation is that the classes $v$ and $v'$ have no common member, as is indeed evident.

The above classification is purely founded on mathematical distinctions.   We shall now inquire what is the logical division to which it corresponds.

The lawful cases of the first class comprehend all those in which, from two universal premises, a universal conclusion may be drawn.   We see that they include the premises of *barbara* and *celarent* in the first figure, of *cesare* and *camestres* in the second, and of *bramantip* and *camenes* in the fourth. [40] The premises of *bramantip* are included, because they admit of an universal conclusion, although not in the same figure.

The lawful cases of the second class are those in which a particular conclusion only is deducible from two universal premises.

The lawful cases of the third class are those in which a conclusion is deducible from two premises, one of which is universal and the other particular.

The fourth class has no lawful cases.

Among the cases in which no inference of any kind is possible, we find six in the fourth class distinguishable from the others by the circumstance, that the result of elimination does not assume the form $0 = 0$.   The cases are

$$\begin{cases} \text{Some Ys are Xs,} \\ \text{Some Zs are not Ys,} \end{cases} \begin{cases} \text{Some Ys are not Xs,} \\ \text{Some Zs are not Ys,} \end{cases}$$

$$\begin{cases} \text{Some Xs are Ys,} \\ \text{Some Zs are not Ys,} \end{cases}$$

F

and the three others which are obtained by mutation of premises.

It might be presumed that some logical peculiarity would be found to answer to the mathematical peculiarity which we have noticed, and in fact there exists a very remarkable one. If we examine each pair of premises in the above scheme, we shall find that there *is virtually* no middle term, i.e. *no medium of comparison*, in any of them. Thus, in the first example, the individuals spoken of in the first premiss are asserted to belong to the class Y, but those spoken of in the second premiss are *virtually* asserted to belong to the class not-Y : nor can we by any lawful transformation or conversion alter this state of things. The comparison will still be made with the class Y in one premiss, and with the class not-Y in the other.

Now in every case beside the above six, there will be found a middle term, either expressed or implied. I select two of the most difficult cases.

[41] In AO, Fig. 1, viz.

> All Ys are Xs,
> Some Zs are not Ys,

we have, by *negative conversion* of the first premiss,

> All not-Xs are not-Ys,
> Some Zs are not Ys,

and the middle term is now seen to be not-Y.

Again, in EO, Fig. 1,

> No Ys are Xs,
> Some Zs are not Ys,

a proved conversion of the first premiss (see *Conversion of Propositions*), gives

> All Xs are not-Ys,
> Some Zs are not-Ys,

and the middle term, the true medium of comparison, is plainly not-Y, although as the not-Ys in the one premiss *may be* different from those in the other, no conclusion can be drawn.

The mathematical condition in question, therefore,—the irreducibility of the final equation to the form $0 = 0$,—adequately represents the logical condition of there being no middle term, or common medium of comparison, in the given premises.

I am not aware that the distinction occasioned by the presence or absence of a middle term, in the strict sense here understood, has been noticed by logicians before. The distinction, though real and deserving attention, is indeed by no means an obvious one, and it would have been un-noticed in the present instance but for the peculiarity of its mathematical expression.

What appears to be novel in the above case is the proof of the existence of combinations of premises in which there [42] is absolutely no medium of comparison. When such a medium of comparison, or true middle term, does exist, the condition that its quantification in both premises to-gether shall exceed its quantification as a single whole, has been ably and clearly shewn by Professor De Morgan to be necessary to lawful inference (*Cambridge Memoirs*, vol. VIII. Part 3). And this is undoubtedly the true principle of the Syllogism, viewed from the standing-point of Arithmetic.

I have said that it would be possible to impose conditions of interpretation which should restrict the results of this calculus to the Aristotelian forms. Those conditions would be,

1st. That we should agree not to interpret the forms $v(1 - x)$, $v(1 - z)$.

2ndly. That we should agree to reject every interpretation in which the order of the terms should violate the Aristotelian rule.

Or, instead of the second condition, it might be agreed that, the conclusion being determined, the order of the premises should, if necessary, be changed, so as to make the syllogism formal.

From the *general* character of the system it is indeed plain, that it may be made to represent any conceivable scheme of logic, by imposing the conditions proper to the case con-templated.

We have found it, in a certain class of cases, to be necessary to replace the two equations expressive of universal Propositions by their solutions; and it may be proper to remark, that it would have been allowable in all instances to have done this,* so that every case of the Syllogism, without

* It may be satisfactory to illustrate this statement by an example.  In *Barbara*, we should have :

$$\begin{aligned} \text{All Ys are Xs,} \quad & y = vx \\ \text{All Zs are Ys,} \quad & z = v'y \\ \hline & z = vv'x \\ & \therefore \text{ All Zs are Xs.} \end{aligned}$$

Or, we may multiply the resulting equation by $1 - x$, which gives

$$z(1 - x) = 0,$$

whence the same conclusion, All Zs are Xs.

Some additional examples of the application of the system of equations in the text to the demonstration of general theorems, may not be inappropriate.

Let $y$ be the term to be eliminated, and let $x$ stand indifferently for either of the other symbols, then each of the equations of the premises of any given syllogism may be put in the form

$$ay + bx = 0, \quad (a)$$

if the premiss is affirmative, and in the form

$$ay + b(1 - x) = 0, \quad (\beta)$$

if it is negative, $a$ and $b$ being either constant, or of the form $\pm v$. To prove this in detail, let us examine each kind of proposition, making $y$ successively subject and predicate.

| | |
|---|---|
| A, All Ys are Xs, | $y - vx = 0,$ $\quad(\gamma),$ |
| All Xs are Ys, | $x - vy = 0,$ $\quad(\delta),$ |
| E, No Ys are Xs, | $xy = 0,$ |
| No Xs are Ys, | $y - v(1 - x) = 0,$ $\quad(\epsilon),$ |
| I, Some Xs are Ys, | |
| Some Ys are Xs, | $vx - vy = 0,$ $\quad(\zeta),$ |
| O, Some Ys are not Xs, | $vy - v(1 - x) = 0,$ $\quad(\eta),$ |
| Some Xs are not Ys, | $vx = v(1 - y),$ |
| | $\therefore \quad vy - v(1 - x) = 0,$ $\quad(\theta).$ |

The affirmative equations $(\gamma)$, $(\delta)$ and $(\zeta)$, belong to $(a)$, and the negative equations $(\epsilon)$, $(\eta)$ and $(\theta)$, to $(\beta)$. It is seen that the two last negative equations are alike, but there is a difference of interpretation. In the former

$$v(1 - x) = \text{Some not-Xs,}$$

in the latter,

$$v(1 - x) = 0.$$

The utility of the two general forms of reference, $(a)$ and $(\beta)$, will appear from the following application.

1st. *A conclusion drawn from two affirmative propositions* is itself affirmative.

By (*a*) we have for the given propositions,

$$ay + bx = 0,$$
$$a'y + b'z = 0,$$

and eliminating          $ab'z - a'bx = 0,$

which is of the form (*a*).  Hence, if there is a conclusion, it is affirmative.

2nd.  *A conclusion drawn from an affirmative and a negative propositions is negative.*

By (*a*) and (*β*), we have for the given propositions

$$ay + bx = 0,$$
$$a'y + b' (1 - z) = 0,$$
$$\therefore \quad a'bx - ab' (1 - z) = 0,$$

which is of the form (*β*).  Hence the conclusion, if there is one, is negative.

3rd.  *A conclusion drawn from two negative premises will involve a negation, (not-X, not-Z) in both subject and predicate, and will therefore be inadmissible in the Aristotelian system, though just in itself.*

For the premises being

$$ay + b (1 - x) = 0,$$
$$a'y + b' (1 - z) = 0,$$

the conclusion will be

$$ab' (1 - z) - a'b (1 - x) = 0,$$

which is only interpretable into a proposition that has a negation in each term.

4th.  *Taking into account those syllogisms only, in which the conclusion is the most general, that can be deduced from the premises,—if, in an Aristotelian syllogism, the minor premises be changed in quality (from affirmative to negative or from negative to affirmative), whether it be changed in quantity or not, no conclusion will be deducible in the same figure.*

An Aristotelian proposition does not admit a term of the form not-Z in the subject.—Now on changing the quantity of the minor proposition of a syllogism, we transfer it from the general form

$$ay + bz = 0,$$

to the general form          $a'y + b' (1 - z) = 0,$

see (*a*) *and* (*β*), or *vice versâ*.  And therefore, in the equation of the conclusion, there will be a change from *z* to $1 - z$, or *vice versâ*.  But this is equivalent to the change of Z into not-Z, or not-Z into Z.  Now the subject of the original conclusion must have involved a Z and not a not-Z, therefore the subject of the new conclusion will involve a not-Z, and the conclusion will not be admissible in the Aristotelian forms, except by conversion, which would render necessary a change of Figure.

Now the conclusions of this calculus are always the most general that can be drawn, and therefore the above demonstration must not be supposed to extend to a syllogism, in which a particular conclusion is deduced, when a universal one is possible.  This is the case with *bramantip* only, among the Aristotelian forms, and therefore the transformation of *bramantip* into *camenes*, and *vice versâ*, is the case of restriction contemplated in the preliminary statement of the theorem.

5th.  *If for the minor premiss of an Aristotelian syllogism, we substitute its contradictory, no conclusion is deducible in the same figure.*

It is here only necessary to examine the case of *bramantip*, all the others being determined by the last proposition.

On changing the minor of *bramantip* to its contradictory, we have AO, Fig. 4, and this admits of no legitimate inference.

Hence the theorem is true without exception.  Many other general theorems may in like manner be proved.

ex[43]ception, might have been treated by equations comprised in the general forms

$$y = vx, \qquad \text{or} \qquad y - vx = 0 \ldots\ldots A,$$
$$y = v(1 - x), \qquad \text{or } y + vx - v = 0 \ldots\ldots E,$$
$$vy = vx, \qquad\qquad vy - vx = 0 \ldots\ldots I,$$
$$vy = v(1 - x), \qquad vy + vx - v = 0 \ldots\ldots O.$$

[44] Perhaps the system we have actually employed is better, as distinguishing the cases in which $v$ only *may* be employed, [45] from those in which it *must*. But for the demonstration of certain general properties of the Syllogism, the above system is, from its simplicity, and from the mutual analogy of its forms, very convenient. We shall apply it to the following theorem.*

Given the three propositions of a Syllogism, prove that there is but one order in which they can be legitimately arranged, and determine that order.

All the forms above given for the expression of propositions are particular cases of the general form,

$$a + bx + cy = 0.$$

* This elegant theorem was communicated by the Rev. Charles Graves, Fellow and Professor of Mathematics in Trinity College, Dublin, to whom the Author desires further to record his grateful acknowledgments for a very judicious examination of the former portion of this work, and for some new applications of the method. The following example of Reduction *ad impossibile* is among the number :

| Reducend Mood, *Baroko* | All Xs are Ys, | $1 - y = v'(1 - x)$ |
|---|---|---|
| | Some Zs are not Ys | $vz = v(1 - y)$ |
| | Some Zs are not Xs | $vz = vv'(1 - x)$ |
| Reduct Mood, *Barbara* | All Xs are Ys | $1 - y = v'(1 - x)$ |
| | All Zs are Xs | $z(1 - x) = 0$ |
| | All Zs are Ys | $z(1 - y) = 0.$ |

The conclusion of the reduct mood is seen to be the contradictory of the suppressed minor premiss. Whence, &c. It may just be remarked that the mathematical test of contradictory propositions is, that on eliminating one elective symbol between their equations, the other elective symbol vanishes. The *ostensive* reduction of *Baroko* and *Bokardo* involves no difficulty.

Professor Graves suggests the employment of the equation $x = vy$ for the primary expression of the Proposition All Xs are Ys, and remarks, that on multiplying both members by $1 - y$, we obtain $x(1 - y) = 0$, the equation from which we set out in the text, and of which the previous one is a solution.

[46] Assume, then, for the premises of the given syllogism, the equations

$$a + bx + cy = 0, \quad (18),$$
$$a' + b'z + c'y = 0, \quad (19),$$

then, eliminating $y$, we shall have for the conclusion

$$ac' - a'c + bc'x - b'cz = 0, \quad (20).$$

Now taking this as one of our premises, and either of the original equations, suppose (18), as the other, if by elimination of a common term $x$, between them, we can obtain a result equivalent to the remaining premiss (19), it will appear that there are more than one order in which the Propositions may be lawfully written; but if otherwise, one arrangement only is lawful.

Effecting then the elimination, we have

$$bc(a' + b'z + c'y) = 0, \quad (21),$$

which is equivalent to (19) multiplied by a factor $bc$. Now on examining the value of this factor in the equations A, E, I, O, we find it in each case to be $v$ or $-v$. But it is evident, that if an equation expressing a given Proposition be multiplied by an extraneous factor, derived from another equation, its interpretation will either be limited or rendered impossible. Thus there will either be no result at all, or the result will be a *limitation* of the remaining Proposition.

If, however, one of the original equations were

$$x = y, \quad \text{or } x - y = 0,$$

the factor $bc$ would be $-1$, and would *not* limit the interpretation of the other premiss. Hence if the first member of a syllogism should be understood to represent the double proposition All Xs are Ys, and All Ys are Xs, it would be indifferent in what order the remaining Propositions were written.

[47] A more general form of the above investigation would be, to express the premises by the equations

$$a + bx + cy + dxy = 0, \quad (22),$$
$$a' + b'z + c'y + d'zy = 0, \quad (23).$$

After the double elimination of $y$ and $x$ we should find

$$(bc - ad)(a' + b'z + c'y + d'zy) = 0;$$

and it would be seen that the factor $bc - ad$ must in every case either vanish or express a limitation of meaning.

The determination of the order of the Propositions is sufficiently obvious.


[48]                    OF HYPOTHETICALS

A hypothetical Proposition is defined to be *two or more categoricals united by a copula* (or conjunction), and the different kinds of hypothetical Propositions are named from their respective conjunctions, viz. conditional (if), disjunctive (either, or), &c.

In conditionals, that categorical Proposition from which the other results is called the *antecedent*, that which results from it the *consequent*.

Of the conditional syllogism there are two, and only two formulæ.

1st.   The constructive,

                    If A is B, then C is D,
                    But A is B, therefore C is D.

2nd.   The Destructive,

                    If A is B, then C is D,
                    But C is not D, therefore A is not B.

A dilemma is a complex conditional syllogism, with several antecedents in the major, and a disjunctive minor.

IF we examine either of the forms of conditional syllogism above given, we shall see that the validity of the argument does not depend upon any considerations which have reference to the terms A, B, C, D, considered as the representatives of individuals or of classes.   We may, in fact, represent the Propositions A is B, C is D, by the arbitrary symbols X and Y respectively, and express our syllogisms in such forms as the following :

                    If X is true, then Y is true,
                    But X is true, therefore Y is true.

Thus, what we have to consider is not objects and classes of objects, but the truths of Propositions, namely, of those [49] elementary Propositions which are embodied in the terms of our hypothetical premises.

To the symbols X, Y, Z, representative of Propositions, we may appropriate the elective symbols $x, y, z$, in the following sense.

The hypothetical Universe, 1, shall comprehend all conceivable cases and conjunctures of circumstances.

The elective symbol $x$ attached to any subject expressive of such cases shall select those cases in which the Proposition X is true, and similarly for Y and Z.

If we confine ourselves to the contemplation of a given proposition X, and hold in abeyance every other consideration, then two cases only are conceivable, viz. first that the given Proposition is true, and secondly that it is false.* As these cases together make up the Universe of the Proposition, and as the former is determined by the elective symbol $x$, the latter is determined by the symbol $1 - x$.

But if other considerations are admitted, each of these cases will be resolvable into others, individually less extensive, the [50] number of which will depend upon the number of foreign considerations admitted. Thus if we associate the Proposition X and Y, the total number of conceivable cases will be found as exhibited in the following scheme.

| Cases. | Elective expressions. |
|---|---|
| 1st   X true, Y true .......... | $xy$ |
| 2nd   X true, Y false .......... | $x(1 - y)$ |
| 3rd   X false, Y true .......... | $(1 - x)y$ |
| 4th   X false, Y false .......... | $(1 - x)(1 - y)$   (24). |

If we add the elective expressions for the two first of the

---

* It was upon the obvious principle that a Proposition is either true or false, that the Stoics, applying it to assertions respecting future events, endeavoured to establish the doctrine of Fate. It has been replied to their argument, that it involves " an abuse of the word *true*, the precise meaning of which is id quod res *est*. An assertion respecting the future is neither true nor false."—*Copleston on Necessity and Predestination*, p. 36. Were the Stoic axiom, however, presented under the form, It is either certain that a given event will take place, or certain that it will not; the above reply would fail to meet the difficulty. The proper answer would be, that no merely verbal definition can settle the question, what is the actual course and constitution of Nature. When we affirm that it is either certain that an event will take place, or certain that it will not take place, we tacitly assume that the order of events is necessary, that the Future is but an evolution of the Present; so that the state of things which is, completely determines that which shall be. But this (at least as respects the conduct of moral agents) is the very question at issue. Exhibited under its proper form, the Stoic reasoning does not involve an abuse of terms, but a *petitio principii*.

It should be added, that enlightened advocates of the doctrine of Necessity in the present day, viewing the end as appointed only in and through the means, justly repudiate those practical ill consequences which are the reproach of Fatalism.

above cases the sum is $x$, which is the elective symbol appropriate to the more general case of X being true independently of any consideration of Y; and if we add the elective expressions in the two last cases together, the result is $1 - x$, which is the elective expression appropriate to the more general case of X being false.

Thus the extent of the hypothetical Universe does not at all depend upon the number of circumstances which are taken into account. And it is to be noted that however few or many those circumstances may be, the sum of the elective expressions representing every conceivable case will be unity. Thus let us consider the three Propositions, X, It rains, Y, It hails, Z, It freezes. The possible cases are the following :

| Cases. | Elective expressions. |
|---|---|
| 1st  It rains, hails, and freezes, | $xyz$ |
| 2nd  It rains and hails, but does not freeze .................... | $xy(1 - z)$ |
| 3rd  It rains and freezes, but does not hail ...................... | $xz(1 - y)$ |
| 4th  It freezes and hails, but does not rain ...................... | $yz(1 - x)$ |
| 5th  It rains, but neither hails nor freezes ................... | $x(1 - y)(1 - z)$ |
| 6th  It hails, but neither rains nor freezes ................... | $y(1 - x)(1 - z)$ |
| 7th  It freezes, but neither hails nor rains ................... | $z(1 - x)(1 - y)$ |
| 8th  It neither rains, hails, nor freezes | $(1 - x)(1 - y)(1 - z)$ |

$$1 = \text{sum}$$

[51]    *Expression of Hypothetical Propositions.*

To express that a given Proposition X is true.

The symbol $1 - x$ selects those cases in which the Proposition X is false. But if the Proposition is true, there are no such cases in its hypothetical Universe, therefore

$$1 - x = 0,$$
or $$x = 1, \quad (25).$$

To express that a given Proposition X is false.

The elective symbol $x$ selects all those cases in which the Proposition is true, and therefore if the Proposition is false,

$$x = 0, \quad (26).$$

And in every case, having determined the elective expression appropriate to a given Proposition, we assert the truth of that Proposition by equating the elective expression to unity, and its falsehood by equating the same expression to 0.

To express that two Propositions, X and Y, are simultaneously true.

The elective symbol appropriate to this case is $xy$, therefore the equation sought is

$$xy = 1, \quad (27).$$

To express that two Propositions, X and Y, are simultaneously false.

The condition will obviously be

$$(1 - x)(1 - y) = 1,$$

or $\qquad x + y - xy = 0, \quad (28).$

To express that either the Proposition X is true, or the Proposition Y is true.

To assert that either one or the other of two Propositions is true, is to assert that it is not true, that they are both false. Now the elective expression appropriate to their both being false is $(1 - x)(1 - y)$, therefore the equation required is

$$(1 - x)(1 - y) = 0,$$

or $\qquad x + y - xy = 1, \quad (29).$

[52] And, by indirect considerations of this kind, may every disjunctive Proposition, however numerous its members, be expressed. But the following general Rule will usually be preferable.

RULE. *Consider what are those distinct and mutually exclusive cases of which it is implied in the statement of the given Proposition, that some one of them is true, and equate the sum of their elective expressions to unity. This will give the equation of the given Proposition.*

For the sum of the elective expressions for all distinct conceivable cases will be unity. Now all these cases being mutually exclusive, and it being asserted in the given Proposition that some one case out of a given set of them is true, it follows that all which are not included in that set are false, and that their elective expressions are severally equal to 0. Hence the sum of the elective expressions for the remaining cases, viz. those included in the given set, will be unity. Some one of those cases will therefore be true, and as they are mutually exclusive, it is impossible that more than one should be true. Whence the Rule in question.

And in the application of this Rule it is to be observed, that if the cases contemplated in the given disjunctive Proposition are not mutually exclusive, they must be resolved into an equivalent series of cases which are mutually exclusive.

Thus, if we take the Proposition of the preceding example, viz. Either X is true, or Y is true, and assume that the two members of this Proposition are not exclusive, insomuch that in the enumeration of possible cases, we must reckon that of the Propositions X and Y being both true, then the mutually exclusive cases which fill up the Universe of the Proposition, with their elective expressions, are

$$1\text{st,} \quad \text{X true and Y false,} \quad x(1 - y),$$
$$2\text{nd,} \quad \text{Y true and X false,} \quad y(1 - x),$$
$$3\text{rd,} \quad \text{X true and Y true,} \quad xy,$$

[53] and the sum of these elective expressions equated to unity gives

$$x + y - xy = 1, \quad (30),$$

as before. But if we suppose the members of the disjunctive Proposition to be exclusive, then the only cases to be considered are

$$1\text{st,} \quad \text{X true, Y false,} \quad x(1 - y),$$
$$2\text{nd,} \quad \text{Y true, X false,} \quad y(1 - x),$$

and the sum of these elective expressions equated to 1, gives

$$x - 2xy + y = 1, \quad (31).$$

The subjoined examples will further illustrate this method.

To express the Proposition, Either X is not true, or Y is not true, the members being exclusive.

The mutually exclusive cases are

1st,  X not true, Y true,     $y(1-x)$,
2nd, Y not true, X true,     $x(1-y)$,

and the sum of these equated to unity gives

$$x - 2xy + y = 1, \quad (32),$$

which is the same as (31), and in fact the Propositions which they represent are equivalent.

To express the Proposition, Either X is not true, or Y is not true, the members not being exclusive.

To the cases contemplated in the last Example, we must add the following, viz.

X not true, Y not true,     $(1-x)(1-y)$.

The sum of the elective expressions gives

$$x(1-y) + y(1-x) + (1-x)(1-y) = 1,$$
or
$$xy = 0, \quad (33).$$

To express the disjunctive Proposition, Either X is true, or Y is true, or Z is true, the members being exclusive.

[54] Here the mutually exclusive cases are

1st,  X true, Y false, Z false,    $x(1-y)(1-z)$,
2nd, Y true, Z false, X false,    $y(1-z)(1-x)$,
3rd,  Z true, X false, Y false,    $z(1-x)(1-y)$,

and the sum of the elective expressions equated to 1, gives, upon reduction,

$$x + y + z - 2(xy + yz + zx) + 3xyz = 1, \quad (34).$$

The expression of the same Proposition, when the members are in no sense exclusive, will be

$$(1-x)(1-y)(1-z) = 0, \quad (35).$$

And it is easy to see that our method will apply to the expression of any similar Proposition, whose members are subject to any specified amount and character of exclusion.

To express the conditional Proposition, If X is true, Y is true.

Here it is implied that all the cases of X being true, are

cases of Y being true. The former cases being determined by the elective symbol $x$, and the latter by $y$, we have, in virtue of (4),

$$x(1 - y) = 0, \quad (36).$$

To express the conditional Proposition, If X be true, Y is not true.

The equation is obviously

$$xy = 0, \quad (37);$$

this is equivalent to (33), and in fact the disjunctive Proposition, Either X is not true, or Y is not true, and the conditional Proposition, If X is true, Y is not true, are equivalent.

To express that If X is not true, Y is not true.

In (36) write $1 - x$ for $x$, and $1 - y$ for $y$, we have

$$(1 - x)y = 0.$$

[55] The results which we have obtained admit of verification in many different ways. Let it suffice to take for more particular examination the equation

$$x - 2xy + y = 1, \quad (38),$$

which expresses the conditional Proposition, Either X is true, or Y is true, the members being in this case exclusive.

First, let the Proposition X be true, then $x = 1$, and substituting, we have

$$1 - 2y + y = 1, \qquad \therefore \quad -y = 0, \text{ or } y = 0,$$

which implies that Y is not true.

Secondly, let X be not true, then $x = 0$, and the equation gives

$$y = 1, \quad (39),$$

which implies that Y is true. In like manner we may proceed with the assumptions that Y is true, or that Y is false.

Again, in virtue of the property $x^2 = x$, $y^2 = y$, we may write the equation in the form

$$x^2 - 2xy + y^2 = 1,$$

and extracting the square root, we have

$$x - y = \pm 1, \quad (40),$$

and this represents the actual case; for, as when X is true
or false, Y is respectively false or true, we have

$$x = 1 \text{ or } 0,$$
$$y = 0 \text{ or } 1,$$
$$\therefore \quad x - y = 1 \text{ or } -1.$$

There will be no difficulty in the analysis of other cases.

### Examples of Hypothetical Syllogism.

The treatment of every form of hypothetical Syllogism will
consist in forming the equations of the premises, and
eliminating the symbol or symbols which are found in more
than one of them.   The result will express the conclusion.

[56] 1st. Disjunctive Syllogism.

| | |
|---|---|
| Either X is true, or Y is true (exclusive), | $x + y - 2xy = 1$ |
| But X is true, | $x = 1$ |

| | |
|---|---|
| Therefore Y is not true, | $\therefore \quad y = 0$ |
| Either X is true, or Y is true (not exclusive), | $x + y - xy = 1$ |
| But X is not true, | $x = 0$ |

| | |
|---|---|
| Therefore Y is true, | $\therefore \quad y = 1$ |

2nd. Constructive Conditional Syllogism.

| | |
|---|---|
| If X is true, Y is true, | $x(1 - y) = 0$ |
| But X is true, | $x = 1$ |
| Therefore Y is true, | $\therefore \quad 1 - y = 0 \text{ or } y = 1.$ |

3rd. Destructive Conditional Syllogism.

| | |
|---|---|
| If X is true, Y is true, | $x(1 - y) = 0,$ |
| But Y is not true, | $y = 0,$ |
| Therefore X is not true, | $\therefore \quad x = 0.$ |

4th. Simple Constructive Dilemma, the minor premiss
exclusive.

| | | |
|---|---|---|
| If X is true, Y is true, | $x(1 - y) = 0,$ | (41), |
| If Z is true, Y is true, | $z(1 - y) = 0,$ | (42), |
| But Either X is true, or Z is true, | $x + z - 2xz = 1,$ | (43), |

From the equations (41), (42), (43), we have to eliminate $x$ and $z$. In whatever way we effect this, the result is

$$y = 1;$$

whence it appears that the Proposition Y is true.

5th. Complex Constructive Dilemma, the minor premiss not exclusive.

If X is true, Y is true,                    $x(1 - y) = 0,$
If W is true, Z is true,                    $w(1 - z) = 0,$
Either X is true, or W is true,      $x + w - xw = 1.$

From these equations, eliminating $x$, we have

$$y + z - yz = 1,$$

[57] which expresses the Conclusion, Either Y is true, or Z is true, the members being non-exclusive.

6th. Complex Destructive Dilemma, the minor premiss exclusive.

If X is true, Y is true,                    $x(1 - y) = 0$
If W is true, Z is true,                    $w(1 - z) = 0$
Either Y is not true, or Z is not true,      $y + z - 2yz = 1.$

From these equations we must eliminate $y$ and $z$. The result is

$$xw = 0,$$

which expresses the Conclusion, Either X is not true, or Y is not true, the members *not being exclusive*.

7th. Complex Destructive Dilemma, the minor premiss not exclusive.

If X is true, Y is true,                    $x(1 - y) = 0$
If W is true, Z is true,                    $w(1 - z) = 0$
Either Y is not true, or Z is not true,      $yz = 0.$

On elimination of $y$ and $z$, we have

$$xw = 0,$$

which indicates the same Conclusion as the previous example.

It appears from these and similar cases, that whether the members of the minor premiss of a Dilemma are exclusive or not, the members of the (disjunctive) Conclusion are never exclusive. This fact has perhaps escaped the notice of logicians.

The above are the principal forms of hypothetical Syllogism which logicians have recognised. It would be easy, however, to extend the list, especially by the blending of the disjunctive and the conditional character in the same Proposition, of which the following is an example.

If X is true, then either Y is true, or Z is true,

$$x(1 - y - z + yz) = 0$$

But Y is not true,                    $y = 0$

Therefore If X is true, Z is true,    $\therefore \quad x(1 - z) = 0.$

[58] That which logicians term a *Causal* Proposition is properly a conditional Syllogism, the major premiss of which is suppressed.

The assertion that the Proposition X is true, *because* the Proposition Y is true, is equivalent to the assertion,

> The Proposition Y is true,
> *Therefore* the Proposition X is true;

and these are the minor premiss and conclusion of the conditional Syllogism,

> If Y is true, X is true,
> But Y is true,
> Therefore X is true.

And thus causal Propositions are seen to be included in the applications of our general method.

Note, that there is a family of disjunctive and conditional Propositions, which do not, of right, belong to the class considered in this Chapter. Such are those in which the force of the disjunctive or conditional particle is expended upon the predicate of the Proposition, as if, speaking of the inhabitants of a particular island, we should say, that they are all *either Europeans or Asiatics ;* meaning, that it is true of each individual, that he is either a European or an Asiatic. If we appropriate the elective symbol $x$ to the inhabitants, $y$ to Europeans, and $z$ to Asiatics, then the equation of the above Proposition is

$$x = xy + xz, \text{ or } x(1 - y - z) = 0, \quad (a);$$

G

to which we might add the condition $yz = 0$, since no Europeans are Asiatics. The nature of the symbols $x$, $y$, $z$, indicates that the Proposition belongs to those which we have before designated as *Categorical*. Very different from the above is the Proposition, Either all the inhabitants are Europeans, or they are all Asiatics. Here the disjunctive particle separates Propositions. The case is that contemplated in (31) of the present Chapter; and the symbols by which it is expressed, [59] although subject to the same laws as those of (*a*), have a totally different interpretation.*

The distinction is real and important. Every Proposition which language can express may be represented by elective symbols, and the laws of combination of those symbols are in all cases the same; but in one class of instances the symbols have reference to collections of objects, in the other, to the truths of constituent Propositions.

## [60]    PROPERTIES OF ELECTIVE FUNCTIONS

SINCE elective symbols combine according to the laws of quantity, we may, by Maclaurin's theorem, expand a given function $\phi(x)$, in ascending powers of $x$, known cases of failure excepted. Thus we have

$$\phi(x) = \phi(0) + \phi'(0)x + \frac{\phi''(0)}{1 \cdot 2}x^2 + \&c., \quad (44).$$

Now $x^2 = x$, $x^3 = x$, &c., whence

$$\phi(x) = \phi(0) + x\{\phi'(0) + \frac{\phi''(0)}{1 \cdot 2} + \&c.\}, \quad (45).$$

---

* Some writers, among whom is Dr. Latham (*First Outlines*), regard it as the exclusive office of conjunction to connect *Propositions*, not *words*. In this view I am not able to agree. The Proposition, Every animal is *either* rational *or* irrational, cannot be resolved into, *Either* every animal is rational, *or* every animal is irrational. The former belongs to pure categoricals, the latter to hypotheticals. In *singular* Propositions, such conversions would seem to be allowable. This animal is *either* rational *or* irrational, is equivalent to, *Either* this animal is rational, *or* it is irrational. This peculiarity of *singular* Propositions would almost justify our ranking them, though truly universals, in a separate class, as Ramus and his followers did.

Now if in (44) we make $x = 1$, we have

$$\phi(1) = \phi(0) + \phi'(0) + \frac{\phi''(0)}{1 \cdot 2} + \&c.,$$

whence

$$\phi'(0) + \frac{\phi''(0)}{1 \cdot 2} + \frac{\phi'''(0)}{1 \cdot 2 \cdot 3} + \&c. = \phi(1) - \phi(0).$$

Substitute this value for the coefficient of $x$ in the second member of (45), and we have *

$$\phi(x) = \phi(0) + \{\phi(1) - \phi(0)\}x, \quad (46),$$

[61] which we shall also employ under the form

$$\phi(x) = \phi(1)x + \phi(0)(1 - x), \quad (47).$$

Every function of $x$, in which integer powers of that symbol are alone involved, is by this theorem reducible to the first order. The quantities $\phi(0)$, $\phi(1)$, we shall call the moduli of the function $\phi(x)$. They are of great importance in the theory of elective functions, as will appear from the succeeding Propositions.

PROP. 1. Any two functions $\phi(x)$, $\psi(x)$, are equivalent, whose corresponding moduli are equal.

* Although this and the following theorems have only been proved for those forms of functions which are expansible by Maclaurin's theorem, they may be regarded as true for all forms whatever; this will appear from the applications. The reason seems to be that, as it is only through the one form of expansion that elective functions become interpretable, no conflicting interpretation is possible.

The development of $\phi(x)$ may also be determined thus. By the known formula for expansion in factorials.

$$\phi(x) = \phi(0) + \Delta\phi(0) \, x + \frac{\Delta^2\phi(0)}{1 \cdot 2} \, x(x - 1) + \&c.$$

Now $x$ being an elective symbol, $x(x - 1) = 0$, so that all the terms after the second, vanish. Also $\Delta\phi(0) = \phi(1) - \phi(0)$, whence

$$\phi(x) = \phi(0) + \{\phi(1) - \phi(0)\}x.$$

The mathematician may be interested in the remark, that this is not the only case in which an expansion stops at the second term. The expansions of the compound operative functions $\phi\left(\frac{d}{dx} + x^{-1}\right)$ and $\phi\left\{x + \left(\frac{d}{dx}\right)^{-1}\right\}$ are,

respectively,     $$\phi\left(\frac{d}{dx}\right) + \phi'\left(\frac{d}{dx}\right)x^{-1},$$

and     $$\phi(x) + \phi'(x)\left(\frac{d}{dx}\right)^{-1}.$$

See *Cambridge Mathematical Journal*, vol. IV. p. 219.

This is a plain consequence of the last Proposition. For since

$$\phi(x) = \phi(0) + \{\phi(1) - \phi(0)\}x,$$
$$\psi(x) = \psi(0) + \{\psi(1) - \psi(0)\}x,$$

it is evident that if $\phi(0) = \psi(0)$, $\phi(1) = \psi(1)$, the two expansions will be equivalent, and therefore the functions which they represent will be equivalent also.

The converse of this Proposition is equally true, viz.

If two functions are equivalent, their corresponding moduli are equal.

Among the most important applications of the above theorem, we may notice the following.

Suppose it required to determine for what forms of the function $\phi(x)$, the following equation is satisfied, viz.

$$\{\phi(x)\}^n = \phi(x).$$

[62] Here we at once obtain for the expression of the conditions in question,

$$\{\phi(0)\}^n = \phi(0). \quad \{\phi(1)\}^n = \phi(1), \quad (48).$$

Again, suppose it required to determine the conditions under which the following equation is satisfied, viz.

$$\phi(x)\psi(x) = \chi(x).$$

The general theorem at once gives

$$\phi(0)\psi(0) = \chi(0). \quad \phi(1)\psi(1) = \chi(1), \quad (49).$$

This result may also be proved by substituting for $\phi(x)$, $\psi(x)$, $\chi(x)$, their expanded forms, and equating the coefficients of the resulting equation properly reduced.

All the above theorems may be extended to functions of more than one symbol. For, as different elective symbols combine with each other according to the same laws as symbols of quantity, we can first expand a given function with reference to any particular symbol which it contains, and then expand the result with reference to any other symbol, and so on in succession, the order of the expansions being quite indifferent.

Thus the given function being $\phi(xy)$ we have

$$\phi(xy) = \phi(x0) + \{\phi(x1) - \phi(x0)\}y,$$

and expanding the coefficients with reference to $x$, and reducing

$$\phi(xy) = \phi(00) + \{\phi(10) - \phi(00)\}x + \{\phi(01) - \phi(00)\}y \\ + \{\phi(11) - \phi(10) - \phi(01) + \phi(00)\}xy, \quad (50),$$

to which we may give the elegant symmetrical form

$$\phi(xy) = \phi(00)(1 - x)(1 - y) + \phi(01)y(1 - x) \\ + \phi(10)x(1 - y) + \phi(11)xy, \quad (51),$$

wherein we shall, in accordance with the language already employed, designate $\phi(00)$, $\phi(01)$, $\phi(10)$, $\phi(11)$, as the moduli of the function $\phi(xy)$.

By inspection of the above general form, it will appear that any functions of two variables are equivalent, whose corresponding moduli are all equal.

[63] Thus the conditions upon which depends the satisfaction of the equation,

$$\{\phi(xy)\}^n = \phi(xy)$$

are seen to be

$$\{\phi(00)\}^n = \phi(00), \qquad \{\phi(01)\}^n = \phi(01), \\ \{\phi(10)\}^n = \phi(10), \qquad \{\phi(11)\}^n = \phi(11), \quad (52).$$

And the conditions upon which depends the satisfaction of the equation

$$\phi(xy)\psi(xy) = \chi(xy),$$

are

$$\phi(00)\psi(00) = \chi(00), \qquad \phi(01)\psi(01) = \chi(01), \\ \phi(10)\psi(10) = \chi(10), \qquad \phi(11)\psi(11) = \chi(11), \quad (53).$$

It is very easy to assign by induction from (47) and (51), the general form of an expanded elective function. It is evident that if the number of elective symbols is $m$, the number of the moduli will be $2^m$, and that their separate values will be obtained by interchanging in every possible way the values 1 and 0 in the places of the elective symbols of the given function. The several terms of the expansion of which the moduli serve as coefficients, will then be formed by writing for each 1 that recurs under the functional sign, the elective symbol $x$, &c., which it represents, and for each 0 the corresponding $1 - x$, &c., and regarding these as factors, the product of which, multiplied by the modulus from which they are obtained, constitutes a term of the expansion.

Thus, if we represent the moduli of any elective function $\phi(xy\ldots)$ by $a_1, a_2,\ldots a_r$, the function itself, when expanded and arranged with reference to the moduli, will assume the form

$$\phi(xy) = a_1 t_1 + a_2 t_2 \ldots + a_r t_r, \quad (54),$$

in which $t_1 t_2 \ldots t_r$ are functions of $x, y\ldots$, resolved into factors of the forms $x, y,\ldots 1 - x, 1 - y,\ldots$ &c. These functions satisfy individually the index relations

$$t_1{}^n = t_1, \; t_2{}^n = t_2, \; \&c. \quad (55),$$

and the further relations,

$$t_1 t_2 = 0 \ldots t_1 t_2 = 0, \; \&c. \quad (56),$$

[64] the product of any two of them vanishing. This will at once be inferred from inspection of the particular forms (47) and (51). Thus in the latter we have for the values of $t_1, t_2$, &c., the forms

$$xy, \; x(1 - y), \; (1 - x)y, \; (1 - x)(1 - y);$$

and it is evident that these satisfy the index relation, and that their products all vanish. We shall designate $t_1 t_2 \ldots$ as the constituent functions of $\phi(xy)$, and we shall define the peculiarity of the vanishing of the binary products, by saying that those functions are *exclusive*. And indeed the classes which they represent are mutually exclusive.

The sum of all the constituents of an expanded function is unity. An elegant proof of this Proposition will be obtained by expanding 1 as a function of any proposed elective symbols. Thus if in (51) we assume $\phi(xy) = 1$, we have $\phi(11) = 1$, $\phi(10) = 1$, $\phi(01) = 1$, $\phi(00) = 1$, and (51) gives

$$1 = xy + x(1 - y) + (1 - x)y + (1 - x)(1 - y), \quad (57).$$

It is obvious indeed, that however numerous the symbols involved, all the moduli of unity are unity, whence the sum of the constituents is unity.

We are now prepared to enter upon the question of the general interpretation of elective equations. For this purpose we shall find the following Propositions of the greatest service.

PROP. 2. If the first member of the general equation $\phi(xy\ldots) = 0$, be expanded in a series of terms, each of which is of the form $at$, $a$ being a modulus of the given function, then for every numerical modulus $a$ which does not vanish, we shall have the equation

$$at = 0,$$

and the combined interpretations of these several equations will express the full significance of the original equation.

For, representing the equation under the form

$$a_1t_1 + a_2t_2 \ldots + a_rt_r = 0, \quad (58).$$

Multiplying by $t_1$, we have, by (56),

$$a_1t_1 = 0, \quad (59),$$

[65] whence if $a_1$ is a numerical constant which does not vanish,

$$t_1 = 0,$$

and similarly for all the moduli which do not vanish. And inasmuch as from these constituent equations we can form the given equation, their interpretations will together express its entire significance.

Thus if the given equation were

$$x - y = 0, \quad \text{Xs and Ys are identical,} \quad (60),$$

we should have $\phi(11) = 0, \phi(10) = 1, \phi(01) = -1, \phi(00) = 0$, so that the expansion (51) would assume the form

$$x(1 - y) - y(1 - x) = 0,$$

whence, by the above theorem,

$$x(1 - y) = 0, \qquad \text{All Xs are Ys,}$$
$$y(1 - x) = 0, \qquad \text{All Ys are Xs,}$$

results which are together equivalent to (60).

It may happen that the simultaneous satisfaction of equations thus deduced, may require that one or more of the elective symbols should vanish. This would only imply the nonexistence of a class : it may even happen that it may lead to a final result of the form

$$1 = 0,$$

which would indicate the nonexistence of the logical Universe. Such cases will only arise when we attempt to unite contradictory Propositions in a single equation. The manner in which the difficulty seems to be evaded in the result is characteristic.

It appears from this Proposition, that the differences in the interpretation of elective functions depend solely upon the number and position of the vanishing moduli. No change in the value of a modulus, but one which causes it to vanish, produces any change in the interpretation of the equation in which it is found. If among the infinite number of different values which we are thus permitted to give to the moduli which do not vanish in a proposed equation, any one value should be [66] preferred, it is unity, for when the moduli of a function are all either 0 or 1, the function itself satisfies the condition

$$\{\phi(xy..)\}^n = \phi(xy...),$$

and this at once introduces symmetry into our Calculus, and provides us with fixed standards for reference.

PROP. 3. If $w = \phi(xy..)$, $w$, $x$, $y$,.. being elective symbols, and if the second member be completely expanded and arranged in a series of terms of the form $at$, we shall be permitted to equate separately to 0 every term in which the modulus $a$ does not satisfy the condition

$$a^n = a,$$

and to leave for the value of $w$ the sum of the remaining terms.

As the nature of the demonstration of this Proposition is quite unaffected by the number of the terms in the second member, we will for simplicity confine ourselves to the supposition of there being four, and suppose that the moduli of the two first only, satisfy the index law.

We have then

$$w = a_1 t_1 + a_2 t_2 + a_3 t_3 + a_4 t_4, \quad (61),$$

with the relations    $a_1^n = a_1, \quad a_2^n = a_2,$

in addition to the two sets of relations connecting $t_1$, $t_2$, $t_3$, $t_4$, in accordance with (55) and (56).

Squaring (61), we have

$$w = a_1 t_1 + a_2 t_2 + a^2_3 t_3 + a^2_4 t_4,$$

and subtracting (61) from this,

$$(a_3{}^2 - a_3)t_3 + (a_4{}^2 - a_4)t_4 = 0;$$

and it being an hypothesis, that the coefficients of these terms do not vanish, we have, by Prop. 2,

$$t_3 = 0, \quad t_4 = 0, \quad (62),$$

whence (61) becomes

$$w = a_1 t_1 + a_2 t_2.$$

The utility of this Proposition will hereafter appear.

[67] Prop. 4. The functions $t_1 t_2 .. t_r$ being mutually exclusive, we shall always have

$$\psi(a_1 t_1 + a_2 t_2 .. + a_r t_r) = \psi(a_1)t_1 + \psi(a_2)t_2 .. + \psi(a_r)t_r, \quad (63),$$

whatever may be the values of $a_1 a_2 .. a_r$ or the form of $\psi$.

Let the function $a_1 t_1 + a_2 t_2 .. + a_r t_r$ be represented by $\phi(xy...)$, then the moduli $a_1 a_2 .. a_r$ will be given by the expressions

$$\phi(11..), \ \phi(10..), \ (...)\phi(00..).$$

Also $\psi(a_1 t_1 + a_2 t_2 .. + a_r t_r) = \psi\{\phi(xy..)\}$

$$= \psi\{\phi(11..)\}xy.. + \psi\{\phi(10)\}x(1 - y)...$$
$$+ \psi\{\phi(00)\}(1 - x)(1 - y)...$$
$$= \psi(a_1)xy.. + \psi(a_2)x(1 - y)... + \psi(a_r)(1 - x)(1 - y)...$$
$$= \psi(a_1)t_1 + \psi(a_2)t_2 .. + \psi(a_r)t_r, \quad (64).$$

It would not be difficult to extend the list of interesting properties, of which the above are examples. But those which we have noticed are sufficient for our present requirements. The following Proposition may serve as an illustration of their utility.

Prop. 5. Whatever process of reasoning we apply to a single given Proposition, the result will either be the same Proposition or a limitation of it.

Let us represent the equation of the given Proposition under its most general form,

$$a_1 t_1 + a_2 t_2 .. + a_r t_r = 0, \quad (65),$$

resolvable into as many equations of the form $t = 0$ as there are moduli which do not vanish.

Now the most general transformation of this equation is

$$\psi(a_1 t_1 + a_2 t_2 \ldots + a_r t_r) = \psi(0), \quad (66),$$

provided that we attribute to $\psi$ a perfectly arbitrary character, allowing it even to involve new elective symbols, having *any proposed relation* to the original ones.

[68] The development of (66) gives, by the last Proposition,

$$\psi(a_1) t_1 + \psi(a_2) t_2 \ldots + \psi(a_r) t_r = \psi(0).$$

To reduce this to the general form of reference, it is only necessary to observe that since

$$t_1 + t_2 \ldots + t_r = 1,$$

we may write for $\psi(0)$,

$$\psi(0)(t_1 + t_2 \ldots + t_r),$$

whence, on substitution and transposition,

$$\{\psi(a_1) - \psi(0)\} t_1 + \{\psi(a_2) - \psi(0)\} t_2 \ldots + \{\psi(a_r) - \psi(0)\} t_r = 0.$$

From which it appears, that if $a$ be any modulus of the original equation, the corresponding modulus of the transformed equation will be

$$\psi(a) - \psi(0).$$

If $a = 0$, then $\psi(a) - \psi(0) = \psi(0) - \psi(0) = 0$, whence there are no *new terms* in the transformed equation, and therefore there are no *new Propositions* given by equating its constituent members to 0.

Again, since $\psi(a) - \psi(0)$ may vanish without $a$ vanishing, terms may be wanting in the transformed equation which existed in the primitive. Thus some of the constituent truths of the original Proposition may entirely disappear from the interpretation of the final result.

Lastly, if $\psi(a) - \psi(0)$ do not vanish, it must either be a numerical constant, or it must involve new elective symbols. In the former case, the term in which it is found will give

$$t = 0,$$

which is one of the constituents of the original equation : in the latter case we shall have

$$\{\psi(a) - \psi(0)\}t = 0,$$

in which $t$ has a limiting factor. The interpretation of this equation, therefore, is a limitation of the interpretation of (65).

[69] The purport of the last investigation will be more apparent to the mathematician than to the logician. As from any mathematical equation an infinite number of others may be deduced, it seemed to be necessary to shew that when the original equation expresses a logical Proposition, every member of the derived series, even when obtained by expansion under a functional sign, admits of exact and consistent interpretation.

[70]   OF THE SOLUTION OF ELECTIVE EQUATIONS.

In whatever way an elective symbol, considered as unknown, may be involved in a proposed equation, it is possible to assign its complete value in terms of the remaining elective symbols considered as known. It is to be observed of such equations, that from the very nature of elective symbols, they are necessarily linear, and that their solutions have a very close analogy with those of linear differential equations, arbitrary elective symbols in the one, occupying the place of arbitrary constants in the other. The method of solution we shall in the first place illustrate by particular examples, and, afterwards, apply to the investigation of general theorems.

Given $(1 - x)y = 0$, (All Ys are Xs), to determine $y$ in terms of $x$.

As $y$ is a function of $x$, we may assume $y = vx + v'(1 - x)$ (such being the expression of an arbitrary function of $x$), the moduli $v$ and $v'$ remaining to be determined. We have then

$$(1 - x)\{vx + v'(1 - x)\} = 0,$$

or, on actual multiplication,

$$v'(1 - x) = 0 :$$

that this may be generally true, without imposing any restriction upon $x$, we must assume $v' = 0$, and there being no condition to limit $v$, we have

$$y = vx, \quad (67).$$

This is the complete solution of the equation. The condition that $y$ is an elective [71] symbol requires that $v$ should be an elective symbol also (since it must satisfy the index law), its interpretation in other respects being arbitrary.

Similarly the solution of the equation, $xy = 0$, is

$$y = v(1 - x), \quad (68).$$

Given $(1 - x)zy = 0$, (All Ys which are Zs are Xs), to determine $y$.

As $y$ is a function of $x$ and $z$, we may assume

$$y = v(1 - x)(1 - z) + v'(1 - x)z + v''x(1 - z) + v'''zx.$$

And substituting, we get

$$v'(1 - x)z = 0,$$

whence $v' = 0$. The complete solution is therefore

$$y = v(1 - x)(1 - z) + v''x(1 - z) + v'''xz, \quad (69),$$

$v'$, $v''$, $v'''$, being arbitrary elective symbols, and the rigorous interpretation of this result is, that Every Y is *either* a not-X and not-Z, or an X and not-Z, or an X and Z.

It is deserving of note that the above equation may, in consequence of its linear form, be solved by adding the two particular solutions with reference to $x$ and $z$; and replacing the arbitrary constants which each involves by an arbitrary function of the other symbol, the result is

$$y = x\phi(z) + (1 - z)\psi(x), \quad (70).$$

To shew that this solution is equivalent to the other, it is only necessary to substitute for the arbitrary functions $\phi(z)$, $\psi(x)$, their equivalents

$$wz + w'(1 - z) \text{ and } w''x + w'''(1 - x),$$

we get $\quad y = wxz + (w' + w'')x(1 - z) + w'''(1 - x)(1 - z).$

In consequence of the perfectly arbitrary character of

$w'$ and $w''$, we may replace their sum by a single symbol $w'$, whence

$$y = wxz + w'x(1 - z) + w'''(1 - x)(1 - z),$$

which agrees with (69).

[72] The solution of the equation $wx(1 - y)z = 0$, expressed by arbitrary functions, is

$$z = (1 - w)\phi(xy) + (1 - x)\psi(wy) + y\chi(wx),   (71).$$

These instances may serve to shew the analogy which exists between the solutions of elective equations and those of the corresponding order of linear differential equations. Thus the expression of the integral of a partial differential equation, either by arbitrary functions or by a series with arbitrary coefficients, is in strict analogy with the case presented in the two last examples. To pursue this comparison further would minister to curiosity rather than to utility. We shall prefer to contemplate the problem of the solution of elective equations under its most general aspect, which is the object of the succeeding investigations.

To solve the general equation $\phi(xy) = 0$, with reference to $y$.

If we expand the given equation with reference to $x$ and $y$, we have

$$\phi(00)(1 - x)(1 - y) + \phi(01)(1 - x)y + \phi(10)x(1 - y)$$
$$+ \phi(11)xy = 0,   (72),$$

the coefficients $\phi(00)$ &c. being numerical constants.

Now the general expression of $y$, as a function of $x$, is

$$y = vx + v'(1 - x),$$

$v$ and $v'$ being unknown symbols to be determined. Substituting this value in (72), we obtain a result which may be written in the following form,

$$[\phi(10) + \{\phi(11) - \phi(10)\}v]x + [\phi(00)$$
$$+ \{\phi(00) - \phi(00)\}v'](1 - x) = 0;$$

and in order that this equation may be satisfied without any way restricting the generality of $x$, we must have

$$\phi(10) + \{\phi(11) - \phi(10)\}v = 0,$$
$$\phi(00) + \{\phi(01) - \phi(00)\}v' = 0,$$

[73] from which we deduce

$$v = \frac{\phi(10)}{\phi(10) - \phi(11)}, \qquad v' = \frac{\phi(00)}{\phi(01) - \phi(00)},$$

wherefore

$$y = \frac{\phi(10)}{\phi(10) - \phi(11)} x + \frac{\phi(00)}{\phi(00) - \phi(01)} (1 - x), \quad (73).$$

Had we expanded the original equation with respect to $y$ only, we should have had

$$\phi(x0) + \{\phi(x1) - \phi(x0)\}y = 0;$$

but it might have startled those who are unaccustomed to the processes of Symbolical Algebra, had we from this equation deduced

$$y = \frac{\phi(x0)}{\phi(x0) - \phi(x1)},$$

because of the apparently meaningless character of the second member. Such a result would however have been perfectly lawful, and the expansion of the second member would have given us the solution above obtained. I shall in the following example employ this method, and shall only remark that those to whom it may appear doubtful, may verify its conclusions by the previous method.

To solve the general equation $\phi(xyz) = 0$, or in other words to determine the value of $z$ as a function of $x$ and $y$.

Expanding the given equation with reference to $z$, we have

$$\phi(xy0) + \{\phi(xy1) - \phi(xy0)\} . z = 0;$$

$$\therefore \quad z = \frac{\phi(xy0)}{\phi(xy0) - \phi(xy1)} \ldots(74),$$

and expanding the second member as a function of $x$ and $y$ by aid of the general theorem, we have

$$z = \frac{\phi(110)}{\phi(110) - \phi(111)} xy + \frac{\phi(100)}{\phi(100) - \phi(101)} x (1 - y)$$

$$+ \frac{\phi(010)}{\phi(010) - \phi(011)} (1 - x)y$$

$$+ \frac{\phi(000)}{\phi(000) - \phi(001)} (1 - x) (1 - y) \ldots \ldots \ldots (75)$$

[74] and this is the complete solution required. By the same method we may resolve an equation involving any proposed number of elective symbols.

In the interpretation of any general solution of this nature, the following cases may present themselves.

The values of the moduli $\phi(00)$, $\phi(01)$, &c. being constant, one or more of the coefficients of the solution may assume the form $\frac{0}{0}$ or $\frac{1}{0}$. In the former case, the indefinite symbol $\frac{0}{0}$ must be replaced by an arbitrary elective symbol $v$. In the latter case, the term, which is multiplied by a factor $\frac{1}{0}$ (or by any numerical constant except 1), must be separately equated to 0, and will indicate the existence of a subsidiary Proposition. This is evident from (62).

Ex. Given $x(1 - y) = 0$, All Xs are Ys, to determine $y$ as a function of $x$.

Let $\phi(xy) = x(1 - y)$, then $\phi(10) = 1$, $\phi(11) = 0$, $\phi(01) = 0$, $\phi(00) = 0$; whence, by (73),

$$y = \frac{1}{1 - 0}x + \frac{0}{0 - 0}(1 - x)$$
$$= x + \tfrac{0}{0}(1 - x)$$
$$= x + v(1 - x), \quad (76),$$

$v$ being an arbitrary elective symbol. The interpretation of this result is that the class Y consists of the entire class X with an indefinite remainder of not-Xs. This remainder is indefinite in the highest sense, *i.e.* it may vary from 0 up to the entire class of not-Xs.

Ex. Given $x(1 - z) + z = y$, (the class Y consists of the entire class Z, with such not-Zs as are Xs), to find Z.

Here $\phi(xyz) = x(1 - z) - y + z$, whence we have the following set of values for the moduli,

$\phi(110) = 0$, $\quad \phi(111) = 0$, $\quad \phi(100) = 1$, $\quad \phi(101) = 1$,
$\phi(010) = -1$, $\quad \phi(011) = 0$, $\quad \phi(000) = 0$, $\quad \phi(001) = 1$,

and substituting these in the general formula (75), we have

$$z = \tfrac{0}{0}xy + \tfrac{1}{0}x(1 - y) + (1 - x)y, \quad (77),$$

[75] the infinite coefficient of the second term indicates the equation

$$x(1 - y) = 0, \text{ All Xs are Ys};$$

and the indeterminate coefficient of the first term being replaced by $v$, an arbitrary elective symbol, we have

$$z = (1 - x)y + vxy,$$

the interpretation of which is, that the class Z consists of all the Ys which are not Xs, and an *indefinite* remainder of Ys which are Xs. Of course this indefinite remainder may vanish. The two results we have obtained are logical inferences (not very obvious ones) from the original Propositions, and they give us all the information which it contains respecting the class Z, and its constituent elements.

Ex. Given $x = y(1 - z) + z(1 - y)$. The class X consists of all Ys which are not-Zs, and all Zs which are not-Ys : required the class Z.

We have

$$\phi(xyz) = x - y(1 - z) - z(1 - y),$$
$$\phi(110) = 0, \quad \phi(111) = 1, \quad \phi(100) = 1, \quad \phi(101) = 0,$$
$$\phi(010) = -1, \quad \phi(011) = 0, \quad \phi(000) = 0, \quad \phi(001) = -1;$$

whence, by substituting in (75),

$$z = x(1 - y) + y(1 - x), \quad (78),$$

the interpretation of which is, the class Z consists of all Xs which are not Ys, and of all Ys which are not Xs; an inference strictly logical.

Ex. Given $y\{1 - z(1 - x)\} = 0$, All Ys are Zs and not-Xs.

Proceeding as before to form the moduli, we have, on substitution in the general formulæ,

$$z = \tfrac{1}{0}xy + \tfrac{0}{0}x(1 - y) + y(1 - x) + \tfrac{0}{0}(1 - x)(1 - y),$$
$$\text{or } z = y(1 - x) + vx(1 - y) + v'(1 - x)(1 - y)$$
$$= y(1 - x) + (1 - y)\phi(x), \quad (79),$$

with the relation $\qquad xy = 0 :$

from these it appears that No Ys are Xs, and that the class Z [76] consists of all Ys which are not Xs, and of an indefinite remainder of not-Ys.

This method, in combination with Lagrange's method of indeterminate multipliers, may be very elegantly applied to the treatment of simultaneous equations. Our limits only permit us to offer a single example, but the subject is well deserving of further investigation.

Given the equations $x(1 - z) = 0$, $z(1 - y) = 0$, All Xs are Zs, All Zs are Ys, to determine the complete value of $z$ with any subsidiary relations connecting $x$ and $y$.

Adding the second equation multiplied by an indeterminate constant $\lambda$, to the first, we have

$$x(1 - z) + \lambda z(1 - y) = 0,$$

whence determining the moduli, and substituting in (75),

$$z = xy + \frac{1}{1 - \lambda}x(1 - y) + \tfrac{0}{0}(1 - x)y, \quad (80),$$

from which we derive

$$z = xy + v(1 - x)y,$$

with the subsidiary relation

$$x(1 - y) = 0 :$$

the former of these expresses that the class Z consists of all Xs that are Ys, with an indefinite remainder of not-Xs that are Ys; the latter, that All Xs are Ys, being in fact the conclusion of the syllogism of which the two given Propositions are the premises.

By assigning an appropriate meaning to our symbols, all the equations we have discussed would admit of interpretation in hypotheticals, but it may suffice to have considered them as examples of categoricals.

That peculiarity of elective symbols, in virtue of which every elective equation is reducible to a system of equations $t_1 = 0$, $t_2 = 0$, &c., so constituted, that all the binary products $t_1 t_2$, $t_1 t_3$, &c., vanish, represents a general doctrine in Logic with reference to the ultimate analysis of Propositions, of which it may be desirable to offer some illustration.

[77] Any of these constituents $t_1$, $t_2$, &c. consists only of factors of the forms $x$, $y,\ldots 1 - w$, $1 - z$, &c. In categoricals it therefore represents a compound class, *i.e.* a class defined by the presence of certain qualities, and by the absence of certain other qualities.

Each constituent equation $t_1 = 0$, &c. expresses a denial of the existence of some class so defined, and the different classes are mutually exclusive.

*Thus all categorical Propositions are resolvable into a denial of the existence of certain compound classes, no member of one such class being a member of another.*

H

The Proposition, All Xs are Ys, expressed by the equation $x(1 - y) = 0$, is resolved into a denial of the existence of a class whose members are Xs and not-Ys.

The Proposition Some Xs are Ys, expressed by $v = xy$, is resolvable as follows.   On expansion,

$$v - xy = vx(1 - y) + vy(1 - x) + v(1 - x)(1 - y)$$
$$-xy(1 - v);$$
$$\therefore \quad vx(1 - y) = 0, \quad vy(1 - x) = 0, \quad v(1 - x)(1 - y) = 0,$$
$$(1 - v)xy = 0.$$

The three first imply that there is no class whose members belong to a certain unknown Some, and are 1st, Xs and not Ys; 2nd, Ys and not Xs; 3rd, not-Xs and not-Ys.   The fourth implies that there is no class whose members are Xs and Ys without belonging to this unknown Some.

From the same analysis it appears that *all hypothetical Propositions may be resolved into denials of the coexistence of the truth or falsity of certain assertions.*

Thus the Proposition, If X is true, Y is true, is resolvable by its equation $x(1 - y) = 0$, into a denial that the truth of X and the falsity of Y coexist.

And the Proposition Either X is true, or Y is true, members exclusive, is resolvable into a denial, first, that X and Y are both true; secondly, that X and Y are both false.

But it may be asked, is not something more than a system of negations necessary to the constitution of an affirmative Proposition? is not a positive element required? Undoubtedly [78] there is need of one; and this positive element is supplied in categoricals by the assumption (which may be regarded as a prerequisite of reasoning in such cases) that there *is* a Universe of conceptions, and that each individual it contains either belongs to a proposed class or does not belong to it; in hypotheticals, by the assumption (equally prerequisite) that there is a Universe of conceivable cases, and that any given Proposition is either true or false.   Indeed the question of the existence of conceptions ($\epsilon\grave{\iota}\ \check{\epsilon}\sigma\tau\iota$) is preliminary to any statement of their qualities or relations ($\tau\acute{\iota}\ \check{\epsilon}\sigma\tau\iota$).—*Aristotle, Anal. Post.* lib. II. cap. 2.

It would appear from the above, that Propositions may be

regarded as resting at once upon a positive and upon a negative foundation. Nor is such a view either foreign to the spirit of Deductive Reasoning or inappropriate to its Method; the latter ever proceeding by limitations, while the former contemplates the particular as derived from the general.

---

*Demonstration of the Method of Indeterminate Multipliers, as applied to Simultaneous Elective Equations.*

To avoid needless complexity, it will be sufficient to consider the case of three equations involving three elective symbols, those equations being the most general of the kind. It will be seen that the case is marked by every feature affecting the character of the demonstration, which would present itself in the discussion of the more general problem in which the number of equations and the number of variables are both unlimited.

Let the given equations be

$$\phi(xyz) = 0, \quad \psi(xyz) = 0, \quad \chi(xyz) = 0, \quad (1).$$

Multiplying the second and third of these by the arbitrary constants $h$ and $k$, and adding to the first, we have

$$\phi(xyz) + h\psi(xyz) + k\chi(xyz) = 0, \quad (2);$$

[79] and we are to shew, that in solving this equation with reference to any variable $z$ by the general theorem (75), we shall obtain not only the general value of $z$ independent of $h$ and $k$, but also any subsidiary relations which may exist between $x$ and $y$ independently of $z$.

If we represent the general equation (2) under the form $F(xyz) = 0$, its solution may by (75) be written in the form

$$z = \frac{xy}{1 - \dfrac{F(111)}{F(110)}} + \frac{x(1 - y)}{1 - \dfrac{F(101)}{F(100)}} + \frac{y(1 - x)}{1 - \dfrac{F(011)}{F(010)}} + \frac{(1 - x)(1 - y)}{1 - \dfrac{F(001)}{F(000)}};$$

and we have seen, that any one of these four terms is to be equated to 0, whose modulus, which we may represent by $M$, does not satisfy the condition $M^n = M$, or, which is here the same thing, whose modulus has any other value than 0 or 1.

Consider the modulus (suppose $M_1$) of the first term, viz. $\dfrac{1}{1 - \dfrac{F(111)}{F(110)}}$, and giving to the symbol $F$ its full meaning,

we have

$$M_1 = \cfrac{1}{1 - \cfrac{\phi(111) + h\psi(111) + k\chi(111)}{\phi(110) + h\psi(110) + k\chi(110)}}.$$

It is evident that the condition $M_1{}^n = M_1$ cannot be satisfied unless the right-hand member be independent of $h$ and $k$; and in order that this may be the case, we must have the function $\dfrac{\phi(111) + h\psi(111) + k\chi(111)}{\phi(110) + h\psi(110) + k\chi(110)}$ independent of $h$ and $k$.

Assume then

$$\frac{\phi(111) + h\psi(111) + k\chi(111)}{\phi(110) + h\psi(110) + k\chi(110)} = c,$$

$c$ being independent of $h$ and $k$; we have, on clearing of fractions and equating coefficients,

$$\phi(111) = c\phi(110), \quad \psi(111) = c\psi(110), \quad \chi(111) = c\chi(110);$$

whence, eliminating $c$,

$$\frac{\phi(111)}{\phi(110)} = \frac{\psi(111)}{\psi(110)} = \frac{\chi(111)}{\chi(110)},$$

[80] being equivalent to the triple system

$$\left. \begin{aligned} \phi(111)\psi(110) - \phi(110)\psi(111) &= 0 \\ \psi(111)\chi(110) - \psi(110)\chi(111) &= 0 \\ \chi(111)\phi(110) - \chi(110)\phi(111) &= 0 \end{aligned} \right\} \quad (3);$$

and it appears that if any one of these equations is not satisfied, the modulus $M_1$ will not satisfy the condition $M_1{}^n = M_1$, whence the first term of the value of $z$ must be equated to 0, and we shall have

$$xy = 0,$$

a relation between $x$ and $y$ independent of $z$.

Now if we expand in terms of $z$ each pair of the primitive equations (1), we shall have

$$\phi(xy0) + \{\phi(xy1) - \phi(xy0)\}z = 0,$$
$$\psi(xy0) + \{\psi(xy1) - \psi(xy0)\}z = 0,$$
$$\chi(xy0) + \{\chi(xy1) - \chi(xy0)\}z = 0,$$

and successively eliminating $z$ between each pair of these equations, we have

$$\phi(xy1)\psi(xy0) - \phi(xy0)\psi(xy1) = 0,$$
$$\psi(xy1)\chi(xy0) - \psi(xy0)\chi(xy1) = 0,$$
$$\chi(xy1)\phi(xy0) - \chi(xy0)\phi(xy1) = 0,$$

which express all the relations between $x$ and $y$ that are formed by the elimination of $z$. Expanding these, and writing in full the first term, we have

$$\{\phi(111)\psi(110) - \phi(110)\psi(111)\}xy + \&c. = 0,$$
$$\{\psi(111)\chi(110) - \psi(110)\chi(111)\}xy + \&c. = 0,$$
$$\{\chi(111)\phi(110) - \chi(110)\phi(111)\}xy + \&c. = 0:$$

and it appears from Prop. 2, that if the coefficient of $xy$ in any of these equations does not vanish, we shall have the equation

$$xy = 0;$$

but the coefficients in question are the same as the first members of the system (3), and the two sets of conditions exactly agree. Thus, as respects the first term of the expansion, the method of indeterminate coefficients leads to the same result as ordinary elimination; and it is obvious that from their similarity of form, the same reasoning will apply to all the other terms.

[81] Suppose, in the second place, that the conditions (3) are satisfied so that $M_1$ is independent of $h$ and $k$. It will then indifferently assume the equivalent forms

$$M_1 = \frac{1}{1 - \dfrac{\phi(111)}{\phi(110)}} = \frac{1}{1 - \dfrac{\psi(111)}{\psi(110)}} = \frac{1}{1 - \dfrac{\chi(111)}{\chi(110)}}.$$

These are the exact forms of the first modulus in the expanded values of $z$, deduced from the solution of the three primitive equations singly. If this common value of $M_1$

is 1 or $\frac{0}{0} = v$, the term will be retained in $z$; if any other constant value (except 0), we have a relation $xy = 0$, not given by elimination, but deducible from the primitive equations singly, and similarly for all the other terms. Thus in every case the expression of the subsidiary relations is a necessary accompaniment of the process of solution.

It is evident, upon consideration, that a similar proof will apply to the discussion of a system indefinite as to the number both of its symbols and of its equations.

## POSTSCRIPT

SOME additional explanations and references which have occurred to me during the printing of this work are subjoined.

The remarks on the connexion between Logic and Language, p. 5, are scarcely sufficiently explicit. Both the one and the other I hold to depend very materially upon our ability to form general notions by the faculty of abstraction. Language is an instrument of Logic, but not an indispensable instrument.

To the remarks on Cause, p. 12,* I desire to add the following : Considering Cause as an invariable antecedent in Nature, (which is Brown's view), whether associated or not with the idea of Power, as suggested by Sir John Herschel, the knowledge of its existence is a knowledge which is properly expressed by the word *that* (τὸ ὅτι), not by *why* (τὸ διότι). It is very remarkable that the two greatest authorities in Logic, modern and ancient, agreeing in the latter interpretation, differ most widely in its application to Mathematics. Sir W. Hamilton says that Mathematics [82] exhibit only the *that* (τὸ ὅτι) : Aristotle says, The *why* belongs to mathematicians, for they have the demonstrations of Causes.—*Anal. Post.* lib. I., cap. XIII. It must be added that Aristotle's view is consistent with the sense (albeit an erroneous one) which in various parts of his writings he virtually assigns to the word Cause, viz. an antecedent in

---

* [Of the original edition: shown in square brackets above.]

Logic, a sense according to which the premises might be said to be the cause of the conclusion. This view appears to me to give even to his physical inquiries much of their peculiar character.

Upon reconsideration, I think that the view on p. 41, as to the presence or absence of a medium of comparison, would readily follow from Professor De Morgan's doctrine, and I therefore relinquish all claim to a discovery. The mode in which it appears in this treatise is, however, remarkable.

I have seen reason to change the opinion expressed in pp. 42, 43. The system of equations there given for the expression of Propositions in Syllogism is *always* preferable to the one before employed—first, in generality—secondly, in facility of interpretation.

In virtue of the principle, that a Proposition is either true or false, every elective symbol employed in the expression of hypotheticals admits only of the values 0 and 1, which are the only quantitative forms of an elective symbol. It is in fact possible, setting out from the theory of Probabilities (which is purely quantitative), to arrive at a system of methods and processes for the treatment of hypotheticals exactly similar to those which have been given. The two systems of elective symbols and of quantity osculate, if I may use the expression, in the points 0 and 1. It seems to me to be implied by this, that unconditional truth (categoricals) and probable truth meet together in the constitution of contingent truth, (hypotheticals). The general doctrine of elective symbols and all the more characteristic applications are quite independent of any quantitative origin.

---

## LATER NOTES

[The Royal Society manuscripts include Boole's own inter-leaved copy of the *Mathematical Analysis of Logic*. In this he has written fairly full revisions or fresh discussions of certain topics. And he has added twelve manuscript pages as an appendix, in which he revises and alters what he has

written in the manuscript pages of the volume. The principal changes or additions are in the chapter on syllogisms,
the chapter on hypotheticals, and the chapter on the solution
of elective equations. They were not all made at the same
time,—not even the manuscript additions to the text,
evidently. What is written in the appendix is generally
later than these; and the last eight pages of the appendix
are later than the first four. But they are all of them earlier
than the *Laws of Thought*, though at least one of them has
been largely included there.

On p. 47 above Boole says that " it is largely in the general
theorems which occupy the latter portion of this work . . .
that the claims of the method as a Calculus of Deductive
Reasoning are most fully set forth ". In the *Calculus of
Logic* and in the *Laws of Thought* those theorems come before
the treatment of syllogism. He says in the *Calculus of Logic*
that syllogistic inference corresponds to elimination and is
therefore a subsidiary part of logic,—" subsidiary to the more
general problem of the solution of elective equations " (p. 139).
And for the exposition of that general problem he uses
development,—as he had done here (p. 109). But he still
has not formulated a general method for syllogisms in terms
of development. He came later to that—with a more
general theory of elimination—in his theory of reduction.

In the *Laws of Thought*—p. (231) 244—he says of the
Syllogism that " its resolution is, indeed, a particular
application of the process for the reduction of systems of
propositions ". In these manuscript notes he was evidently
working towards a method for the reduction of systems of
propositions, which would be an improvement in the
" Method of Indeterminate Multipliers, as applied to Simultaneous Elective Equations ", given at the end of the last
chapter. The importance of this for syllogism is explicitly
recognized only in the last notes of the appendix.

In his earlier notes—which may be later than the *Calculus
of Logic*—he still eliminates between the premises as they
stand and uses development to solve the conclusion reached.
He begins :]

All combinations of premises will here be admitted, the

separate propositions of which can be referred to any of the following forms [cf. p. 86, using $x$ and $z$] at the same time that they involve in their expression a common symbol $y$. . . .

So far, then, as reasoning or analytical process is concerned, all cases of the syllogism depend upon the two following :

$$vx = v'y,$$
$$wz = w'y; \quad (1)$$

$$vx = v'y,$$
$$wz = w'(1 - y); \quad (2)$$

the former representing the general case in which the *middle* terms, i.e. those which involve $y$ in their expression, are *alike in quality*, the latter that in which they are unlike. . . .

[This classification appears in the *Laws of Thought*. He then goes on to give a case with " like middles ".]

$$vx = v'y \quad \cdots \cdots \quad (1),$$
$$wz = w'y \quad \cdots \cdots \quad (2).$$

Solving the equations with reference to $y$, we obtain the relations

$$vx(1 - v') = 0 \quad \cdots \cdots \quad (3),$$
$$wz(1 - w') = 0 \quad \cdots \cdots \quad (4),$$

and eliminating $y$ from (1) and (2),

$$w'vx = v'wz \quad \cdots \cdots \quad (5).$$

Now assuming $x$ as the symbol entering into the subject of the conclusion, it is necessary to interpretation that it should either enter universally, as $x$ or $1 - x$, or as it does in the first premiss, in the form $vx$. We must therefore obtain by solution of (5) the most general values of $x$, $1 - x$ and $vx$, reducing them by the conditions (3) and (4), till there shall enter into them nothing superfluous.

[For the solution of (5) he uses the methods for the solution of elective equations which are given in his last two chapters. It is perhaps important to emphasize that he solves the equation for each of the three symbols he has mentioned. He was already demanding—his general methods were leading him to demand—that the solution of a syllogism should be " exhaustive ". And in later writings he criticized the traditional logical methods because the conclusions which they furnished were incomplete,—they did not show all that could be deduced from the premises. But as it stands here, Boole's method is still in its beginnings,—although it is a marked change from that in the printed text. The relations between expansion, elimination and reduction had to be further worked out before he could reach the view of logical inference which he later held. The use of expansion in the solution of syllogisms in this place would be one thing pointing to a more exhaustive conclusion. And the theory of the reduction of propositions, which he develops in his last chapter, would go together with this. But the theory of the reduction of *systems* of propositions does not appear there, beyond the statement that for the treatment of simultaneous equations Lagrange's method of indeterminate multipliers may be applied in combination with the method for solving single equations; and when he speaks, e.g., of every elective equation as " reducible to a system of equations $t = 0$, $t = 0$, etc.," that " reduction " is rather the inverse of reduction in the other sense. When he speaks of " reducing " in the present passage, this is the reduction of a solution in an expanded form to its " reduced value.' This is not the sense in which he later spoke of the reduction of a system of equations to a single general equation. This is obvious enough; and all that needs emphasis here is the measure in which the method for " simultaneous equations " had still to be developed.

The following passage is from the manuscript appendix.]

### General Method for the Treatment of Simultaneous Elective Equations

In the first place, it is clear that if we have any system of equations,

$$V = 0, \ V' = 0, \ V'' = 0, \ldots \quad \cdot \quad \cdot \quad (1),$$

the aggregate system may be represented by the single equation,

$$V + \lambda V' + \lambda' V'' \ldots = 0 \quad \cdot \quad \cdot \quad \cdot \quad (2),$$

—for whatever constituents are found in the separate equations (1) are found in (2). And it is upon the number and character of the constituents only that the value and interpretation of an equation depend.

In the second place, let $\phi(xyz) = 0$ represent any proposed equation. Then expanding with reference to $z$,

$$\phi(xy1)z + \phi(xy0)\overline{1 - z} = 0,$$

or, $\qquad \phi(xy0) + \{\phi(xy1) - \phi(xy0)\}z = 0 \quad . \quad . \quad (3).$

And by multiplying by $z$,

$$\phi(xy1)z = 0 \quad . \quad . \quad . \quad . \quad (4).$$

Eliminating $z$ between (3) and (4),

$$\phi(xy1)\phi(xy0) = 0 \quad . \quad . \quad . \quad (5).$$

Hence if there are implied in the existence of the equation $\phi(xyz) = 0$ any relations between $x$ and $y$ independent of $z$, they are given by (5).

And if we had an equation with four or more symbols, such as,

$$\phi(xyzw) = 0,$$

we should similarly have, after one elimination,

$$\phi(xyz1)\phi(xyz0) = 0;$$

after a second,

$$\phi(xy11)\phi(xy10)\phi(xy01)\phi(xy00) = 0,$$

and so on.

These present us with the laws of the most general result of elimination in any proposed case.

Now the most general problem which can be proposed with reference to elective equations is the following.

Given any system of elective equations involving any system of symbols, $v$, $w$, $x$, $y$, $z$, &c., to determine the value of any one of those symbols in terms of any others (some or all), excluding those which we do not wish to take into account.

For example, if we had two equations, $\phi(xyz) = 0$ and $\psi(xyz) = 0$, and desired to determine $y$ in terms of $x$ irrespectively of $z$, we should be permitted to proceed thus. We should have

$$\phi(xyz) + \lambda\psi(xyz) = 0 . \quad . \quad . \quad . \quad (1),$$

for our single equation. Then eliminating $z$,

$$\{\phi(xy1) + \lambda\psi(xy1)\}\{\phi(xy0) + \lambda\psi(xy0)\} = 0.$$

And solving this equation with reference to $y$, vide (73), we should obtain the results sought.

When the elective symbols are numerous, it will be best to solve the final equation as if it were algebraic, and, putting the values of $y$ in the form of a rational function, to develope it by the general formula of development.

The method in fact consists in reducing the system of equations to a single general equation, eliminating the variables which are to disappear from this by the fundamental relations $x^2 = x$, $y^2 = y$ &c., and then solving the resulting equation. This method is perfectly general. We may depend upon its giving us an *exhaustive* solution. On the contrary, if we merely eliminate between the primitive equations, we cannot depend upon the completeness of our solution, and are compelled to employ subsequent reductions, as is seen in the previous treatment of the general equations of syllogism.

The same equations are in the following pages solved by the new and more general method. . . .

[The solutions which follow are more direct than those given in the passage referred to before. But they are fairly long,—like most of his solutions, they include long and complicated expansions,—and they will not be given here. The last few sentences in this passage do something to emphasize the step that has been taken.]

## THE CALCULUS OF LOGIC *

IN a work lately published † I have exhibited the application of a new and peculiar form of Mathematics to the expression of the operations of the mind in reasoning. In the present essay I design to offer such an account of a portion of this treatise as may furnish a correct view of the nature of the system developed. I shall endeavour to state distinctly those positions in which its characteristic distinctions consist, and shall offer a more particular illustration of some features which are less prominently displayed in the original work. The part of the system to which I shall confine my observations is that which treats of categorical propositions, and the positions which, under this limitation, I design to illustrate, are the following :—

(1) That the business of Logic is with the relations of classes, and with the modes in which the mind contemplates those relations.

(2) That antecedently to our recognition of the existence of propositions, there are laws to which the conception of a class is subject—laws which are dependent upon the constitution of the intellect, and which determine the character and form of the reasoning process.

(3) That those laws are capable of mathematical expression, and that they thus constitute the basis of an interpretable calculus.

(4) That those laws are, furthermore, such that all equations which are formed in subjection to them, even though expressed under functional signs, admit of perfect solution, so that every problem in logic can be solved by reference to a general theorem.

(5) That the forms under which propositions are actually

* [The Cambridge & Dublin Mathematical Journal, May 1848.]
† The Mathematical Analysis of Logic, being an Essay towards a Calculus of Deductive Reasoning. Cambridge, Macmillan : London, G. Bell.

exhibited, in accordance with the principles of this calculus, are analogous with those of a philosophical language.

(6) That although the symbols of the calculus do not depend for their interpretation upon the idea of quantity, they nevertheless, in their particular application to syllogism, conduct us to the quantitative conditions of inference.

It is specially of the two last of these positions that I here desire to offer illustration, they having been but partially exemplified in the work referred to. Other points will, however, be made the subjects of incidental discussion. It will be necessary to premise the following notation.

The universe of conceivable objects is represented by 1 or unity. This I assume as the primary and subject conception. All subordinate conceptions of class are understood to be formed from it by limitation, according to the following scheme.

Suppose that we have the conception of any group of objects consisting of Xs, Ys, and others, and that $x$, which we shall call an elective symbol, represents the mental operation of selecting from that group all the Xs which it contains, or of fixing the attention upon the Xs to the exclusion of all which are not Xs, $y$ the mental operation of selecting the Ys, and so on; then, 1 or the universe being the subject conception, we shall have

$x1$ or $x =$ the class X,
$y1$ or $y =$ the class Y,
$xy1$ or $xy =$ the class each member of which is both X and Y, and so on.

In like manner we shall have

$1 - x =$ the class not-X,
$1 - y =$ the class not-Y,
$x(1 - y) =$ the class whose members are Xs but not-Ys,
$(1 - x)(1 - y) =$ the class whose members are neither Xs nor Ys, &c.

Furthermore, from consideration of the nature of the mental operation involved, it will appear that the following laws are satisfied.

Representing by $x, y, z$, any elective symbols whatever,

$$x(y + z) = xy + xz \quad . \quad . \quad . \quad . \quad (1),$$
$$xy = yx, \&c. \quad . \quad . \quad . \quad . \quad (2),$$
$$x^n = x, \&c. \quad . \quad . \quad . \quad . \quad (3).$$

From the first of these it is seen that elective symbols are distributive in their operation; from the second that they are commutative. The third I have termed the index law; it is peculiar to elective symbols.

The truth of these laws does not at all depend upon the nature of the number, or the mutual relations, of the individuals included in the different classes. There may be but one individual in a class, or there may be a thousand. There may be individuals common to different classes, or the classes may be mutually exclusive. All elective symbols are distributive, and commutative, and all elective symbols satisfy the law expressed by (3).

These laws are in fact embodied in every spoken or written language. The equivalence of the expressions " good wise man " and " wise good man ", is not a mere truism, but an assertion of the law of commutation exhibited in (2). And there are similar illustrations of the other laws.

With these laws there is connected a general axiom. We have seen that algebraic operations performed with elective symbols represent mental processes. Thus the connexion of two symbols by the sign $+$ represents the aggregation of two classes into a single class, the connexion of two symbols $xy$ as in multiplication, represents the mental operation of selecting from a class Y those members which belong also to another class X, and so on. By such operations the conception of a class is modified. But beside this the mind has the power of perceiving relations of equality among classes. The axiom in question, then, is, that *if a relation of equality is perceived between two classes, that relation remains unaffected when both subjects are equally modified by the operations above described*. (A). This axiom, and not " Aristotle's dictum ", is the real foundation of all reasoning, the form and character of the process being, however, determined by the three laws already stated.

It is not only true that every elective symbol representing a class satisfies the index law (3), but it may be rigorously demonstrated that any combination of elective symbols $\phi(xyz..)$, which satisfies the law $\phi(xyz..)^n = \phi(xyz..)$, represents an intelligible conception,—a group or class defined by a greater or less number of properties and consisting of a greater or less number of parts.

The four categorical propositions upon which the doctrine of ordinary syllogism is founded are,

|  |  |
|---|---|
| All Ys are Xs. | A, |
| No Ys are Xs. | E, |
| Some Ys are Xs. | I, |
| Some Ys are not Xs. | O. |

We shall consider these with reference to the classes among which relation is expressed.

A. The expression All Ys represents the class Y and will therefore be expressed by $y$, the copula *are* by the sign $=$, the indefinite term, Xs, is equivalent to Some Xs. It is a convention of language, that the word Some is expressed in the subject, but not in the predicate of a proposition. The term Some Xs will be expressed by $vx$, in which $v$ is an elective symbol appropriate to a class V, some members of which are Xs, but which is in other respects arbitrary. Thus the proposition A will be expressed by the equation

$$y = vx \quad . \quad . \quad . \quad . \quad . \quad (4)$$

E. In the proposition, No Ys are Xs the negative particle appears to be attached to the subject instead of to the predicate to which it manifestly belongs.* We do not intend

---

* There are but two ways in which the proposition, No Xs are Ys, can be understood. 1st, in the sense of All Xs are not-Y. 2nd, in the sense of It is not true that any Xs are Ys, i.e. the proposition "Some Xs are Ys" is false. The former of these is a single categorical proposition. The latter is *an assertion respecting a proposition*, and its expression belongs to a distinct part of the elective system. It appears to me that it is the latter sense, which is really adopted by those who refer the negative, *not*, to the copula. To refer it to the predicate is not a useless refinement, but a necessary step, in order to make the proposition truly a *relation between classes*. I believe that it will be found that this step is really taken in the attempts to demonstrate the Aristotelian rules of distribution.

The transposition of the negative is a very common feature of language. Habit renders us almost insensible to it in our own language, but when in another language the same principle is differently exhibited, as in the Greek, οὐ φημὶ for φημὶ οὐ, it claims attention.

to say that those things which are not-Ys are Xs, but that things which are Ys are not-Xs. Now the class Not-Xs is expressed by $1 - x$; hence the proposition No Ys are Xs, or rather All Ys are not-Xs, will be expressed by

$$y = v(1 - x) \quad . \quad . \quad . \quad . \quad (5).$$

I. In the proposition Some Ys are Xs, or Some Ys are Some Xs, we might regard the Some in the subject and the Some in the predicate as having reference to the same arbitrary class V, and so write

$$vy = vx,$$

but it is less of an assumption to refrain from doing this. Thus we should write

$$vy = v'x \quad . \quad . \quad . \quad . \quad (6),$$

$v'$ referring to another arbitrary class V'.

O. Similarly, the proposition Some Ys are not-Xs, will be expressed by the equation

$$vy = v'(1 - x) \quad . \quad . \quad . \quad . \quad (7).$$

It will be seen from the above that the forms under which the four categorical propositions A, E, I, O, are exhibited in the notation of elective symbols are analogous with those of pure language, i.e. with the forms which human speech would assume, were its rules entirely constructed upon a scientific basis. In a vast majority of the propositions which can be conceived by the mind, the laws of expression have not been modified by usage, and the analogy becomes more apparent, e.g. the interpretation of the equation

$$z = x(1 - y) + y(1 - x),$$

is, the class Z consists of all Xs which are not-Ys, and of all Ys which are not-Xs.

### General Theorems relating to Elective Functions

We have now arrived at this step,—that we are in possession of a class of symbols, $x, y, z$, &c. satisfying certain laws, and applicable to the rigorous expression of any categorical proposition whatever. It will be our next business to exhibit a few of the general theorems of the calculus which rests upon

I

the basis of those laws, and these theorems we shall afterwards apply to the discussion of particular examples.

Of the general theorems I shall only exhibit two sets : those which relate to the development of functions, and those which relate to the solution of equations.

### Theorems of Development

(1) If $x$ be any elective symbol, then

$$\phi(x) = \phi(1)x + \phi(0)(1 - x) \quad . \quad . \quad . \quad (8),$$

the coefficients $\phi(1)$, $\phi(0)$, which are the quantitative or common algebraic functions, are called the moduli, and $x$ and $1 - x$ the constituents.

(2) $\phi(xy) = \phi(11)xy + \phi(10)x(1 - y) + \phi(01)(1 - x)y$
$$+ \phi(00)(1 - x)(1 - y) \quad . \quad (9),$$

in which $\phi(11)$, $\phi(10)$, &c. are quantitative, and are called the moduli, and $xy$, $x(1 - y)$, &c. the constituents.

(3) Functions of three symbols,

$\phi(xyz) = \phi(111)xyz + \phi(110)xy(1 - z)$
$\qquad + \phi(101)x(1 - y)z + \phi(100)x(1 - y)(1 - z)$
$\qquad + \phi(011)(1 - x)yz + \phi(010)(1 - x)y(1 - z)$
$\qquad + \phi(001)(1 - x)(1 - y)z$
$\qquad + \phi(000)(1 - x)(1 - y)(1 - z) \quad . \quad . \quad . \quad (10).$

in which $\phi(111)$, $\phi(110)$, &c. are the moduli, and $xyz$, $xy(1 - z)$, &c. the constituents.

From these examples the general law of development is obvious. And I desire it to be noted that this law is a mere consequence of the primary laws which have been expressed in (1), (2), (3).

THEOREM. *If we have any equation $\phi(xyz..) = 0$, and fully expand the first member, then every constituent whose modulus does not vanish may be equated to 0.*

This enables us to interpret any equation by a general rule.

RULE. *Bring all the terms to the first side, expand this in terms of all the elective symbols involved in it, and equate to 0 every constituent whose modulus does not vanish.*

For the demonstration of these and many other results, I must refer to the original work. It must be noted that on

p. 66, $z$ has been, through mistake, substituted for $w$, and that the reference on p. 80 should be to Prop. 2*.

As an example, let us take the equation

$$x + 2y - 3xy = 0 \quad . \quad . \quad . \quad (11).$$

Here $\phi(xy) = x + 2y - 3xy$, whence the values of the moduli are $\phi(11) = 0$, $\phi(10) = 1$, $\phi(01) = 2$, $\phi(00) = 0$, so that the expansion (9) gives

$$x(1 - y) + 2y(1 - x) = 0,$$

which is in fact only another form of (11). We have, then, by the Rule

$$x(1 - y) = 0 \quad . \quad . \quad . \quad (11),$$
$$y(1 - x) = 0 \quad . \quad . \quad . \quad (12);$$

the former implies that there are no Xs which are not-Ys, the latter that there are no Ys which are not-Xs, these together expressing the full significance of the original equation.

We can, however, often recombine the constituents with a gain of simplicity. In the present instance, subtracting (12) from (11) we have

$$x - y = 0$$
or
$$x = y$$

that is, the class X is identical with the class Y. This proposition is equivalent to the two former ones.

All equations are thus of equal significance which give, on expansion, the same series of constituent equations, and *all are interpretable.*

### General Solution of Elective Equations

(1) The general solution of the equation $\phi(xy) = 0$, in which two elective symbols only are involved, $y$ being the one whose value is sought, is

$$y = \frac{\phi(10)}{\phi(10) - \phi(11)} x + \frac{\phi(00)}{\phi(00) - \phi(01)} (1 - x) \quad . \quad (13).$$

The coefficients

$$\frac{\phi(10)}{\phi(10) - \phi(11)}, \quad \frac{\phi(00)}{\phi(00) - \phi(01)}$$

are here the moduli.

* [The mistakes have been corrected above.]

(2) The general solution of the equation $\phi(xyz) = 0$, $z$ being the symbol whose value is to be determined, is

$$z = \frac{\phi(110)}{\phi(110) - \phi(111)}xy + \frac{\phi(100)}{\phi(100) - \phi(101)}x(1 - y)$$

$$+ \frac{\phi(010)}{\phi(010) - \phi(011)}(1 - x)y$$

$$+ \frac{\phi(000)}{\phi(000) - \phi(001)}(1 - x)(1 - y) \quad . \quad (14),$$

the coefficients of which we shall still term the moduli. The law of their formation will readily be seen, so that the general theorems which have been given for the solution of elective equations of two and three symbols, may be regarded as examples of a more general theorem applicable to all elective equations whatever. In applying these results, it is to be observed, that if a modulus assume the form $\frac{0}{0}$, it is to be replaced by an arbitrary elective symbol $w$, and that if a modulus assume any numerical value except 0 or 1, the constituent of which it is a factor must be separately equated to 0. Although these conditions are deduced solely from the laws to which the symbols are obedient, and without any reference to interpretation, they nevertheless render the solution of every equation interpretable in logic. To such formulæ also *every question upon the relations of classes may be referred.* One or two very simple illustrations may suffice.

(1) Given $\quad\quad yx = yz + x(1 - z) \quad . \quad . \quad . \quad (a)$
The Ys which are Xs consist of the Ys which are Zs and the Xs which are not-Zs. Required the class Z.
Here

$$\phi(xyz) = yx - yz - x(1 - z),$$
$$\phi(111) = 0, \quad\quad \phi(110) = 0, \quad\quad \phi(101) = 0,$$
$$\phi(100) = -1, \quad \phi(011) = -1, \quad \phi(010) = 0,$$
$$\phi(001) = 0, \quad\quad \phi(000) = 0,$$

and substituting in (14), we have

$$z = \frac{0}{0}xy + x(1 - y) + \frac{0}{0}(1 - x)(1 - y)$$
$$= x(1 - y) + wxy + w'(1 - x)(1 - y) \quad . \quad (15).$$

Hence the class Z includes all Xs which are not-Ys, an indefinite number of Xs which are Ys, and an indefinite number of individuals which are neither Xs nor Ys. The classes $w$ and $w'$ being quite arbitrary, the indefinite remainder is equally so; it may vanish or not.*

Since $1 - z$ represents a class, not-Z, and satisfies the index law
$$(1 - z)^n = 1 - z,$$
as is evident on trial, we may, if we choose, determine the value of this element just as we should determine that of $z$.

Let us take, in illustration of this principle, the equation $y = vx$, (All Ys are Xs), and seek the value of $1 - x$, the class not-X.

Put $1 - x = z$, then $y = v(1 - z)$, and if we write this in the form $y - v(1 - z) = 0$ and represent the first member by $\phi(vyz)$, $v$ here taking the place of $x$, in (14), we shall have

$$\phi(111) = 1, \quad \phi(110) = 0, \quad \phi(101) = 0, \quad \phi(100) = -1,$$
$$\phi(011) = 1, \quad \phi(010) = 1, \quad \phi(001) = 0, \quad \phi(000) = 0;$$

the solution will thus assume the form

$$z = \frac{0}{0-1}vy + \frac{-1}{-1-0}v(1 - y) + \frac{1}{1-1}(1 - v)y$$
$$+ \frac{0}{0-0}(1 - v)(1 - y),$$

or   $1 - x = v(1 - y) + \frac{1}{0}(1 - v)y + \frac{0}{0}(1 - v)(1 - y)$   (16).

The infinite coefficient of the second term in the second member permits us to write

$$y(1 - v) = 0 \quad . \quad . \quad . \quad . \quad (17).$$

---

* This conclusion may be illustrated and verified by considering as example such as the following :—

Let $x$ denote all steamers, or steam-vessels,
  $y$ ..................... armed vessels,
  $z$ ........ vessels of the Mediterranean.

Equation (a) would then express that *armed steamers consist of the armed vessels of the Mediterranean, and the steam-vessels not of the Mediterranean.* From this it follows :—

(1) That there are no armed vessels except steamers in the Mediterranean.
(2) That all unarmed steamers are in the Mediterranean (since the steam-vessels not of the Mediterranean are armed). Hence we infer that *the vessels of the Mediterranean consist of all unarmed steamers; any number of armed steamers; and any number of unarmed vessels without steam.* This, expressed symbolically, is equation (15).

the coefficient $\dfrac{0}{0}$ being then replaced by $w$, an arbitrary elective symbol, we have

$$1 - x = v(1 - y) + w(1 - v)(1 - y),$$
or $\qquad 1 - x = \{v + w(1 - v)\}(1 - y) \quad . \quad . \quad (18).$

We may remark upon this result that the coefficient $v + w(1 - v)$ in the second member satisfies the condition

$$\{v + w(1 - v)\}^n = v + w(1 - v),$$

as is evident on squaring it. It therefore represents a *class*. We may replace it by an elective symbol $u$; we have then

$$1 - x = u(1 - y) \quad . \quad . \quad . \quad (19),$$

the interpretation of which is

All not-Xs are not-Ys.

This is a known transformation in logic, and is called conversion by contraposition, or negative conversion. But it is far from exhausting the solution we have obtained. Logicians have overlooked the fact, that when we convert the proposition All Ys are (some) Xs, into All not-Xs are (some) not-Ys, there is a relation between the two (*somes*), understood in the predicates. The equation (18) shows that whatever may be that condition which limits the Xs in the original proposition,—the Not-Ys in the converted proposition consist of all which are subject to the same condition, and of an arbitrary remainder which are not subject to that condition. The equation (17) further shows that there are no Ys which are not subject to that condition.

We can similarly reduce the equation $y = v(1 - x)$, No Ys are Xs, to the form $x = v'(1 - y)$ No Xs are Ys, with a like relation between $v$ and $v'$. If we solve the equation $y = vx$, All Ys are Xs, with reference to $v$, we obtain the subsidiary relation $y(1 - x) = 0$ No Ys are not-Xs, and similarly from the equation $y = v(1 - x)$ (No Ys are Xs) we get $xy = 0$. These equations, which may also be obtained in other ways, I have employed in the original treatise. All equations whose interpretations are connected are similarly connected themselves, by solution or development.

## On Syllogism

The forms of categorical proposition already deduced are

$$y = vx,$$     All Ys are Xs,
$$y = v(1 - x),$$     No Ys are Xs,
$$vy = v'x,$$     Some Ys are Xs,
$$vy = v'(1 - x),$$     Some Ys are not-Xs,

whereof the two first give by solution, $1 - x = v'(1 - y)$, All not-Xs are not-Ys, $x = v'(1 - y)$, No Xs are Ys. To the above scheme, which is that of Aristotle, we might annex the four categorical propositions

$$1 - y = vx$$     All not-Ys are Xs,
$$1 - y = v(1 - x),$$     All not-Ys are not-Xs,
$$v(1 - y) = v'x,$$     Some not-Ys are not-Xs,
$$v(1 - y) = v'(1 - x),$$     Some not-Ys are not-Xs,

the two first of which are similarly convertible into

$$1 - x = v'y,$$     All not-Xs are Ys,
$$x = v'y,$$     All Xs are Ys,
or     No not-Xs are Ys.

If now the two premises of any syllogism are expressed by equations of the above forms, the elimination of the common symbol $y$ will lead us to an equation expressive of the conclusion.

Ex. 1.     All Ys are Xs, $y = vx$,
     All Zs are Ys, $z = v'y$,

the elimination of $y$ gives

$$z = vv'x,$$

the interpretation of which is

All Zs are Xs;

the form of the coefficient $vv'$ indicates that the predicate of the conclusion is limited by both the conditions which separately limit the predicates of the premises.

Ex. 2.     All Ys are Xs, $y = vx$.
     All Ys are Zs, $y = v'z$.

The elimination of $y$ gives

$$v'z = vx,$$

which is interpretable into Some Zs are Xs. It is always necessary that one term of the conclusion should be interpretable by means of the equations of the premises. In the above case, both are so.

Ex. 3.    All Xs are Ys, $x = vy,$
No Zs are Ys, $z = v'(1 - y).$

Instead of directly eliminating $y$ let either equation be transformed by solution as in (19). The first gives

$$1 - y = u(1 - x),$$

$u$ being equivalent to $v + w(1 - v)$, in which $w$ is arbitrary. Eliminating $1 - y$ between this and the second equation of the system, we get

$$z = v'u(1 - x),$$

the interpretation of which is

No Zs are Xs.

Had we directly eliminated $y$, we should have had

$$vz = v'(v - x),$$

the reduced solution of which is

$$z = v'\{v + w(1 - v)\}(1 - x),$$

in which $w$ is an arbitrary elective symbol. This exactly agrees with the former result.

These examples may suffice to illustrate the employment of the method in particular instances. But its applicability to the demonstration of general theorems is here, as in other cases, a more important feature. I subjoin the results of a recent investigation of the Laws of Syllogism. While those results are characterized by great simplicity, and bear, indeed, little trace of their mathematical origin, it would, I conceive, have been very difficult to arrive at them by the examination and comparison of particular cases.

*Laws of Syllogism Deduced from the Elective Calculus*

We shall take into account all propositions which can be made out of the classes X, Y, Z, and referred to any of the forms embraced in the following system

| A, All Xs are Zs. | A', All not-Xs are Zs. |
|---|---|
| E, No Xs are Zs. | E', {No not-Xs are Zs, or (All not-Xs are not-Zs). |
| I, Some Xs are Zs. | I', Some not-Xs are Zs. |
| O, Some Xs are not-Zs. | O', Some not-Xs are not-Zs. |

It is necessary to recapitulate that quantity (universal and particular) and quality (affirmative and negative) are understood to belong to the *terms* of propositions which is indeed the correct view.*

Thus, in the proposition All Xs are Ys, the subject All Xs is universal-affirmative, the predicate (some) Ys particular-affirmative.

In the proposition, Some Xs are Zs, both terms are particular-affirmative.

The proposition No Xs are Zs would in philosophical language be written in the form All Xs are not-Zs. The subject is universal-affirmative, the predicate particular-negative.

In the proposition Some Xs are not Zs, the subject is particular-affirmative, the predicate particular-negative. In the proposition All not-Xs are Ys the subject is universal-negative, the predicate particular-affirmative, and so on.

In a pair of premises there are four terms, viz. two subjects and two predicates; two of these terms, viz. those involving the Y or not-Y, may be called the middle terms, the two others the extremes, one of these involving X or not-X, the other Z or not-Z.

The following are then the conditions and the rules of inference.

Case 1st.   The middle terms of like quality.

---

* When *propositions* are said to be affected with quantity and quality, the quality is really that of the *predicate*, which expresses the *nature* of the assertion, and the quantity that of the *subject*, which shews its extent.

Condition of Inference.   One middle term universal.

Rule.   Equate the extremes.

Case 2nd.   The middle terms of opposite qualities.

1st.   Condition of Inference.   One extreme universal.

Rule.   Change the quantity and quality of that extreme, and equate the result to the other extreme.

2nd.   Condition of Inference.   Two universal middle terms.

Rule.   Change the quantity and quality of either extreme, and equate the result to the other extreme.

I add a few examples,

1st,                    All Ys are Xs.
                       All Zs are Ys.

This belongs to Case 1.   All Ys is the universal middle term.   The extremes equated give All Zs are Xs, the stronger term becoming the subject.

2nd.     $\left. \begin{array}{l} \text{All Xs are Ys} \\ \text{No Zs are Ys} \end{array} \right\} = \left\{ \begin{array}{l} \text{All Xs are Ys.} \\ \text{All Zs are not-Ys.} \end{array} \right.$

This belongs to Case 2, and satisfies the first condition. The middle term is particular-affirmative in the first premise, particular-negative in the second.   Taking All Zs as the universal extreme, we have, on changing its quantity and quality, Some not-Zs, and this equated to the other extreme gives

All Xs are (some) not-Zs = No Xs are Zs.

If we take All Xs as the universal extreme we get

No Zs are Xs.

3rd.                    All Xs are Ys.
                       Some Zs are not Ys.

This also belongs to Case 2, and satisfies the first condition.   The universal extreme All Xs becomes, Some not-Xs, whence

Some Zs are not-Xs.

4th.                    All Ys are Xs.
                       All not-Ys are Zs.

This belongs to Case 2, and satisfies the second condition. The extreme Some Xs becomes All not-Xs,

$$\therefore \quad \text{All not-Xs are Zs.}$$

The other extreme treated in the same way would give

$$\text{All not-Zs are Xs,}$$

which is an equivalent result.

If we confine ourselves to the Aristotelian premises A, E, I, O, the second condition of inference in Case 2 is not needed. The conclusion will not necessarily be confined to the Aristotelian system.

Ex.   $\left.\begin{array}{l}\text{Some Ys are not-Xs}\\ \text{No Zs are Ys}\end{array}\right\} = \left\{\begin{array}{l}\text{Some Ys are not-Xs.}\\ \text{All Zs are not-Ys.}\end{array}\right.$

This belongs to Case 2, and satisfied the first condition.   The result is

$$\text{Some not-Zs are not-Xs.}$$

These appear to me to be the ultimate laws of syllogistic inference.   They apply to every case, and they completely abolish the distinction of figure, the necessity of conversion, the arbitrary and partial * rules of distribution, &c.   If all logic were reducible to the syllogism these might claim to be regarded as the rules of logic.   But logic, considered as the science of the relations of classes has been shown to be of far greater extent.   Syllogistic inference, in the elective system, corresponds to elimination.   But this is not the highest in the order of its processes.   All questions of elimination may in that system be regarded as subsidiary to the more general problem of the solution of elective equations.   To this problem all questions of logic and of reasoning, without exception, may be referred.   For the fuller illustrations of this principle I must, however, refer to the original work.   The theory of hypothetical propositions, the analysis of the positive and negative elements, into which all propositions are ultimately resolvable, and other similar topics are also there discussed.

* Partial, because they have reference only to the quantity of the X, even when the proposition relates to the not-X.   It would be possible to construct an exact counterpart to the Aristotelian rules of syllogism, by quantifying only the not-X.   The system in the text is *symmetrical* because it is complete.

Undoubtedly, the final aim of speculative logic is to assign the conditions which render reasoning possible, and the laws which determine its character and expression. The general axiom (A) and the laws (1), (2), (3), appear to convey the most definite solution that can at present be given to this question. When we pass to the consideration of hypothetical propositions, the same laws and the same general axiom which ought perhaps also to be regarded as a law, continue to prevail; the only difference being that the subjects of thought are no longer classes of objects, but cases of the coexistent truth or falsehood of propositions. Those relations which logicians designate by the terms conditional, disjunctive, &c., are referred by Kant to distinct conditions of thought. But it is a very remarkable fact that the expressions of such relations can be deduced the one from the other by mere analytical process. From the equation $y = vx$, which expressed the *conditional* proposition, " If the proposition Y is true the proposition X is true ", we can deduce

$$yx + (1 - y)x + (1 - y)(1 - x) = 1,$$

which expresses the *disjunctive* proposition, " Either Y and X are together true, or X is true and Y false, or they are both false ", and again the equation $y(1 - x) = 0$, which expresses a relation of coexistence, viz. that the truth of Y and the falsehood of X do not coexist. The distinction in the mental regard, which has the best title to be regarded as fundamental, is, I conceive, that of the affirmative and the negative. From this we deduce the direct and the inverse in operations, the true and the false in propositions, and the opposition of qualities in their terms.

The view which these inquiries present of the nature of language is a very interesting one. They exhibit it not as a mere collection of signs, but as a system of expression, the elements of which are subject to the laws of the thought which they represent. That those laws are as rigorously mathematical as are the laws which govern the purely quantitative conceptions of space and time, of number and magnitude, is a conclusion which I do not hesitate to submit to the exactest scrutiny.

# III

## SKETCH OF A THEORY AND METHOD OF PROB-ABILITIES FOUNDED UPON THE CALCULUS OF LOGIC *

IT will be necessary to give some account of the method and objects of the Calculus of Logic before entering upon its derived applications, which are in part at least of a different nature.

I have already, in a special treatise on this subject, and in a paper entitled " The Calculus of Logic " published in the *Cambridge and Dublin Mathematical Journal*, established the laws upon which the calculus is based, and I have endeavoured to found upon them certain methods having for their object the analysis of propositions and the deduction of inference from premises. To the system of laws above referred to, I have nothing here to add. They appear to me to be the essential laws of language, whether it is considered as a medium of communication of thought or as an organon of the reasoning faculty.

The general conclusion to which this investigation points may be briefly stated as follows. That language in the twofold capacity above described is resolvable into a system of elementary signs or symbols, which, if represented by the letters $x$, $y$, $z$ &c., will be subject, 1st, to the laws of those symbols which are employed in the science of Algebra to represent numbers and magnitudes, and 2ndly, to a peculiar law which may be expressed by the equations $x^2 = x$, $y^2 = y$, $z^2 = z$, the index implying the repetition of the operations symbolized by the letters $x$, $y$, $z$, to which it is attached.

There are some general principles having reference to the

---

* [This essay is written in parts of two note-books—marked " 2 Logic " and " 6 Logic "—among the Boole manuscripts in the Royal Society Library. It obviously was written after the publication of the *Calculus of Logic* and before the *Laws of Thought*. It may have been written before 1851; see p. 250 of this volume.]

nature and requirements of a system of Logic which a very slight consideration of the subject will warrant us in assuming, and to these it will be convenient to direct attention before entering upon an account of the method which it is intended to establish.

But the special methods which I have in the aforementioned work founded upon this system of laws are susceptible of great improvement, and in fact merge in a certain more general method which I intend briefly to establish here. That method may, I think, be regarded as universal; for I am not aware of any general object that can be conceived as attainable by a method in Logic which it does not suffice to accomplish, nor am I acquainted with any cases of failure or exception in the application of it which I have actually made.

All demonstration essentially consists of the deduction of conclusions from premises,—a conclusion once deduced being itself admissible as a premiss. And it is in this order that reasoning usually proceeds. Certain premises are laid down, either from experience or from testimony, or from some other extralogical source; from these are deduced conclusions which simply or combined with other premises derived from the same class of sources as those first given, serve as bases for further inference, until the chain of argument is completed. At any stage of the process we may find ourselves dealing with two sorts of data, viz., such as have been deduced in the previous course of argument from given data, and such as have not before appeared. A very slight examination of any actual specimen of demonstrative reasoning will shew that such are the materials of its composition and such the order of its progress.

It is obviously possible in every instance to separate the *original* premises from those which are merely derived. We may upon attentive examination of any train of argument ascertain which propositions are to be reckoned as the primary data, and what are in themselves conclusions albeit employed in their turn as principles.

And supposing the real data of the question thus separately exhibited, it is clear that in them are implicitly involved all the conclusions to which the chain of argument, howsoever extended, can conduct us.    The knowledge of the original premises is *potentially* the knowledge of all the truths which are derivable from them.    And it is equally clear that our implicit possession of such knowledge does not depend upon the order in which the premises are arranged.    For the purposes of ordinary reasoning a certain order is indeed necessary to be observed.    But the dependence of each or all of the conclusions upon the premises is not at all affected thereby.    Hence with reference to any particular train or argument directed to a particular end, the object of a method ought to be thus expressed.    Given any order in the entire series of original premises, it is required to ascertain whether a particular conclusion is true or false.

But this is far from being the most general object which can be effected.    Perhaps it would not be possible to settle *a priori* the question which is the most general object of a method in Logic.    Judging of this question *a posteriori*, i.e. with the knowledge which is derived from the possession of a method, I should be led to assign the following as the ultimate object which it is within the power of a method to accomplish.

The subject of any argumentative discourse may be resolvable into certain elements, the mutual dependence of which is expressed in the original premises.    Thus, if one of the premises be expressed by the proposition, " If the thermometer falls, the weather will be rainy ", we may regard that proposition as expressing the nature of the connexion which exists between the elements of the subject of discussion, viz., the falling of the thermometer and the occurrence of rain.    And this remark may be extended to any other form of proposition which may be exhibited in the given premises.

Now it will commonly happen that many elements of the above kind will appear in the premises which we do not desire to retain in the conclusion.    They serve as links or middle terms which are actually employed for the purpose of inference alone.    These elements, therefore, must be *eliminated*.    In addition to this it may be required that among the elements to be retained in the conclusion a certain order of antecedence and of consequence should be observed. From a given assumption with reference to a given element or set of elements, we may require to ascertain what consequences follow with reference to certain other elements assumed at pleasure, or we may require to know what relations connect certain elements independently of any connexion with others. The latter problem is, however, really involved in the former.

For example, we may require a train of argument of which the original premises take account of such relations as the following, viz., the connexion of virtue with happiness, of virtue also with advancing knowledge, with civilization and with wealth. And from such a system of premises it may be required to determine the dependence of wealth and civilization upon virtue, or the relations of wealth and civilization to each other. In such a case, the element of " knowledge " would require to be disposed of, and our object would be to determine the relations among the remaining elements according to a certain order of antecedence and consequence previously assigned (viz., virtue antecedent, wealth consequent), together with any absolute relation between the elements " wealth " and " civilization " which might exist independently of their connexion with the antecedent element " virtue ". In complex trains of argument many elements may thus require to be eliminated, and it is conceivable that many may yet remain both in that portion of the conclusion which constitutes the antecedent and in that which forms the consequent.

All that is contemplated above is within the province of the method which it is here designed to exemplify,—and indeed much more than this. For it is not even requisite that the elements of the conclusion should have appeared at all in the premises, the defective information of the latter being supplied by *necessary* truths, in such manner as to save the generality of the method. I can conceive of nothing more nearly approaching to universality than this; and I apprehend that the object which is thus accomplished may be esteemed the most general which it can fall within the sphere of the logician to desire to accomplish.

The actual processes of the method may be referred to one or the other of the three following heads.

1st. The expression of propositions, and the converse, interpretation.

2nd. The development of functions into interpretable forms.

3rd. The general canon of elimination.

These will be considered separately.

## *The Laws of Expression*

It has been remarked that every proposition expresses a relation among elements. Those elements may either be *things*, in which case the proposition belongs to that class which logicians designate as categorical; or they may be facts or events represented by elementary propositions, in which case the connecting proposition belongs to that division which logicians term conditional or hypothetical.

Of the former case we have an illustration in the proposition,

All men are mortal,

which expresses a relation between the classes of things designated by the names " men " and " mortal ".

Of the latter case we have an illustration in the proposition,

If the thermometer falls, it will rain,

which expresses a relation between the facts or events designated by the elementary propositions, " The thermometer falls ", and " It will rain ". It is with this case that we have to do in the theory of probabilities.

In the expression of categorical propositions the symbols $x$, $y$, $z$ are names expressive of qualities or attributes, and as such are used according to the laws of naming. Thus if $x$ represent a certain name " white ", and $y$ a certain name " cloud ", then $xy$ or $yx = $ " white cloud " will represent a name applicable to those things which answer at once to the descriptions " white " and " cloud ". Hence, since the repetition of a name does not affect its signification, we have $xx = x$, or in the language of Algebra,

$$x^2 = x.$$

K

In other respects the laws of the combination of these symbols with one another are the same as the laws of combination of symbols of numerical magnitude in Algebra. The laws may be established *à priori* by regarding the symbols as expressive of certain operations of the mind. (See *Mathematical Analysis of Logic*, p. [15] 60.)

The numerical values 0 and 1 satisfy the same laws as the above symbols of naming, and they actually admit of interpretation taken in the same system, the 0 as Nothing, the 1 as the Universe.

In the division of hypothetical and conditional propositions we have the same *laws* but another *interpretation*. It has been seen that such propositions express relations among the elementary propositions which they connect together. Accordingly I have, in the work above referred to, interpreted the symbols *x, y, z* as here expressing the *cases* in which those elementary propositions are true. This is in agreement with the ordinary doctrine * of the " Reduction of Hypotheticals ". But a more exact analysis has led me to another conclusion. And without stopping here to assign the reason upon which that interpretation is founded,† I shall simply state that it consists in regarding the symbols *x, y, z* as representing the *times* in which the elementary propositions to which they refer are true. In strict accordance with this interpretation, the symbols will be subject to the same laws as those which prevail in the expression of categorical propositions. Thus if *x* represent the time during which a particular proposition X is true, *y* the time during which another proposition Y is true, then *xy* or *yx* will represent the time during which the propositions are both true. The law whose expression is $x^2 = x$, $y^2 = y$ &c., will equally be satisfied, and the numerical values 0 and 1 will be equally admissible with this system of interpretation, —the former as the representative of the nothing of time or *never*: the latter as the Universe of time, which when unlimited is *Eternity*, when limited the duration to which our discourse refers. (See Appendix I to the present paper.)

* Wallis's ?  [Cf. *Laws of Thought*, p. (176) 187.]
† [See Appendix I to this essay.]

Upon this theoretical foundation are established the following rules of expression, which may be used without any distinct reference to the element of time upon which they are based.

To express any single proposition such as " It rains " by means of the symbol $x$, we write

$$x = 1.$$

To express the proposition " It hails " we in like manner appropriate a symbol $y$, so that by $y = 1$ we represent the proposition " It hails ", by $y = 0$ the proposition " It does not hail ". Then the different combinations of these two propositions will be expressed thus,

1st. $xy = 1$.   It rains and hails.
2nd. $x(1 - y) = 1$.   It rains but does not hail.
3rd. $(1 - x)y = 1$.   It hails but does not rain.
4th. $(1 - x)(1 - y) = 1$.   It neither hails nor rains.

To express any disjunctive combination of propositions, we employ the sign $+$ in place of each disjunctive particle *either* or *or*, and express the separate terms as before. Thus, for the proposition, " It either rains and hails simultaneously, or it neither rains nor hails ", we have

$$xy + (1 - x)(1 - y) = 1.$$

It is specially in each case to be noted whether the separate operations which are thus disjunctively connected are really *exclusive*, so that the truth of the one precludes the possibility of the truth of the other; and if such is not the case, the really exclusive assertion to which they are equivalent must be determined and the rule applied. Thus if we desire to express the proposition " It either rains or hails " without excluding the case of both events happening, we have for the really exclusive case,

1st. It rains and hails.   $xy = 1$.
2nd. It rains and does not hail.   $x(1 - y) = 1$.
3rd. It hails but does not rain.   $(1 - x)y = 1$.

Whence the proposition " Either it rains or it hails " will be expressed by the equation

$$xy + x(1 - y) + (1 - x)y = 1.$$

The conditional proposition " If it rains, it hails " is expressed by the equation

$$x = vy,$$

in which $v$ is the representative of *time partially indefinite* and is a symbol of the same kind as $x$ and $y$. In general, a conditional proposition is expressed by placing the antecedent and consequent on different sides of an equation and prefixing to any term which enters only into the consequent an indefinite symbol $v$. Thus if $x$ be appropriated as before to the proposition " It rains ", $y$ to the proposition " It hails ", and if we appropriate $z$ to the proposition " The thermometer falls ", then such interpretations as the following may be established.

$z = v(x\overline{1-y} + y\overline{1-z})$. If the thermometer falls, it either rains or hails.

$zx = v(1 - y)$. If the thermometer falls and it rains, it does not hail.

And so on.

When some terms in either member have the indefinite prefix $v$ and others not, which is the most general case conceivable and is really inclusive of all the others, the following rule of interpretation applies.

The sum of those terms in either member which are free from the prefix $v$ may be interpreted into an antecedent, and all the terms of the opposite member into a consequent. Thus we should have the following interpretations :

$$z = x(1 - y) + v(1 - x)y.$$

1st. If the thermometer falls, either it rains and does not hail or hails and does not rain.

2nd. If it rains and does not hail, the thermometer falls.

Both interpretations are involved in the given equation,— the second of them is obtained by taking the first term of the second member which is free from $v$ as an antecedent, and the first member as a consequent.

$$z + vx(1 - z) = y.$$

1st. If the thermometer falls, it hails.

2nd. If it hails, either the thermometer falls or it rains without the thermometer falling.

There will be no difficulty in the interpretation of any case, provided only that we attend to the following principles.

1st. To take our antecedent from one member and our consequent from the other.

2nd. To include no term in an antecedent which has a factor $v$.

3rd. To connect the different terms, when there are more than one, of the antecedent and of the consequent by the signs *either* and *or*.

The interpretation of the equation,

$$x = y,$$

is comprised in the propositions : 1st, " If it rains, it hails ", 2nd, " If it hails, it rains ".

## The Development of Functions

Since $x$ is a symbol subject to the law $x^2 = x$, it is evident that any function of $x$, as $\phi(x)$, if it be susceptible of development at all, may be expanded in the form

$$\phi(x) = A + Bx \quad . \quad . \quad . \quad . \quad (1).$$

It is then required to determine the values of A and B.

As the expansion of (1) is warranted by the condition that the symbol $x$ is subject to the law,

$$x^2 = x . \quad . \quad . \quad . \quad . \quad (2),$$

it is clear that it will hold true if $x$ is a quantitative symbol satisfying (2) when regarded as the expression of a relation of *quantity*. The solutions of (2) thus considered are,

$$x = 0, \ x = 1.$$

Make, then, in (1), $x = 0$ and $x = 1$, and we get

$$\phi(0) = A, \ \ \phi(1) = A + B.$$

Whence $A = \phi(0)$, $B = \phi(1) - \phi(0)$; and the expansion now becomes,

$$\phi(x) = \phi(0) + \{\phi(1) - \phi(0)\}x$$
$$= \phi(1)x + \phi(0)(1 - x).$$

From hence we obtain by induction,

$$\phi(xy) = \phi(11)xy + \phi(10)x(1 - y) + \phi(01)(1 - x)y$$
$$+ \phi(00)(1 - x)(1 - y),$$

with corresponding forms for the development of functions including a greater number of symbols. In the above form the terms, $xy$, $x(1-y)$ &c., are called constituents, and their multipliers, $\phi(11)$, $\phi(10)$ &c., the corresponding coefficients. The examination of the above theorems conducts us to the general rule for the expansion of functions.

### To expand any function of x, y, z &c.

Rule : Write down the product of the symbols $x$, $y$, $z$; then in that product change any symbol $z$ into $1-z$, and write down the results; and in the forms thus obtained, change any other symbol $x$ into $1-x$, and write down the results,—continuing the process until every symbol has been thus changed. The series of terms thus obtained will be the *constituents* of the expansion.

To determine the coefficient of any constituent, substitute in the original function for the different symbols the numerical value (0 or 1) which will make the factors of the constituent respectively equal to 1. Thus, for the coefficient of the constituent $xyz$, make

$x = 1, y = 1, z = 1$; for the coefficient of $xy(1-z)$, make $x = 1, y = 1, z = 0$; and so on.

The proper coefficient being thus attached to each constituent, and the result connected by the sign $+$, the expansion will be completed.

Thus if we were required to expand the function, $\dfrac{x+y-z}{x+y}$, we should have for the series of constituents, $xyz$, $xy(1-z)$, $x(1-y)z$, $x(1-y)(1-z)$, $(1-x)yz$, $(1-x)y(1-z)$ $(1-x)(1-y)z$, $(1-x)(1-y)(1-z)$.

The coefficient of the first constituent, $xyz$, would be found by making $x = 1, y = 1, z = 1$ in the original function, the resulting value being $\dfrac{1+1-1}{1+1}$, or $\dfrac{1}{2}$; the coefficient of $xy(1-z)$ would be found by making $x = 1, y = 1, z = 0$ in the same function, the result being $\dfrac{1+1}{1+1}$, or $1$; and so on for the rest.   The final expansion would thus be

$$\frac{1}{2}xyz + xy(1 - z) + x(1 - y)(1 - z) + (1 - x)y(1 - z)$$

$$+ \frac{1}{0}(1 - x)(1 - y)z + \frac{0}{0}(1 - x)(1 - y)(1 - z).$$

The mode in which the forms of the coefficients affect the interpretation of a result like the above, will be hereafter considered.

### The Canon of Elimination

Suppose the system of original premises to be expressed symbolically, and that it is required to eliminate some particular symbol, as $x$.   And let it be supposed in the first place that $x$ only enters into a single equation of the system.

Let the given equation be reduced to the form,

$$V = 0,$$

in which V is a function of $x$ and of the other symbols.   Then in V make $x = 1$, and let the result be represented $V_1$. Again, in V let $x = 0$, and represent the result by $V_0$.   The result of the elimination of $x$ from the given equation will be represented by the equation,

$$V_1 V_0 = 0.$$

Thus if it were required to eliminate $v$ from the equation,

$$y - vx = 0,$$

the first member becomes, on making $v = 1$,

$$y - x;$$

and on making $v = 0$, it becomes $y$.

Whence                  $y(y - x) = 0.$

For an example of the transformation here given, see Cicero, *de Fato* (Cap. 8).*

The proof of the above rule may be exhibited as follows.

---

\* [The passage is quoted in *Laws of Thought*, p. (179) 190.   On elimination, compare the discussion in *Laws of Thought*, Ch. VII.   The present essay does not notice the way in which the law of duality makes elimination in Logic different from elimination in Algebra.   That came later, as did the method of reduction without arbitrary constants.   But contrast the present discussion with that in the *Mathematical Analysis of Logic*.]

Let $\phi(x) = 0$ represent the given equation in which $\phi(x)$ represents a function of $x$ and of the other symbols. Then expanding the equation with reference to $x$, we have,

$$\phi(1)x + \phi(0)\overline{1 - x} = 0,$$

$$\therefore \quad \phi(0) + \{\phi(1) - \phi(0)\}x = 0 \quad . \quad . \quad (1).$$

Multiply the above equation by $x$, and we have,

$$\phi(0)x + \{\phi(1) - \phi(0)\}x = 0,$$

or $$\phi(1)x = 0 \quad . \quad . \quad . \quad . \quad (2).$$

Now the result of the elimination of $x$ from the two simple equations,

$$a + bx = 0 \quad . \quad . \quad . \quad . \quad (3),$$

$$a' + b'x = 0 \quad . \quad . \quad . \quad . \quad (4),$$

is $$ab' - a'b = 0 \quad . \quad . \quad . \quad . \quad (5).$$

Comparing (1) and (2) with (3) and (4), we have,

$$a = \phi(0),\ b = \phi(1) - \phi(0),\ a' = 0,\ b' = \phi(1),$$

Whence (5) becomes $\phi(0)\,\phi(1) = 0$, and the rule is manifest.

In the next place, suppose that the symbol which it is required to eliminate enters into more than one equation of the system. Let the equations into which it does enter be represented by $U_x = 0$, $V_x = 0$, $W_x = 0$ &c. Then form the equation,

$$U_x + cV_x + c'W_x = 0,$$

in which $c$, $c'$ etc. are arbitrary quantities, and proceed with the equation according to the rule above stated. Thus, making $x = 0$, we have for the first member, $U_0 + cV_0 + c'W_0$; and making $x = 1$, we have $U_1 + cV_1 + c'W_1$. The product of these factors equated to 0 gives,

$$(U_0 + cV_0 + c'W_0)(U_1 + cV_1 + c'W_1) = 0.$$

(See Appendix II.)

## General Method in Logic

We are now prepared to exhibit a general Rule for the treatment of any system of equations so as to accomplish any proposed object.

The most general object, and one which includes all others, may be thus defined.

Given a system of propositions, to determine the relations of antecedence and of consequence which connect any element entering into those propositions with any other element or set of elements.

Each element being represented by a distinct symbol, the following Rule will apply to every case.

Rule.—*Eliminate by the general method all those symbols which are not required to appear in the conclusion. Reduce the resulting equation, if necessary, to a single equation, by multiplying all but one by an arbitrary constant and adding the results. Supposing x to be an element whose connexion with other elements is sought, this result may be exhibited in the form,*

$$A x = B \quad . \quad . \quad . \quad . \quad . \quad (1),$$

*whence*
$$x = \frac{B}{A} . \quad . \quad . \quad . \quad . \quad (2).$$

*Expand the function $\frac{B}{A}$ in terms of all the symbols which it involves ; retain unaltered every term whose coefficient is unity ; for every coefficient $\frac{0}{0}$ write q, an indefinite symbol ; reject all terms whose coefficient is 0 separately ; and equate to 0 all other terms.*

*Then the equation exhibiting the reduced value of x will, on interpretation, express the relations both of antecedence and of consequence which are sought, and the remaining equations, if any, will exhibit the relations which exist among the remaining elements independently of the element represented by x.*

It may be remarked that this rule never fails,—not even when elements are introduced into the conclusion which are absent from the premises. If $x$, the element whose value is sought, do not enter into the equation represented by (1), in which case $A = 0$, still the development of the second member of (2) according to the literal direction of the rule will give a result both true and interpretable,—true, although it may only express a *necessary* truth. If A and B both vanish, which implies that some of the elements of the conclusion have been found in the premises, still the development of (2) will conduct to a true result, albeit a *necessary* one and adding nothing to our previous knowledge. . . .

[There follows an illustration of the Rule by reference to Dr. Clarke's " Demonstration of the Being and Attributes of God ".   Compare *Laws of Thought*, Chapter XIII. The earlier version uses the methods just outlined.]

## Of Probabilities

I shall in this Essay designate as a simple proposition, one of which the expression is effected by an equation involving a single symbol. Thus we may express the proposition, " It rains ", by the equation, $x = 1$, and the proposition, " It does not rain ", by the equation $x = 0$; and either of these I therefore designate as a simple proposition.

The event of which the occurrence is expressed by a simple proposition I shall call a simple event; and I here use the term to signify not only an occurrence, but also a condition or state of a thing.

A proposition which is represented by an equation involving two or more symbols, I shall designate as a compound proposition, and the state of things represented by it as a compound event. Thus if $x = 1$ represent the proposition, " It rains ", $y = 1$ the proposition " It hails ", then the propositions,

$$xy = 1, \quad \text{It rains and hails,}$$
$$x(1 - y) + y(1 - x) = 1, \quad \text{It either rains or hails,}$$

will be designated as compound propositions, and the states of things which they represent as compound events. I adopt this language merely for convenience.

I intend in the introduction of [this part of] this Essay to speak of assertive and disjunctive propositions, and not of conditional ones, and for this obvious reason, that our experience informs us immediately of the frequency of occurrence of events or alternations of events,—but only mediately and inferentially of the frequency of the occur rence of events under conditions; for it is necessary to compare the frequency of occurrence of the events with the frequency of occurrence of the conditions under which they happen. I shall speak more particularly of this subject in the sequel.

Now if $x$ and $y$ represent two simple events, of which the probabilities are $p$ and $q$, then the equations,

$$xy = 1, \; x(1 - y) = 1 \;\&\text{c.},$$

will represent compound events, of which the probabilities are $pq$, $p(1 - q)$ &c.

Also, it is evident that the equation,

$$x(1 - y) + y(1 - x) = 1,$$

represents a compound event, of which the probability is $p(1 - q) + q(1 - p)$.

These are examples of the simplest cases of events represented by assertive and disjunctive propositions. And it is hence evident by induction that if $x$, $y$, $z$ represent any simple events of which the respective probabilities are $p$, $q$, $r$, then the probabilities of the compound event whose probability is represented by the equation,

$$(xyz\ldots) = 1, \; . \quad . \quad . \quad . \quad . \quad (1)$$

will be represented by the function,

$$(pqr\ldots),$$

obtained by changing, in the first member of (1), $x$ into $p$, $y$ into $q$, $z$ into $r$ etc. This proposition may, however, be formally proved.

It is obviously supposed in the above case that the probabilities of the simple events $x$, $y$, $z$, ... are given by independent observations. This is, I apprehend, what is really meant by events being spoken of as independent. For if the events are not independent (according to the ordinary acceptation of that term), the knowledge that they are not so can only be derived from experiences in which they are mutually involved, not from observations upon them as simple and unconnected. And hence if our knowledge is derived from experience, the independence of events is only another name for the independence of our observations of them.

To the case above contemplated, the ordinary theory of probabilities is confined. It cannot be applied to observations made upon compound events, because the hypothesis that the simple events which are involved in their expression are independent cannot then be maintained. In fact, the very observance of events occurring in any mutual connexion is a presupposition that they are not independent.

An instance of an erroneous extension of the common theory of probabilities to the case in which one of the observations is compound, occurs in the able article on Probabilities in the *Encyclopedia Metropolitana* *. The following principle is there laid down.

" Principle IV. Knowing the probability of a compound event and that of one of its components, we find the probability of the other by dividing the first by the second."

Here it is assumed that the simple events are independent; whereas if the probability of the occurrence of the compound event is a result of observations upon prior instances of its occurrence, it is clear that we have no right to regard the simple events as unconnected and independent.

For suppose the probability of its thundering upon a particular day to be $p$, and that of its thundering and raining on the same day $q$, each probability being determined by a set of previous observations,—the one set upon the frequency of thunder, the other upon the frequency of rain and thunder conjointly. We know from the physical connexion of the two simple events, that $p$ and $q$, *thus determined by observation*, would be fractions having *very nearly the same value*. Hence the probability of its raining upon the given day, as given by the above principle, viz. $\frac{p}{q}$, would be very nearly equal to unity, i.e. it would, according to that principle, be *almost certain* that it would rain upon a given day. Such a conclusion is obviously unwarranted. The observed occurrence of rain and thunder, from which the probability of their simultaneously happening upon a given occasion is ascertained, [should be taken] to afford a presumption that the events are not independent.

* [The article is by De Morgan.]

The received theory, then, rests upon the hypothesis that simple events are independent.

In place of this hypothesis I lay down the following one.

*The events, whether simple or compound, whose probabilities are given by observation, are to be regarded as independent of any but a logical connexion.*

How events may have a logical connexion, will appear in the next chapter. Postulating that they may have, it is clear that such a connexion is *necessary*, and therefore *must* according to the laws of the reasoning faculty be recognized. If they have any other connexion, it is a physical one, respecting which our experience gives us no information.

### On the Logical connexion of Events

Let $x$, $y$, $z$ &c. represent any simple events, the occurrence of which will therefore be expressed by the propositions, $x = 1, y = 1, z = 1$.

Let $\phi(xyz)$, $\psi(xyz)$, $\cdots \chi(xyz)$ represent any compound events, the occurrence of which is, of course, expressed by the equations,

$$\phi(xyz) = 1, \psi(xyz) = 1, \ldots \chi(xyz) = 1.$$

Suppose it is required to determine the logical dependence of the event whose occurrence is asserted by the last proposition, upon those whose occurrence is implied by the other equations.

Let $u$ represent a simple event so related to the compound event $\phi(xyz)$ that whenever the one occurs the other occurs also. Let $v \ldots t$ be also simple events, similarly related to the compound events represented by $\psi(xyz) \ldots \chi(xyz)$. Then the logical connexion of $u$, $v$, $t$ with $x$, $y$, $z$ will be represented by the system of equations,

$$\phi(xyz) = u,$$
$$\psi(xyz) = v,$$
$$\chi(xyz) = t.$$

From these equations the symbols $x, y, z$, whatever their number, may be eliminated, according to the general rule for equations in Logic, and a result obtained of the form,

$$F(uvt) = 0.$$

If this equation then be solved with reference to $t$, and the solution developed with reference to $u$ and $v$, we shall be in possession of the logical dependence of $t$ upon $u$ and $v$; and this will represent the logical dependence of $\phi(xyz)$ upon $\psi(xyz)$ and $\chi(xyz)$. For from the definition of $u$, $v$ and $t$, it is evident that the probability of $u$ occurring is the same as the probability of $\phi(xyz)$ occurring, and similarly for the others.

The value of $t$, as established in terms of $u$ and $v$, will be of the form,

$$t = \mathrm{P} + c\mathrm{Q}, \text{ with the condition } \mathrm{R} = 0\,;$$

P, Q and R being functions of $u$ and $v$, and $c$, which occupies the place of $q^{*}$ in the Logic, representing an arbitrary class; and R $= 0$ exhibiting those relations among $u$ and $v$ which are independent of $t$.

To such a form of solution we shall arrive, whatever may be the number of simple events $x$, $y$, $z$, or of the compound events into which they enter.

Given the probabilities of any events, simple or compound, to ascertain the probability of any other event.

Let $\phi(xyz)$, $\psi(xyz)$, ... be the events whose probabilities are given, and let $\chi(xyz)$ be the event whose probability is sought. Let the probability of $\phi(xyz)$ be $p$, and that of $\psi(xyz)$, $q$.

Proceeding as in the last proposition, we shall obtain an equation of the form,

$$t = \mathrm{P} + c\mathrm{Q}, \text{ with } \mathrm{R} = 0, \quad . \quad . \quad . \quad (1)$$

in which P and Q and R are functions of $u$ and $v$, the actual probability of the event represented by $u$ being $p$, that of the event represented by $v$ being $q$, and the probability of $t$ being the element sought.

Since R $= 0$, it is obvious that all the combinations of $u$ and $v$ which actually occur will be represented by the function, $1 - \mathrm{R}$. This is the logical restriction already referred to. The quantities $p$ and $q$ represent the proba-

* [Or $v$. See above, p. 153; but also p. 148. In the manuscript of that passage Boole has written $v$ and $q$ interchangeably, and he would undoubtedly have made the usage uniform if he had revised it. In some other manuscripts he uses $q$ for the arbitrary symbol, but he generally keeps to $v$, and that has been kept there. In the immediate context before us, $v$ might have been confusing.]

bilities of $u$ and $v$, regarded as *subject to that restriction*. In other respects the events $u$ and $v$ are independent.

We shall form a better idea of the case we have to do with, by considering a question, the theory of which has been previously established. This I merely adduce by way of *analogy*, not of *authority*. If there are two independent testimonies, of the values of $p'$ and $q'$, to the truth of an event, the probability of its truth is

$$\frac{p'q'}{p'q' + (1 - p')(1 - q')}.$$ (De Morgan, *Formal Logic*, p. 195.)

Here the veracities of the individuals are represented by $p'$ and $q'$; these are the *antecedent* probabilities of their speaking the truth. *When it is known that they have given the same testimony*, the only admissible combinations are those of both speaking the truth and both speaking falsehood. The probability that either individual speaks the truth is now no longer $p'$ or $q'$, but $\dfrac{p'q'}{p'q' + (1 - p')(1 - q')}$. This may be called the actual probability, as distinguished from $p'$ or $q'$, the antecedent probability, i.e. the probability of such an event *antecedent* to our knowledge of the agreement of the testimonies.

Now the case before us is one in which the restriction is given, and the *actual probabilities* of the events $u$ and $v$ subject to that restriction. And it will be our first care to express these functions of the antecedent probabilities.

Let $p'$, $q'$, be the antecedent probabilities of $u$ and $v$ considered as independent and occurring in an unlimited universe. Now actually $u$ does not occur in every possible combination with $v$, but only in such combinations as are found in $1 - R$; the whole of the combinations in which $u$ actually occurs is represented by $u(1 - R)$ (the multiplication being performed), the whole of those in which $v$ occurs by $v(1 - R)$, and so on. The probability of these events occurring in the unlimited universe represented by 1, would be $[u(1 - R)][v(1 - R)]$, when the [ ] indicates the change of $u$ into $p'$, $v$ into $q'$ in the expressions $u(1 - R)$ and $v(1 - R)$ reduced as above.

The probability of the same events occurring in a limited universe of possible events, will be greater than the above by the ratio in which the number of events in the universe is less than in the universe 1. But the ratio in which the universe 1 — R is less than the universe 1, is 1 — R. Hence the probabilities of the occurrence of the events $u$, $v$ in the universe 1 — R are represented by

$$\frac{[u(1 - R)]}{[1 - R]} \qquad \frac{[v(1 - R)]}{[1 - R]}$$

respectively. But these probabilities are $p$ and $q$, by the data of the question. Whence

$$\frac{[u(1 - R)]}{[1 - R]} = p, \qquad \frac{[v(1 - R)]}{[1 - R]} = q, \text{ \&c. } \quad . \quad (2)$$

Now the value of $t$ is $P + cQ$, which will not be affected by multiplying 1 — R. For R, P and Q being constituents, $RP = 0$, $RQ = 0$, $PQ = 0$. Hence the probability of $t$ will be represented by

$$\frac{[P + cQ]}{[I - R]}, \quad . \quad . \quad . \quad . \quad . \quad (3)$$

$c$ being an arbitrary constant representing the probability of the indefinite event before represented by $c$. The values of $p'$ and $q'$ being determined by the system (2) and substituted in (3) will give the probability sought.

A little consideration will shew that $c$ in the above formula represents the probability that if the proposition $Q = 1$ is true, the proposition $t = 1$ is true; and it will then, when the problem is not determinate, point out what new experience is necessary in order to render it so.

Instead of changing $u$, $v$ &c. into $p'$, $q'$, we may suppose $u$ and $v$ changed in interpretation from logical to algebraic symbols. The results of the investigation will then be embodied in the following rule.

Rule.—*Equate those functions which represent the compound events to a new set of symbols, u, v etc. Eliminate all the symbols which represent events whose probability is either given or sought, and determine according to the rules of the Calculus of Logic the value of the symbol t which corresponds to the event whose probability is sought in terms of those which represent events whose probability is given. The result will be of the form,*

$$t = P + cQ, \text{ with } R = 0.$$

*Also, let $u(1 - R)$, $v(1 - R)$ &c. represent the results obtained by multiplying $1 - R$ by $u$, $v$ &c., according to the rules of the Calculus of Logic.*

*Now let $p$, $q$ etc. be the given probabilities of the events represented by $u$, $v$ etc. Then the values of the probability sought will be represented by the formula,*

$$\frac{P + cQ}{1 - R}, \quad \cdot \quad \cdot \quad \cdot \quad \cdot \quad \cdot \quad (4)$$

*provided that $u$, $v$ etc. be regarded as algebraic quantities, whose values are to be determined by the system of equations,*

$$\frac{u(1 - R)}{1 - R} = p, \frac{v(1 - R)}{1 - R} = q, \dots \&c.$$

*If in the above formula Q does not vanish, the arbitrary constant will express the probability that if the event represented by Q occurs, the event represented by t will follow ; and it thus indicates what new information is necessary to make the probability sought a determinate quantity.*

If all the events whose probability is given are *simple*, the above method conducts us to the same result as the methods already known. . . .

[Boole then gives examples of problems and their solutions. The problems, or similar ones, are discussed in the *Laws of Thought*, Chapters XVII and XVIII. One of them is given briefly in the early paper on Mitchell's Problem of the Distribution of the Fixed Stars; see below, p. 254. But in the present essay the solutions are much longer. He occasionally condenses, with a remark like, " After a somewhat tedious elimination, we get . . .". But his methods appear more cumbersome here than in the *Laws of Thought*.]

## Appendix I

The complete theory of the symbolic expression both of categorical and hypothetical propositions is contained in the following position.*

The office of the adjective in common language is not simply to attribute quality; it also operates by *limiting* the sphere of the subject to which it is applied.  The subject " men ", without any adjective prefixed, means " all men ".  Prefix the adjective " good ", and the term " good men " involves a limitation of the subject from " all men " to " all men who possess a certain attribute expressed by ' good ' ".  Thus the adjective, and every attributive expression, whether single or many-worded, possesses a limiting, or as I have termed it elsewhere, an *elective* power.  The substantive only differs from this in that it is understood to express also the subject to which the attribute is referred.  We abolish the distinction by supposing the common subject " things ", or the Universe, to be always understood.

The symbols *x*, *y* &c., used in this treatise to express categorical propositions, represent, then, this attributive and elective operation, which is thus seen to be common to the substantive and the adjective and the many-worded attributive clause.  Thus *x*, applied to any subject, must be understood to represent the operation of selecting from that subject all the individuals possessing a given character which it contains.  From this definition, the laws of combination of the symbols may be deduced *à priori*.

As we are permitted to give any definition to a symbol, provided that the laws to which it is made subject are such as that definition necessitates, we are at liberty to adopt such a scheme of symbols as the following.  Let the subject be *time*, and let *x* represent the operation of selecting out

* [Among the manuscripts there is a short essay on the interpretation of hypotheticals, which is similar to this Appendix in substance and in various details.  It evidently belongs to the same period,—between the *Calculus of Logic* and the *Laws of Thought*.  At the time, Boole called that essay the " final draft ", and wrote " approved " on it.  The statement there is more formal and rigorous than the present one,—though it is not certain which is earlier.  The general position and argument are the same.  And since this was written for this essay, it has been kept.]

of that subject all those instants of duration in which a certain elementary proposition is true ; $y$ the same operation with reference to another elementary proposition ; and so on.

It is clear then that the equation,

$$x = y,$$

would represent that whenever the one proposition is true, the other is. Upon this basis the laws of combination and of expression, given in the text, are a necessary superstructure. It is equally clear that in this system the ultimate subject is the whole duration to which the propositions we are speaking of are referred, whether as true or false, and therefore the absolute subject is Eternity.

There are some very beautiful analogies between the two systems of interpretation here introduced, which I shall briefly exhibit.

| Categoricals | Hypotheticals |
|---|---|
| Subject the Universe, | Subject Eternity, |
| consisting of individual things to which attributes are referred. | made up of instants of duration to which propositions are referred. |
| 1. To any individual, a given attribute or its contrary may be referred. | 1. At any instant of duration a given proposition or its contrary is true. |
| 2. An attribute and its contrary cannot be referred to the same individual. | 2. A proposition and its contrary are not true at the same instant of duration. |
| 3. A given attribute may be referred to one individual and its contrary to another individual in the same universe. | 3. A given proposition may be true at one time, and its contrary true at another time. |
| 4. The individuals which possess a given attribute, together with those which possess its contrary, make up the Universe. | 4. The instants in which a proposition is true, with those in which it is false, make up Eternity. |

These analogies may easily be multiplied.

One other point of great importance remains to be noticed. By the process which in ordinary treatises on Logic is termed " Reduction of Hypotheticals ", it is shewn that a hypothetical judgment is reducible to a categorical form. But the reduced proposition is always *universal*. There is nothing in the commonly received doctrine of hypotheticals at all analogous to the *particular* propositions of the categorical system. The language of common discourse, which in many respects outstrips the limits within which the logicians would fain have restricted it, recognizes, however, the particular as well as the universal in hypothetical judgments,—and it distinguishes them by the particle " *sometimes* ". The system which I have endeavoured to establish, introduces the same element, *Time*, and in the same manner. This I was not aware of when I was led to form that system, and I accordingly esteem it an interesting verification.

But the system in the text also permits us to introduce Time definitely, and explicitly to deduce conclusions in strict logic from propositions referred to a given period of duration, and ascertain the limits of duration within which those conclusions are accepted as true.

The doctrine of life assurance rests in reality upon the theory of hypothetical propositions regarded as true within certain limits of *time*. A single example will shew this.

Suppose the value of an annuity to be paid during the last survivorship of three given lives, A, B, C, were required. Let $x$ represent the time during which the proposition, " A lives ", is true, $y$ and $z$ the corresponding times for B and C. Thus the time during which some one of these propositions is true, and both the others false, is,

$$x(1 - y)(1 - z) + y(1 - x)(1 - z) + z(1 - x)(1 - y),$$

or multiply out,

$$x + y + z - z(xy + xz + yz) + 3xyz,$$

whence the ordinary rule follows.

Mr. Sylvester pointed out to me some time ago the defective character of the ordinary theory of life assurance. But it was not until lately, and while engaged in pursuits entirely different, that I was led to view the subject in the above connexion.

### Appendix II

The introduction of the numerical constants, $c$, $c'$ &c., into this system, may perhaps be objected to on the following ground. We can interpret $x$ as a logical symbol, it may be said, but we cannot interpret $cx$. A satisfactory answer can be given to this objection upon more than one distinct ground.

In the first place, it may be observed that in every branch of analysis the formal laws of combination of the symbols are of wider extent than the laws of their interpretation. In strict obedience to those laws we can pass from an interpretable to an uninterpretable result, and again from this to an interpretable result. Thus in the arithmetic of sines we employ the form $\sqrt{-1}$, the representation of an operation quite uninterpretable in arithmetic, with perfect security. I apprehend that the philosophical ground of this application is, that we borrow the laws of our symbols from the examination of interpretable cases; that we frame a language or a notation, the symbols of which are subject to this restriction only: that they should obey those laws,—not to the restriction that every combination thus obtained should be interpretable; that the process of reasoning with this general language is formal, and dependent solely upon the general laws to which its symbols are subject; that any interpretation which we are able to assign to such a language is particular; and that the validity of a conclusion is dependent upon these two conditions : first, that the interpretation is consistent with the formal laws to which the symbols are subject, secondly that those formal laws have never been violated in the process of reasoning.

If it is objected that the symbol $\sqrt{-1}$ does admit of interpretation in geometry, the answer is that the validity of results obtained by its aid in the case referred to, the arithmetic of sines, does not depend upon such interpretation.

The introduction of numerical constants into any calculus, the symbols of which represent *operations*, of whatever kind they may be, is however in itself perfectly consistent. We conceive of an operation as capable of being repeated. Hence the idea of integral numerical quantity. With the idea of operation is also connected the antithesis of the Direct and the Inverse, and it is in this way that we pass from the idea of integral number to that of fractional number. It hence follows that the idea of Number is not solely confined to Arithmetic, but that it is an element which may properly be combined with the elements of every system of language which can be employed for the purposes of general reasoning, whatsoever may be the nature of the subject.

I think it important to notice that, while Number thus properly and naturally may be employed in the logical system, the logical symbols themselves, (except perhaps the 0 and the 1), are not in any sense numerical. Let $x$, $y$, $z$ represent three entirely distinct classes of things, together filling up the Universe of discourse. Then,

$$x + y + z = 1.$$

Here none of the symbols, $x$, $y$ and $z$, can be replaced by 0, because none of the classes is supposed to vanish; nor by 1, because otherwise the sum of the three would be more than 1; nor by any other numerical value, because no other numerical value satisfies the law,

$$x^2 = x.$$

Thus they are not numbers, but signs used in subjection to the laws of thought as manifested in language. . . .

[Two more appendices follow. The first applies the theory to a problem in the calculus of probabilities. The second has the title, " Of the probabilities of conditional events, and of the syllogism ". Compare *Laws of Thought*, pp. (281) 297 ff. The discussion of the probabilities of conditional events is short, and does not recognize the difficulties which are brought out in the *Laws of Thought*. The discussion of the probability of the syllogism is more complicated than that in the *Laws of Thought*. It ends with the following remark, which is also the end of the essay.]

It is a commonly received opinion that the probability of the truth of a logical conclusion is equal to the product of the probabilities of the premises. This is only true, as a *limiting case*, in the syllogism, while for the other forms of argument the question requires a distinct examination.

# IV

## OF PROPOSITIONS NUMERICALLY DEFINITE *

BY a proposition numerically definite, I mean a proposition which conveys an assertion respecting the number of individuals contained in a class. If I assert that in a given company of men there are six individuals who possess some particular attribute, the proposition which I affirm is numerically definite. There exist propositions which are numerical but not strictly definite, as when we assert, "most of the trees in a certain park are elms," or that more than two-thirds of a certain company are merchants. Such propositions may certainly be regarded as numerical, although not so far definite as to determine the actual number of individuals spoken of. The theory of propositions numerically definite in the stricter sense will, however, include the theory of those which are so in a less degree. One general investigation will, in fact, conduct us to all the results of which the subject admits.

Professor De Morgan was, I believe, the first to treat of this class of propositions. In his *Formal Logic* he has devoted a chapter to the consideration of the subject. His most important conclusion is expressed in the syllogism

most $Ys$ are $Xs$,
most $Ys$ are $Zs$;
∴ some $Zs$ are $Xs$,

taken in connexion with the condition that the number of

* [From the *Transactions of the Cambridge Philosophical Society*, vol. XI. Part II. Cambridge, 1868. After the title comes, " By the late George Boole, F.R.S., Professor of Mathematics in Queen's College, Cork. Communicated † by A. De Morgan, Esq."]

† This paper appears to me to illustrate, in a very remarkable way, the trains of thought contained in Professor Boole's logical writings. It was written after the publication of my *Formal Logic*, and before the final elaboration of Mr. Boole's *Laws of Thought*, though subsequently to his first tract on the subject which appeared on the same day as my *Formal Logic*. The paper is an interpretation, in terms of the numerical proposition, of forms familiar to all in the theory of probability, and to Mr. Boole in his own system of Logic. December 2, 1867. A. De. M.

*Z*s which are *X*s will be at least equal to the excess of the aggregate of the two numbers of *Y*s spoken of in the two premises over the total number of *Y*s existing.  The other examples of syllogism which Professor De Morgan has given appear to be derived from the above, or at least to be capable of being so derived by conversion of premises and other known transformations of the ordinary logic.

Professor De Morgan has remarked that from forms similar to the above all the known cases of syllogism may be deduced.  Thus the condition that the sum of the quantifications of the middle term in both premises together shall exceed its total quantifications, as a rule of inference, at once leads us to the syllogism

all *Y*s are *X*s,

some *Y*s are *Z*s ;

∴   some *Z*s are *X*s,

and similarly, with the aid of conversion, to the other known forms.

There appear to be two general questions suggested by a consideration of the above.  First.  Does there arise a general method to which the treatment of all systems, propositions involving any and whatsoever amount of numerical definition, may be referred?  Secondly.  Are the ordinary conclusions of logic to be considered as limiting cases of the results of any such general method?  These questions I propose to consider separately.

With respect to the first, it may be well to inquire, *in limine*, what is the most general object which we can propose to ourselves to accomplish by any method applicable to propositions numerically definite.  Now I conceive that the most general object which we can propose may be thus expressed.  Given any system of propositions, any of the terms of which, simple or compound, are made in numerically definite form, required the numerical limits within which the number of individuals contained in any proposed class will be ; whether that class be defined by the presence or the absence of any single attribute, or by the presence of any collection of attributes and the absence of any other collection of attributes, or whether it consist of distinct groups and parcels of individuals each of which is thus defined. The problem thus stated admits of complete and general solution.

## *Notation and Definition*

By the letter $N$ prefixed to any expression representing a class or group of individuals howsoever constituted, I understand the number of individuals contained in that class or group.

Thus by $Nx$, I mean the number of individuals contained in the class $x$, by $Nxy$ the number contained in the class whose members are both $Xs$ and $Ys$, by $N(x + y)$ the number contained in the aggregate class whose divisions are $x$ and $y$. This implies that the classes $x$ and $y$ are mutually exclusive. Similarly, $N(x - y)$, I mean the number of individuals comprised in the remainder by taking the class $Y$ from the class $X$. This in like manner implies that the class $Y$ is entirely included in the class $X$.

By the letter $L$ prefixed to any expression representative of a class or group of individuals, I intend to imply the least number of individuals which can exist in the given class or group in accordance with the conditions expressed by a given system of propositions or relations.

## PROPOSITION I

If $P$, $Q$, $R$, &c. are any expressions representative of classes or groups, in fact any class functions, then

$$NP \pm NQ \pm NR \ldots = N(P \pm Q \pm R \ldots) \quad (1),$$

provided that we develope $P \pm Q \pm R \ldots$ into constituents, apply $N$ to each term of the result, and interpret any term $Nat$ in which $t$ is a constituent and $a$ a numerical coefficient, by $aNt$.

For consider the particular case $Nx \pm Ny$, and assuming the truth of the proposition, we have

$$Nx \pm Ny = N(x \pm y) \quad . \quad . \quad . \quad (2),$$

which gives the binary system

$$Nx + Ny = N(x + y) \quad . \quad . \quad . \quad (3),$$
$$Nx - Ny = N(x - y) \quad . \quad . \quad . \quad (4).$$

Now (3) gives

$$Nx + Ny = N(x + y)$$
$$= N(2xy + x\overline{1 - y} + y\overline{1 - x})$$
$$= Nx\overline{1 - y} + Ny\overline{1 - x} + 2Nxy.$$

That is, on interpretation—The number of individuals in the class $X$ together with the number in the class $Y$ is equal to the number of individuals which are $X$s and not $Y$s, with the number that are $Y$s and not $X$s, and twice the number that are both $X$s and $Y$s. Now this result is evidently true, however the classes $X$ and $Y$ are related.

Again, the equation (4) gives

$$Nx - Ny = N(x - y) = N(x\overline{1 - y} - y\overline{1 - x})$$
$$= Nx\overline{1 - y} - Ny\overline{1 - x},$$

which may be interpreted into the following result, viz. The number of individuals in the class $X$ diminished by the number contained in the class $Y$ is equal to the number of the $X$s that are not $Y$s, diminished by the number of $Y$s that are not $X$s. And this conclusion is equally evident.

The proposition is, therefore, true for the two cases contemplated in (3) and (4) quite independently of the relation which may exist between the two classes $x$ and $y$. It is therefore, by induction true universally, since all cases which are conceivable may be derived from successive aggregations or diminutions, i.e. from successive applications of the above particular forms.

## PROPOSITION II

The expression $aNP + bNQ + cNR$, in which $P$, $Q$, $R$ are any class functions, and $a$, $b$, $c$, numerical constants used as multipliers, is equal to $N(aP + bQ + cR)$ provided that the second member be developed into constituents, with the letter $N$ applied to each term separately within the numerical multiplier.

The proof is exactly the same as in the preceding Proposition, which is in fact only a particular case of the present one.   Thus, if we assume

$$aNx + bNy = N(ax + by)$$
$$= N(\overline{a + b}xy + ax\overline{1 - y} + by\overline{1 - x})$$
$$= \overline{a + b}Nxy + aNx\overline{1 - y} + bNy\overline{1 - x},$$

we have a result which is on interpretation obviously true, whatever may be the connexion between the classes $X$ and $Y$.   The general proposition flows by an easy induction from this particular case.


## PROPOSITION III.   PROBLEM

Given the number of individuals comprised in any proposed classes, required to deduce other numerical relations among classes *ad libitum*.

This is an easy application of the previous propositions, and will be sufficiently illustrated by an example.

Ex. In a company of $r$ individuals, $p$ have coats and $q$ have waistcoats, determine some other relations of number among them.

Let 1 represent the given company which is the universe of the proposition, $x$ the class possessing coats, $y$ the class possessing waistcoats.   Then

$$p = Nx, q = Ny, r = N1.$$

Now form by addition or subtraction any derivative equation, e.g.

$$p + q - r = Nx + Ny - N1.$$

Now, by Prop. I.

$$Nx + Ny - N1 = N(x + y - 1)$$
$$= N(xy - \overline{1 - x}\ \overline{1 - y})$$
$$= Nxy - N\overline{1 - x}\ \overline{1 - y};$$
$$\therefore\ p + q - r = Nxy - N\overline{1 - x}\ \overline{1 - y};$$

wherefore    $Nxy = p + q - r + N\overline{1 - x}\ \overline{1 - y}.$

It may from hence be inferred that the number of persons

in the company who are provided with both articles of dress is at least equal to $p + q - r$, and that it exceeds this quantity by as many individuals as are found destitute of both.

The reader will easily give a similar interpretation to the equivalent result

$$N\overline{1 - x}\ \overline{1 - y} = r - p - q + Nxy.$$

Again, let us form the equation

$$
\begin{aligned}
2p - q - r &= 2Nx - Ny - N1 \\
&= N(2x - y - 1) \\
&= N(x\overline{1 - y} - 2y\overline{1 - x} - \overline{1 - x}\ \overline{1 - y}) \\
&= Nx\overline{1 - y} - 2Ny\overline{1 - x} - N\overline{1 - x}\ \overline{1 - y}.
\end{aligned}
$$

From which we have

$$Nx\overline{1 - y} = 2p - q - r + 2Ny\overline{1 - x} + N\overline{1 - x}\ \overline{1 - y}.$$

Hence we might deduce that the number who had coats but not waistcoats would exceed the number $2p - q - r$ by twice the number who had waistcoats without coats together with the number who had neither coats nor waist-coats. This is not indeed the simplest result with reference to the class in question, but it is a correct one.

## Proposition IV

If $P = Q$, the test of which is that they give the very same development in constituents, then $NP = NQ$ provided that we apply $N$ to every term of $P$ and place it within the numerical multipliers of the several terms.

For by Prop. 2,

$$NP = N(a_1t_1 + a_2t_2 \ldots + a_nt_n) \quad . \quad . \quad (1),$$
$$NQ = N(a_1t_1 + a_2t_2 \ldots + a_nt_n) \quad . \quad . \quad (2),$$

$a_1t_1 + a_2t_2 \ldots + a_nt_n$ being the development in constituents of $P$ or $Q$. And it is assumed in the demonstration of Prop. (1) and (2) that $N$ is applied to each term of $P$ and $Q$ separately. Whence comparing (1) and (2),

$$NP = NQ.$$

COROLLARY. From the above it appears that the symbol $N$ as applied to any expression is distributive, and may thus be applied to each term separately.

## PROPOSITION V

To find the least number of individuals contained in a given compound class $x_1 x_2, \ldots x_n$, having given the number of individuals contained in each of the simple classes $x_1, x_2, \ldots x_n$, and the number in the universe.

Let $\qquad x_1 = 1 - t_1, \ x_2 = 1 - t_2 \ldots x_n = \overline{1 - t_n}$ . (1).

Then
$$x_1 x_2 \ldots x_n = (1 - t_1)(1 - t_2) \ldots (1 - t_n)$$
$$= 1 - t_1 - t_2 \ldots - t_n + \Sigma t_1 t_2 - \Sigma t_1 t_2 t_3 + \&c.$$
$$= 1 - t_1 - t_2 \ldots - t_n + R \qquad . \quad . \quad (2),$$

where $R$ represents the remainder of the development.

For $t_1, t_2, \ldots t_n$ write their values in terms of $x_1, x_2, \ldots x_n$, viz. $1 - x_1, 1 - x_2, \ldots 1 - x_n$, and we have

$$x_1 x_2 \ldots x_n = 1 - (1 - x_1) - (1 - x_2) \ldots - (1 - x_n) + R$$
$$= x_1 + x_2 \ldots + x_n - (n - 1) + R \qquad . \quad . \quad (3).$$

It will be convenient to examine the real nature of the remainder $R$.

To develope $R$ in constituents, we have

$$R = x_1 x_2 \ldots x_n - x_1 - x_2 \ldots - x_n + n - 1,$$

and expanding the second member by the general rule

$$R = \Sigma x_1 x_2 \ldots x_{n-2} \overline{1 - x_{n-1}} \, \overline{1 - x_n}$$
$$+ 2\Sigma x_1 x_2 \ldots x_{n-3} \overline{1 - x_{n-2}} \, \overline{1 - x_{n-1}} \, \overline{1 - x_n}$$
$$+ 3\Sigma x_1 x_2 \ldots x_{n-4} \overline{1 - x_{n-3}} \ldots \overline{1 - x_n} \ldots$$
$$+ \overline{n - 2} \Sigma x_1 \overline{1 - x_2} \, \overline{1 - x_3} \ldots \overline{1 - x_n} \ldots$$
$$+ \overline{n - 1} \, \overline{1 - x_1} \, \overline{1 - x_2} \ldots \overline{1 - x_n} \qquad . \quad . \quad (4).$$

By the prefixing of $\Sigma$ to an expression, I represent the taking of the sum of all the results which will be obtained by interchanging the letters $x_1, x_2, \ldots x_n$ in every possible way in that expression. Thus supposing $n = 3$.

$$\Sigma x_1 x_2 \overline{1 - x_3} = x_1 x_2 \overline{1 - x_3} + x_1 x_3 \overline{1 - x_2} + x_2 x_3 \overline{1 - x_1}.$$

From the above expression (4) it appears that $R$ cannot be negative. It will vanish if all the classes whose expressions enter into it as constituents vanish, but it cannot in any case become negative.

Now prefixing $N$ to each member of (3), we have

$$Nx_1x_2\ldots x_n = Nx_1 + Nx_2\ldots + Nx_n - (n-1)N(1)$$
$$+ NR \quad . \quad . \quad . \quad (5);$$

and it is apparent that $NR$ will either be a positive integer number or 0. On the latter supposition we have

$$Nx_1x_2\ldots x_n = Nx_1 + Nx_2\ldots + Nx_n - (n-1)N(1)$$
$$. \quad . \quad . \quad . \quad (6).$$

of which the second member expresses the least number of individuals which can exist in the class $x_1x_2\ldots x_n$.

Thus if $n = 2$, we get on writing $x$ and $y$ for $x_1$ and $x_2$,

$$Nxy = Nx + Ny - N1.$$

Similarly, if $n = 3$, putting $x, y, z$ for $x_1, x_2, x_3$,

$$Nxyz = Nx + Ny + Nz - 2N1,$$

and so on.

We shall call the second member of (6) the prime value of $Nx_1x_2\ldots x_n$ and $R$ the remainder.

## PROPOSITION VI

If the prime value of the class $x_1x_2\ldots x_n$ be positive the prime value of any of the constituents of its remainder $R$ is negative.

For any such constituent differs in expression from $x_1x_2\ldots x_n$ by more than one factor, as is seen on inspection. Let us then represent any one of them by

$$x_1x_2\ldots x_r\overline{1 - x_{n+1}}\ldots\overline{1 - x_n},$$

in which $n - r \geqq 2$.

Now the prime value of $x_1x_2\ldots x_n$ is $N(x_1 + x_2\ldots + x_n - n + 1)$, which is positive; therefore

$$- Nx_1 - Nx_2\ldots - Nx_n + (n-1)N(1) = \text{a negative}$$
$$\text{quantity.}$$

But $N(x_1 - 1)$, $N(x_2 - 1)$, $\ldots N(x_r - 1)$, &c. are negative or 0.   Add twice their sum, viz. $2\{Nx_1 + Nx_2 \ldots + Nx_r - rN(1)\}$, to the above and we have

$$Nx_1 + Nx_2 \ldots + Nx_r - Nx_{r+1} \ldots$$
$$- Nx_n + (n - 2r - 1)N(1) = \text{a negative quantity,}$$

or    $Nx_1 + Nx_2 \ldots + Nx_r + N(1 - x_{r+1}) \ldots$
$$+ N(1 - x_n) - (r + 1)N(1) = \text{a negative quantity.}$$

Moreover as $n - r \geq 2$, it follows that $n - r - 2 \geq 0$; therefore $r + 2 - n \leq 0$.   And adding this, multiplied by $N(1)$, to the last expression, we have

$$Nx_1 + Nx_2 \ldots + Nx_r + N(1 - x_{r+1}) \ldots$$
$$+ N(1 - x_n) - (n - 1)N(1) = \text{a negative quantity.}$$

Now this is the prime value of the class function $x_1 x_2 \ldots x_r \overline{1 - x_{r+1}} \ldots \overline{1 - x_n}$, which was taken as the common representative of the constituents of the development of $R$. Wherefore the prime value of each of those constituents is negative.

## PROPOSITION VII

If two classes differ in expression by a single factor, the number of individuals comprised in them both will be equal to the least number of individuals comprised in the class represented by the factors which are common to them both.

For the two classes will together make that class; whence the proposition is evident.

Thus the classes $xyz$ and $xy\overline{1 - z}$ together make $xy$, whence    $$Nxyz + Nxy\overline{1 - z} = Nxy.$$

We may, however, with advantage examine the result of the separate evaluation of the two terms :

$$Nxyz = N(x + y + z - 2 + x\overline{1 - y}\ \overline{1 - z} + y\ \overline{1 - x}\ \overline{1 - z}$$
$$+ z\overline{1 - x}\ \overline{1 - y} + 2\overline{1 - x}\ \overline{1 - y}\ \overline{1 - z}) \quad . \quad (1)$$

To each side of (1) add $Nxy\ \overline{1 - z}$, we get

$$Nxyz + Nxy\overline{1 - z} = N(x + y + z - 2 + \overline{1 - z}$$
$$+ z\overline{1 - x}\ \overline{1 - y} + \overline{1 - x}\ \overline{1 - y}\ \overline{1 - z})$$
$$= N(x + y + z - 2 + \overline{1 - z}$$
$$+ \overline{1 - x}\ \overline{1 - y})$$
$$= N(x + y - 1 + \overline{1 - x}\ \overline{1 - y}).$$

$$Nxy \,\overline{1-z} = N(x+y-z-1+xyz+\overline{1-x}yz$$
$$+\,\overline{1-x}\,\overline{1-y}\,\overline{1-z}+2\overline{1-x}\,\overline{1-y}z) \quad . \quad . \quad (2).$$

$$N(xyz+xy\,\overline{1-z}) = N(2x+2y-3+x\overline{1-y}+y\overline{1-x}$$
$$+\,\overline{1-x}\,\overline{1-y}+2\overline{1-x}\,\overline{1-y})$$
$$= N\{2x+2y-3+(x+\overline{1-x})\,\overline{1-y}$$
$$+\,(y+\overline{1-y})\,\overline{1-x}+\overline{1-x}\,\overline{1-y}\}$$
$$= N(2x+2y-3+1-y+1-x$$
$$+\,\overline{1-x}\,\overline{1-y})$$
$$= N(x+y-1+\overline{1-x}\,\overline{1-y}),$$

which is the prime value and remainder of $xy$.

COR. Hence it appears that in the least numerical value of the sum of two classes terms may arise from the addition of the remainders which pass into the prime value of the result; and that this happens when the two classes differ only by a single factor.

It is to be observed that in the above case neither class enters into the remainder of the other.

## PROPOSITION VIII

If the development of a class function $x_1 x_2 \ldots x_n$ have a certain prime value $V$ and remainder $R$, then there will exist for any function $P$ whose development in constituents consists of the sum $x_1 x_2 \ldots x_n$ and certain other constituents differing from this by more than two factors, a development of the form $V+R'$, $V$ being the same prime value as before and $R'$ differing from $R$ only in the difference of the positive values of the coefficients.

For each of the remaining constituents of $P$ differing from $x_1 x_2 \ldots x_n$ by more than one factor will be a constituent of $R$, and therefore, by addition to both members will only alter the value of the coefficient of that constituent in the expansion of $R$.

## PROPOSITION IX

If the prime value of a class function be positive, we cannot increase it by expanding any of the constituents of its remainder into another prime value and remainder.

For the prime value of each of the constituents of the remainder is negative.

## PROPOSITION X

If the prime value of a class function be positive or 0, it cannot be that the prime value of any higher class function is negative.

Let $x_1 x_2 \ldots x_n$ be the given class function, then any immediate superior may be represented by $x_1 x_2 \ldots x_{n-1}$: the prime values of the original and each subordinate class function are

$$Lx_1 x_2 \ldots x_{n-1} = N(x_1 + x_2 \ldots + x_{n-1} - n + 2) = A.$$
$$Lx_1 x_2 \ldots x_n \;\; = N(x_1 + x_2 \ldots + x_n - n + 1) = B,$$

which is not negative.

Hence                 $A = B + 1 - x_n :$
$$\therefore \;\; A \gtrless B, \text{ since } 1 \gtrless x_n.$$

Whence the proposition is manifest.

## PROPOSITION XI

Any function will have all the prime values of its constituents, and of those superior class functions which can be formed by aggregating in any manner its constituents.

This is an immediate consequence of Propositions (7) and (8). For the prime value afforded by any particular constituent can only be augmented by that of another constituent differing from it by a single factor, and if there is no such constituent, it gives an independent prime value. But if there is, we obtain, by aggregation, the prime value and remainder of the class which is common to them both. This is then an independent prime value unless there exists another aggregate class differing from the last by only a single factor, in which case the same operation will be repeated. Hence the highest prime values are those of the highest classes which can be formed by aggregation of the constituents.

M

## Proposition XII

To determine the prime values of $P$, $P$ being a sum of constituents.

As any superior class function is equal to the sum of its subordinate class functions of a given order, it is clear that such function will be entirely found in $P$ if none of its subordinates are found in $1 - P$.

Now the highest class functions are $x_1$, $x_2$, $\ldots x_n$, $\overline{1 - x_1}$, $\overline{1 - x_2}$, $\ldots \overline{1 - x_n}$. Therefore, if any one of these is not found as a factor of any term in $1 - P$ it yields a prime value.

Again, the binary functions $x_1 x_2$, $x_1 \overline{1 - x_2}$, &c. form the next class. Of these, we need only consider such no factor of which has already yielded a prime value. If then any one of these binary products does not enter as a factor of any term in $1 - P$, it yields a prime value.

In like manner we must proceed for the ternary products. Then the highest of the prime values obtained will be the least number of individuals which can enter into the proposed class. The determination of which is the greatest will depend upon the particular values of $Nx_1$, $Nx_2$, $Nx_n$, $N(1)$.

## Proposition XIII

To ascertain the prime values of $P$ having $Q = 0$, $P$ being as in the last proposition and $Q$ also a sum of constituents.

Since $Q = 0$, all the terms of $P$ which do not vanish will be represented by $P(1 - Q)$, and therefore the factors with which we shall have to do will be such only as enter into the terms of $P(1 - Q)$.

Again, all the terms which do not enter into $P$ will be contained in $1 - P$ and therefore in $(1 - P)(1 - Q)$. Hence those factors or superior functions which are entirely contained in $P$ will not enter into any of the terms of $(1 - P)(1 - Q)$.

Wherefore we must examine which of the highest class functions $x_1$, $x_2$, $\ldots$, $x_n$, $1 - x_1$, $1 - x_2$, $\ldots 1 - x_n$ enter into any of the terms of $P(1 - Q)$ and not into any of the terms of $(1 - P)(1 - Q)$.  Then we must examine which of the binary products, rejecting those which are subordinate to the simple factors already retained, enter into $P(1 - Q)$ and not into $(1 - P)(1 - Q)$; and so on.

The best practical Rule in this case is to divide the constituents of $1 - Q$ into two sets, the former including all those constituents which are contained in $P$, the latter those which are not contained in $P$.  Then seek the class functions $x_1$, $1 - x_1$, &c., which are contained in the former and not in the latter; then the binary class functions, &c.  Each class function retained gives a prime value $V$ and a remainder $R$.

Now if any one of the highest class functions $x_1$, ..., $x_n$, $1 - x_1$, ... $1 - x_n$, the numerical amount of which is known, is entirely included in $R$ in such way that we have, supposing $x_1$ to be the one,

$$R = x_1 + R',$$

in which $R'$ is entirely positive, we should of course add $x_1$ to $V$, the numerical amount of which would be thereby increased.  And thus we should proceed until the final remainder $R^{(P)}$ no longer contained the whole of any one of the determinate class functions in question.

In order to ascertain the point and to accomplish this end we may proceed thus.

The class functions $x_1$, $x_2$, ..., $\overline{1 - x_1}$, $\overline{1 - x_2}$, &c. which are entirely contained in $R$, are those which enter into $R(1 - Q)$, i.e. into those terms of $1 - Q$ which are found in $R$, but not into the remaining terms of $1 - Q$.  Or divide $1 - Q$ into two sets of constituents, the one set consisting of those constituents which are contained in $R$, the other of those which are not contained in $R$.  Then the class functions $x_1$, $x_2$, ..., $1 - x_1$, $1 - x_2$, &c., which enter into the former and not into the latter being represented by $t_1 t_2 \ldots t_r$, and we must form the inequality

$$a_1 t_1 (1 - Q) + a_2 t_2 (1 - Q) \cdots + a_r t_r (1 - Q) \gtrless R(1 - Q).$$

$a_1$, $a_2$, ..., $a_r$ being 0 or integers, and compare the coefficients of like constituents in both members.  This will give the relations among $a_1$, $a_2$, $\ldots$, $a_r$, in virtue of which the expression

$$a_1 t_1 + a_2 t_2 \ldots + a_r t_r$$

may form a part of $R$ : and subject to these relations

$$N(V + a_1 t_1 + a_2 t_2 \ldots + a_r t_r)$$

will be the prime value required.

As different sets of values for $a_1$, $a_2$, $\ldots$, $a_r$ may perhaps be found, different expressions for the corrected prime value will be obtained.

## Proposition XIV

Given any system of Propositions involving any amount whatever of numerical definition to ascertain how many individuals at least will be found in any supposed class.

If we equate to a new set of variables $x_1$, $x_2$, $\ldots x_n$, the different compound or aggregate classes whose numerical amounts are given, and to $x$ the one whose amount is required, we shall have a system of equations connecting $x_1$, $x_2$, $\ldots$, $x_n$, and the primitive set of symbols.

From these we may eliminate the primitive variables and determine $x$ as a function of $x_1$, $x_2$, $\ldots$, $x_n$. Let $P$ be the sum of those constituents which have for their coefficient unity, $T$ the sum of those which have for their coefficient $\frac{0}{0}$, and $Q$ the sum of those which have for their coefficients any other value than

$$x = P + vT \text{ with } Q = 0.$$

Now as $vT$ represents an indefinite number of individuals (some, all, or none) included in the aggregate class $T$, it is clear that the least number of individuals in $x$ will be found by taking the least number in $P$, so that we have to find the least number of individuals included in $P$, having given the condition $Q = 0$. The solution of this will be effected by the last Proposition; but the particular circumstances of the case enable us to simplify a part of the process.

Suppose $p_1 p_2 \ldots p_r$ * to be one of the class functions

* Here $p_1$, $p_2$, $\ldots p_r$ stand for any of the symbols $x_1$, $\ldots x_n$, $1 - x_1$, $1 - x_2$, $\ldots 1 - x_n$.

contained in and retained from $P$, we have then

$$p_1 p_2 \ldots p_r = V + R \text{ where } V = p_1 + p_2 \ldots + p_r - r + 1.$$

Now, since there are no constituents of $P$ which are contained in $Q$, the class function $p_1 p_2 \ldots p_r$, which is either itself a constituent or a sum of constituents, has no subordinate function in $Q$. Therefore $p_1 p_2 \ldots p_r$ enters into $1 - Q$, but $p_1 p_2 \ldots p_r$ does not enter into its own remainder $R$, since the constituents of $R$ differ from it by at least two factors. Hence $p_1 p_2 \ldots p_r$ belongs to that part of $1 - Q$ which is not found in $R$. Wherefore $p_1, p_2 \ldots p_r$ are found in that part of $1 - Q$. But $t_1 t_2 \ldots t_r$ of Prop. 13 are *not* found in this part of $1 - Q$, wherefore $t_1, t_2, \ldots t_r$ are entirely distinct from $p_1, p_2, \ldots, p_r$, wherefore they must be taken from $1 - p_1, 1 - p_2, \ldots, 1 - p_r$. Hence we have to seek those factors $1 - p_1, \ldots, 1 - p_2$ which are contained in $(1 - Q)R$ and not in the remaining part of $(1 - Q)$.

Again, those constituents of $1 - Q$ which are contained in $R$ are such as differ by at least two factors from $p_1 p_2 \ldots p_r$. Hence we have to seek those factors $1 - p_1, 1 - p_2, \ldots$ $1 - p_r$ which are found in those constituents of $1 - Q$ which differ from $p_1 p_2 \ldots p_r$ by at least two factors, but not in those constituents which differ in but a single factor.

This latter condition, however, if neglected in the formation of the inequality in Prop. 13, will be introduced in passing to the derived numerical inequalities, for if we retain all the terms $1 - p_1, \ldots, 1 - p_r$, and construct the equation

$$a_1(1 - p_1)(1 - Q) + a_2(1 - p_2)(1 - Q) \ldots$$
$$+ a_r(1 - p_r)(1 - Q) \gtrless R(1 - Q),$$

any coefficient $a_s$ which may be attached to a factor $1 - p_s$ entering into a constituent differing only in this single factor from $p_1 p_2 \ldots p_r$ will be equated to 0 on forming the derivative inequalities. This follows from the fact that no constituent of this nature can enter into the second member, since none such is found in $R$.

Wherefore, $p_1 p_2 \ldots p_r$ being one of the class functions retained, we shall have

$$p_1 p_2 \ldots p_r \gtrless p_1 + p_2 \ldots + p_r - r + 1 + a_1(1 - p_1) \ldots$$
$$+ a_r(1 - p_r),$$

$a_1 a_2 \ldots a_r$ being negative or positive integers determined so as to satisfy the inequality,

$$a_1(1 - p_1)(1 - Q) \ldots + a_r(1 - p_r)(1 - Q) \gtrless R(1 - Q).$$

Now

$$p_1 p_2 \ldots p_r = 1 - (1 - p_1) - (1 - p_2) \ldots - (1 - p_r) + R;$$
$$\therefore \quad R = p_1 p_2 \ldots p_r + (1 - p_1) + (1 - p_2) \ldots$$
$$+ (1 - p_r) - 1,$$

whence the above inequality becomes

$$a_1(1 - p_1)(1 - Q) \ldots + a_r(1 - p_r)(1 - Q) \gtrless p_1 p_2 \ldots p_r$$
$$+ (1 - p_1)(1 - Q) \ldots + (1 - p_r)(1 - Q) - (1 - Q);$$
$$\therefore \quad (a_1 - 1)\overline{1 - p_1}\,\overline{1 - Q} \ldots + (a_r - 1)\overline{1 - p_r}\,\overline{1 - Q}$$
$$+ \overline{1 - Q} \gtrless p_1 p_2 \ldots p_r.$$

The value of $p_1 \ldots p_r$ given above may be put in the form

$$p_1 \ldots p_r \gtrless (1 - \overline{1 - p_1}) \ldots - (1 - p_r) + a_1(1 - p_1) \ldots$$
$$+ a_r(1 - p_r),$$
$$\gtrless 1 + (a_1 - 1)\overline{1 - p_1} \ldots + (a_r - 1)\overline{1 - p_r},$$

from which we might immediately deduce the relation given above, viz.

$$\{1 + (a_1 - 1)\overline{1 - p_1} \ldots$$
$$+ (a_r - 1)\overline{1 - p_r}\}(1 - Q) \gtrless p_1 p_2 \ldots p_r.$$

If for $a_1 - 1$, $a_2 - 1 \ldots a_r - 1$ we write $i_1 i_2 \ldots i_r$ we should have

$$L p_1 p_2 \ldots p_r = N(1 + i_1 \overline{1 - p_1} \ldots + i_r \overline{1 - p_r}),$$

with

$$i_1 \gtrless -1, \ i_2 \gtrless -1, \ \ldots i_r \gtrless -1,$$

and

$$\{1 + i_1 \overline{1 - p_1} \ldots + i_r \overline{1 - p_r}\}(1 - Q) \gtrless p_1 p_2 \ldots p_r,$$

which, being resolved into a system of numerical relations by comparison of constituents, will give with the previous conditions the relations among $i_1 \ldots i_r$, these admitting only of the values −1, 0, 1, 2, &c.

Perhaps the former is the more convenient form in practice. We may put it under the following elegant shape.

The least number of individuals contained in the class $p_1 p_2 \ldots p_r$ will be expressed by the formula

$$N\{1 - (1 - a_1)(1 - p_1) - (1 - a_2)(1 - p_2) \ldots$$
$$- (1 - a_r)(1 - p_r)\},$$

provided that $a_1, a_2, \ldots, a_r$ be determined so as to satisfy the inequality

$$1 - Q - (1 - a_1)(1 - p_1)(1 - Q)$$
$$- (1 - a_2)(1 - p_2)(1 - Q) \ldots$$
$$- (1 - a_r)(1 - p_r)(1 - Q) \leq p_1 p_2 \ldots p_r,$$

the coefficients of like constituents being compared.

We may comprise the results of this investigation in the following general Rule.

To determine the least number of individuals which can possibly exist in a class having any number of propositions given, containing any amount or character of numerical definition.

*General Rule.* Equate to a new set of variables $x_1$, $x_2$, $\ldots$, $x_n$ all those classes, however expressed, whose numerical amount is given, and to a new symbol $x$ that class whose least numerical value in accordance with the conditions is required.

Determine $x$ as a function of $x_1$, $x_2$, $\ldots$, $x_n$, eliminating all the old symbols. Let $P$ be that part of the value of $x$ in which the coefficients are units, and $Q$ the aggregate of the vanishing terms.

Form the functions $1 - Q$, the aggregate of the constituents which do not enter into $Q$, and $1 - P - Q$ the aggregate of those which do not enter into $P$ or $Q$.

Find which of the primary class functions $x_1$, $x_2$, $\ldots$, $x_n$, $1 - x_1$, $1 - x_2$, $\ldots$, $1 - x_n$ enter into $P$ and not into $1 - P - Q$, and write them down. Then of the remaining primary class functions, as certain what binary products are found in $P$ and not in $1 - P - Q$, and retain these; then what ternary products, not including any of the preceding binary products, are found in $P$ and not in $1 - P - Q$, and retain these, and so on. Proceed with each of the class functions thus retained in the following manner.

Supposing $p_1 p_2 \ldots p_r$ to be any such class function, the least number of individuals comprised in it will be represented by the formula

$$N(1) - (1 - a_1)N(1 - p_1) - (1 - a_2)N(1 - p_2)\ldots$$
$$-(1 - a_r)N(1 - p_r) \quad . \quad . \quad (1),$$

provided that $a_1$, $a_2$, $\ldots$, $a_r$ be selected from the system of numbers 0, 1, 2, 3, 4, &c. in such manner as to satisfy the relations implied by the inequality

$$1 - Q - (1 - a_1)(1 - p_1)(1 - Q)$$
$$- (1 - a_2)(1 - p_2)(1 - Q)\ldots$$
$$- (1 - a_r)(1 - p_r)(1 - Q) \gtrless p_1p_2\ldots p_r.$$

These inequalities are obtained by comparing the coefficients of like constituents. They may have different sets of solutions, and of these, such are only to be retained as possess this characteristic, viz. that the value of none of the coefficients $a_1$, $a_2$, $\ldots$, $a_r$ can be increased without at the same time diminishing the value of some other.

As many separate sets of values are thus obtained for $a_1$, $a_2$, $\ldots$, $a_r$, so many different values will the expression (1) assume. And these values, obtained for all the class functions retained, will be so many *lower* limits of the number of individuals contained in the class under consideration.

Particular circumstances may render any of these values positive or any of them negative. It is, of course, the *highest positive* value which must in each instance be retained as the solution applicable to the case in hand.

To find the higher limits of the same class, $x$. *Rule.* Find the lower limits of its contrary $1 - x$, and subtract these severally from $N(1)$. The lowest value of the result will be the maximum limit of $x$.

*Note.* If there be no constituents in $Q$, the rule is greatly simplified, for we have only to seek the class functions which enter into $P$ and not into $1 - P$. Then if $p_1p_2\ldots p_r$ represent one of these class functions, the least number of individuals contained in $p_1p_2\ldots p_r$ will be

$$- N(1) - N(1 - p_1) - N(1 - p_2)\ldots - N(1 - p_r),$$

or

$$N(p_1) + N(p_2)\ldots + N(p_r) - (r + 1)N(1).$$

Ex. 1. In a company consisting of $r$ individuals, there were $q$ in number who knew Latin, and $p$ in number who knew either Latin or French, but not both; between what limits is the number of those who knew French confined?

Let $x$ represent those who knew French.

Let $y$ represent those who knew Latin.

Then $x\overline{1-y} + y\overline{1-x} =$ those who knew one but not the other.   The conditions of the question then are

$$N\{x(1-y) + y(1-x)\} = p, \; Ny = q, \; N(1) = r.$$

Let $x(1-y) + y(1-x) = t$, then we have to find $x$ in terms of $t$ and $y$, the numerical values of which are known :

$$x\overline{1-y} + y\overline{1-x} = t,$$
$$x(1-2y) + y = t,$$
$$x = \frac{t-y}{1-2y}$$
$$= t(1-y) + (1-t)y.$$

Here $P = t\overline{1-y} + \overline{1-t}y$, and $Q = 0$.

Hence we get for the minimum value of $x$ the expressions

$$N(t + \overline{1-y} - 1) \text{ and } N(y + \overline{1-t} - 1),$$

or $\qquad\qquad Nt - Ny$ and $Ny - Nt$

or $\qquad\qquad p - q$ and $q - p$.

For the maximum value, we find

$$1 - x = 1 - \frac{t-y}{1-2y} = \frac{1-y-t}{1-2y}$$
$$= ty + \overline{1-t}\,\overline{1-y}.$$

Whence for the minimum values of $N(1-x)$ we have

$$Nt + Ny - N1 \text{ and } N\overline{1-t} + N\overline{1-y} - N1,$$

or $\qquad Nt + Ny - N1$ and $N1 - Nt - Ny,$

or $\qquad\qquad p + q - r$ and $r - p - q,$

and subtracting these from $N(1)$ or $r$, we have

$$2r - p - q \text{ and } p + q,$$

the least of which is the maximum value of $x$.

Hence the limits of $x$ are,

Lower limit, the greatest value in $p - q$ and $q - p$,

Upper limit, the least value in $2r - p - q$ and $p + q$.

These conclusions may easily be verified.

Ex. 2.  To find the least number of individuals in

$$xy + \overline{1 - x}\ \overline{1 - y}\ \text{having}\ x\overline{1 - y} = 0.$$

This gives $Nx$ and $N\overline{1 - y}$,

or $p$ and $r - q$ for the minimum values.

Ex. 3.  Given

$$N(xy + x\overline{1 - y} + \overline{1 - xy}) = p,\ N(x\overline{1 - y} + \overline{1 - xy}$$
$$+ \overline{1 - x}\ \overline{1 - y}) = q,\ N(1) = 2,$$

to find the least number in

$$x\overline{1 - y} + \overline{1 - xy}.$$

Put

$$xy + x\ \overline{1 - y} + \overline{1 - xy} = t,\ x\overline{1 - y} + \overline{1 - xy}$$
$$+ \overline{1 - x}\ \overline{1 - y} = s,\ x\overline{1 - y} + \overline{1 - xy} = u.$$

We find on elimination and solution

$$u = st\ \text{with}\ \overline{1 - s}\ \overline{1 - t} = 0.$$

Hence the least number sought will be

$$p + q - r.$$

*⁎* As so often happens in writings which do not receive the author's last correction, some obscurities of expression will be found.  These I have thought it best to leave to the reader.  A. De M.

# V

## THE CLAIMS OF SCIENCE,
### Especially as Founded in its Relation to Human Nature *

There are few employments of life in which it is not some-times advantageous to pause for a short time, and reflect upon the nature of the end proposed. The pursuit of knowledge is one of those in which this occasional relinquish-ment of the field of action for that of meditation, is especially needed. We enter upon it at a period when the feelings are quick and ardent, when the desire of distinction is strong, and when many amiable feelings of our nature, the personal affection which we owe to our dearest friends, and the reverence which seems almost to be due to their very opinions, impel us to engage with eagerness in a task which the all but universal consent of mankind has pronounced to be useful and honourable. There is not one of these motives of which I would desire to weaken the force. But valuable as they are as incentives to exertion, they obviously constitute an incomplete ground for any systematic devotion of our maturer powers. The claims of the pursuit of science, like all other claims with which we are concerned, must ultimately rest upon some intrinsic excellency or special suitableness of the object. Qualities such as these can alone give to it an enduring title to our regard. I design, upon the present occasion, to consider the claims of science in the light of the principle just stated. More especially, I wish to direct attention to the ground of those claims, in the immediate or implied relations of science to human nature; in its relations, namely, as an answer to some of the distinctive wants of the human mind, an exercise to its faculties, a discipline of the character and habits, an instrument of conquest and dominion over the powers of surrounding

* [A lecture delivered in Queen's College, Cork, at the opening of the third session, in October, 1851. Published in London, 1851. Its interest for logical theory is chiefly in pp. 194–196, 207–210.]

Nature. In the present divided state of public sentiment, particularly in this country and with reference to this institution, there seems to be need of such a discussion; need also that it should not shrink from occupying the whole field of the inquiry. To ourselves at least, it cannot but be useful to endeavour to form an intelligent conception of what is really implied in the pursuit of science, of the spirit which that pursuit demands, and of the ends to which it points.

It is proper to state in the outset, that under the term Science, I include all general truths, discoverable by the human understanding, whether they are physical truths relating to the material universe, or moral truths relating to the constitution of our own nature, or truths of any other kind. And the order which I design to pursue is the following :—

First, I shall consider the origin of scientific knowledge as respects both its internal and its external sources, and shall briefly examine the nature of its conclusions.

Secondly, I shall, from the previous inquiry, endeavour to draw a just conception of the relations of science to the constitution and design of our own minds, of the benefits which we owe to it, and of the corresponding claims which it possesses upon our regard.

I remark in the first place that all scientific truths are founded upon the observation of facts, that experience, though not the only element, is yet an essential element of their existence. The truths of the natural sciences, as of astronomy, or optics, or electricity, are made known to us by the observation of natural phenomena, and by reflection upon the results of that observation. Nor can our knowledge of them be derived from any other origin. Thus every science is, as to its actual progress, a gradually increasing system of knowledge which, beginning with experience, advances ever onward through successive stages towards that perfection which no science has yet reached, which none, perhaps, ever will reach, but of which the idea becomes clearer and brighter, with every approach that we make. And although in this gradual progress of a science, the necessity for continued observation may become less and less urgent, although in some instances, it may even altogether disappear, yet, in every case, it must have supplied the first point of departure. This doctrine which is now so fully acknowledged that to dwell further upon it would be super-fluous, did not always meet with acceptance. There was a time in which the indispensable necessity of a foundation in experience for all our knowledge of Nature, was not recognised. Among the ancients, it was very imperfectly understood; during the long reign of scholasticism it was all but entirely ignored. And obvious as the principle in question appears to us now to be, it has won its way to general acceptance only through difficulty and opposition. It formed, indeed, with its more important consequences, the chief result of that great review of the sources and the methods of human knowledge, which we owe to the illus-trious Bacon.

But if science begins with experiment and observation, it does not end with them. All the knowledge which the senses have ever communicated to man, has been a mere collection of facts; and were there in the human mind no powers beyond those to which the senses make their direct appeal, that knowledge would never have advanced to any higher condition than that of facts. With such a state of information, however, the mind does not rest satisfied. It feels the pressure of impulses, it is conscious of the exis-tence of powers and faculties which urge it to reduce the scattered details of its knowledge into form and order. It begins to compare and to classify, and to arrange. It examines in what respects different facts agree, and in what respects they differ; and it inquires how far those differences and agreements are constant; how far they are the results of circumstance or accident. Thus, from the contemplation of facts, the mind rises to the perception of their relations. While in the former state it is little more than a passive recipient of the impressions of the external world, in the latter it exercises an unborrowed activity. The faculties of judgment, of abstraction, of comparison, of reason, are an agency of strength and power from within, which it brings to bear upon the lifeless elements before it, shaping them into order, and extracting from them their hidden meaning and significance.

Thus, to take one department of human knowledge. It is not enough to have observed the courses of the heavens, the sun and moon, those greater and lesser lights, or that silent and countless multitude of stars, which, as soon as the light of day is withdrawn, unfold before us the true amplitude and grandeur of the material creation. Neither would it be enough, if every phase of apparent change which has swept across the heavens from the beginning of time until now, were recorded for our information. We desire to understand the nature of the phaenomena which we survey. We would know how far appearances correspond to realities. We would ascertain the law of that " mystic dance "; we would unveil the secret mechanism of causes which produces the order that is seen, and makes that order perpetual. Impatient alike of unconnected and of causeless phaenomena, we would reduce all that we behold around us into subjection to our own understandings. And the frame of nature is so constituted as to permit us in a great measure to accomplish that which we desire. If we are conscious of desires and impulses which cannot rest in the possession of particular and solitary facts, but find only in the contemplation of general truths, of constant and predominating laws, their corresponding goal and end; there is in the constitution of nature that which may answer those desires and satisfy those impulses. If we are sensible of the existence of faculties and powers whose province it is to detect order amid apparent diversity, to discover the indications of cause amid the seeming results of accident, those faculties do not exist in vain. The mind of man is placed amid a scene which can afford to all its powers their appropriate exercise. There is thus a correspondency between the powers of the human understanding and the outward scenes and circumstances which press upon its regard. In this agreement alone is Science made possible to us. The native powers of the mind, cast abroad amid a world of mere chance and disorder, could never have realised the conception of law. On the other hand, the fairest scenes of order, and the most unbroken sequences of causation, would have unfolded themselves in vain before a mind unpossessed of those higher faculties which are necessary to their apprehension. The actual circumstances of our position afford us at once the fairest field of exertion, and the surest guarantee of a success proportioned to the diligence of our labours.

I have dwelt upon this view of the nature of science, because I think it important to our present inquiry that its two-fold origin should be fully recognised. If, before the time of Bacon, the external sources of human knowledge were too little regarded, we may, in the strong reaction of a subsequent age against this form of error, discern perhaps too much of the contrary tendency. Science, in its actual development, may indeed be compared to some stately temple, whose materials have been brought together from many distant regions, some from the forest, and some from the mine and quarry, but in whose fair proportions and goodly order, we read the traces of the designing mind. To all just theory, experience and observation are indeed the necessary pre-requisites, but it is the intellect of man operating by laws and processes of its own, which executes the scheme. To those laws and to those processes there belongs an interest quite independent of the results of material science to which they give birth; and for this reason, they deserve a distinct attention. But it is only when the two studies, the material and the mental, are associated together, that the true relations of science to human nature are recognised. Then it is that in studying the laws of external nature, a light is shed upon our own, which may seem to us even of more value than the source from which it is derived.

We have examined the sources from which scientific knowledge is derived. Let us inquire, in the next place, what are the most general conclusions to which it conducts us, with reference to the constitution of the universe.

Science exhibits to us the material or physical universe as a system of being subject, in all respects, to the dominion of fixed and invariable laws. In that system, to the utmost extent to which either the observations of sense, or the deductions of reason permit us to judge, chance and accident have no place. The condition of its existence is a rigid, unchangeable, necessity. All its successions are uniform; from its settled order, no deviation is either actual or possible. The courses of the stars are justly said to be appointed; " the sun knoweth his going down ". Yet, in the conception of this rigorous and dominant necessity, repellent as it would be to our own natures, we see nothing to shock or to offend when viewed in connexion with the idea of matter. If the courses of nature are settled, they are settled in a consistent harmony. If her laws are so fixed that they cannot be broken, they are so fixed in themselves, so fixed in relation to the wants of sentient and intelligent beings, that regularity and beauty are the most conspicuous features of the world over which they preside.

Thus in the most ancient and most perfect of all the physical sciences, Astronomy, we contemplate not a particular orb or system, but a universe of worlds preserved in their mutual order and relation, through the agency of a single prevailing law. We trace the operation of that law in the most diverse consequences. We see it moulding the drops of rain, guiding the stone thrown from the hand in its course, and regulating the swing of the pendulum. We trace it in a larger circle of operations, renewing the waters of the ocean by the healthful play of the tides, deflecting the moon in its orbit, moulding the forms and determining the motions of planetary worlds, larger, and it may be, fairer, than our own. We are taught by the conclusions of analysis, that this law of gravitation has not merely a governing, but a preserving, agency; that it not only determines the motions of the whole system, but so determines them, as to provide for their stability and perpetuity. And beyond the confines of this system of ours, beyond the reach of the unassisted eye of thought of man, science still reads the indications of the same power. The faint lustre of spiral nebulæ, and the calculated orbits of double stars, tell us of mightier revolutions, accomplished in obedience to the self-same guiding law.

Or to take a more special illustration of the necessity which governs external nature. A comet suddenly makes its appearance in the heavens. Whence it has come we know not, but we are acquainted with the *general* laws by which its motions are directed, and know the particular influences to which in this our region of space it must be subject. Three, or at the most, five exact observations of its position, enable us to apply our knowledge to the determination of its actual motion; or could we, by a single observation, ascertain its exact place and direction, and velocity, at a given moment, the same end would be accomplished. The future path of the erratic stranger is then marked out, among the constellations. And the course thus assigned to it, it is actually observed to follow, until it again becomes invisible by its remoteness. Here we behold the dominion of necessity. Law is obeyed without choice or alternative. There is no deviation, no shortcoming, no excess. In the more recent and less perfect of the physical sciences, we have similar intimations of the nature and character of the material system. We have no reason to think that the law of definite proportions in the science of chemistry, or the laws of the connected agencies of light and heat, of magnetism and electricity, so far as they are actually known by us, are of any less universal character, than the law of gravitation. Upon each and all of these, once that they are determined, we depend with the conviction of perfect certainty. It has been thought by some that this reliance on the constancy of nature, is an instinctive feeling of the human breast, an original impulse of our nature. But be this as it may, the feeling is one which, if accompanied by a proper estimate of circumstances, is never misplaced. We may be deceived by external appearances, but this source of error apart, the uniformity and universality of the laws of nature is, so far as the range of its just application extends, the most solid foundation of human certainty to which we have yet attained.

We have seen how all the generalisations of science point to the one conclusion, that material nature through all her parts is subject to an inflexible necessity, a necessity which seems to inhere in the very idea of matter, and to be inseparable from all the conditions of its existence. Here then, the

N

question suggests itself to us : does the dominion of science terminate with the world of matter, or is there held out to us the promise of something like exact acquaintance, however less in extent, with the interior and nobler province of the mind ?   The inquiry is twofold, and we may consider it as involving the following questions :

First, whether there exist, with reference to our mental faculties, such general laws as are necessary to constitute a science; for we have seen that it is essentially in the recognition of general laws, not of particular facts, that science consists.

Secondly, supposing that such general laws are discoverable, what is the nature of the relation which the mind sustains towards them?   Is it, like that of external nature, a relation of necessary obedience, or is it a relation of some distinct kind having no example and no parallel in the material system?   These I conceive to be questions of a perfectly definite character, and it seems to me that they admit of an equally definite answer.

First, we are to inquire if the mind is a proper object of science.

That in some sense the moral and the intellectual constitution of man are proper objects of scientific inquiry, must be conceded by all who recognise the existence either of general truths in morals, the knowledge of which may be drawn from our own consciousness, or of any fixed principles in the right operations of human reason.   Neither of these can be derived from a merely external source.   How varied soever the materials which are brought before the mind, there exist within, principles of thought and reason, which are of common application to them all, and are borrowed from none.   There are also certain other principles which are of a more special character, yet, equally with the former, have their seat in the mind.   In these principles together are involved the laws of our intellectual nature, even as in the final generalisations of physical science we discern the laws of the material universe.   If it is asked whether out of these common principles of the reason we are able to deduce the actual expressions of its fundamental laws, I reply that this is possible, and that the results constitute the true basis of mathematics. I speak here, not of the mathematics of number and quantity alone, but of mathematics in its larger, and I believe, truer sense, as universal reasoning expressed in symbolical forms, and conducted by laws, which have their ultimate abode in the human mind. That such a science exists is simply a fact, and while it has one development in the particular science of number and quantity, it has another in a perfect logic. Now in this view of the laws of our intellectual nature, are seen proofs of its relation to science, not less convincing than any which are written upon the physical universe. Similar evidence, though of a less formal kind, is presented in the survey of our moral constitution. Though we are conscious that we often do that which our calmer judgment condemns, not as inexpedient, but wrong; in the very fact of this condemnation we read the existence of some internal rule of right, which indeed, we have power to disobey, but which we cannot ignore. To this secret testimony of the heart must be added not only the consenting force of the positive deductions of moral science which are based upon other grounds, but also the full weight of that confirmatory analogy which is drawn from the proved existence of law in our intellectual constitution. The study of Ethics thus becomes an essential part of the study of human nature. We conclude that the mind both in its intellectual and in its moral character is a proper object of science.

Secondly, we are to inquire what relation the mind sustains, to the scientific laws of its constitution.

As it is the office of the laws of reasoning to determine what is correct in the processes of thought, and of the laws of morals to determine what is right in sentiment and conduct, it may safely be inferred that whatever other relations the mind may sustain, it is constituted in some definite relation to those elements which we designate by the terms, Right and True. But in the very nature of these terms it is implied that the relation in question cannot be one of necessary or constrained obedience. Were there no liberty of error, there would be no sense of the peculiar claims and character of truth.   There are also, however, apt to be obscured amid the importunate strivings of interest and passion, eternal rules of right, expressions of the moral character and purpose of their great Author and source.   And neither do those exercise upon us any force of actual constraint.   But they possess a character and a greatness of their own.   They stand before us invested with attributes of reality, and of rightful supremacy, before which every opposing power seems but as a shadow or an usurpation.   In these facts are presented to us the distinguishing features of our own higher nature.   On its ethical side is freedom, associated with the sense of duty; on the intellectual is freedom, conjoined with the perception of the rightful demands of truth.   Let the term, Freedom, be objected to, the fact under whatever name, remains the same.   The optimist may, indeed, inquire whether a condition of existence liable to error and irregularity, is equally perfect with one from which every such possibility is excluded.   But the true idea of human progression lessens, if it does not solve the difficulty.   A state of being, whose just action is maintained, and advanced by conscious effort, is *felt* to be better in itself than all the unintelligent obedience of nature.

I shall not here pause to dwell upon the social and economical sciences, which regard men, not as individuals, but as members of a community, and sharers of a public interest, and which are based upon the consideration of prevailing motives, rather than the requirements of an ideal standard of conduct.   As men cannot be divested of their individuality, such sciences do not profess to attain the formal strictness of those which have been already considered.   They, however, afford us valuable information as to the general tendencies of society and of institutions; and thus constitute a very important branch of knowledge.   It is remarkable with what uniformity those causes operate upon large collections of men, which in the individual seem to merge and be lost amid a variety of conflicting influences.   I pass over in like manner, some other departments of knowledge, which, depending chiefly upon classification, may be regarded as the precursors of science, rather than science.   Let us then revert to what has been said, and endeavour to recapitulate, in a few words, the conclusions which have been arrived at.

Science, then, we may regard as the joint result of the teachings of experience, and the desires and faculties of the human mind. Its inlets are the senses; its form and character are the result of comparison, of reflection, of reason, and of whatever powers we possess, whereby to perceive relations, and trace through its successive links the chain of cause and effect. This order of its progress is from particular facts to collective statements, and so on to universal laws. In Nature, it exhibits to us a system of law *enforcing* obedience, in the Mind a system of law *claiming* obedience. Over the one presides Necessity; over the other, the unforced obligations of Reason and the Moral Law. Such I conceive, to be the true conception of Science. It is a conception in which different elements are involved, partly appertaining to the pure and abstract nature of the object, partly to its more special relation to human conditions. Let us endeavour, from the careful review of these elements, to deduce a reply to the further enquiries,—What are the benefits which science confers? What are the claims it possesses upon our regard?

A narrow estimate of human objects is not likely to be a just one, and even in the sober view of reason, things are valuable upon very different grounds; some things for their own sake, some as means toward the attainment of an ulterior good. It might be well if the actual pursuits of mankind were more often regulated by some deliberate judgment of this nature. Custom, however, and the opinion of others too often prescribe to men what ends they shall pursue, and to what extent they shall follow them. And were it not that in such cases the pursuit often yields that enjoyment which the object sought either does not, or cannot produce, we might be tempted to think that the restless strivings of humanity are even more vain than poet and inspired sage have pronounced them to be. Yet, notwithstanding that the aims of mankind are often misdirected, and their bearing upon private happiness yet oftener misunderstood, it is not to be questioned that there do exist ends which are worthy in themselves; worthy of all the expenditure of toil and time which their acquisition demands. To this regard they may be entitled, either as meeting some positive want of our nature, or as tending to some improvement of faculty or character, some essential convenience of life, or other acknowledged good. Now, we have seen what is the general conception of Science, as presented in the results of previous discussion. Let us, then, consider some of the particulars involved in that conception, with reference to the question of utility, which is more immediately before us.

We have found it to be one of the characteristics of scientific knowledge, that it owes its origin in part to the desires and faculties of the human mind, and that it bears to them a certain relation of fitness and correspondency. Upon this fact, its first claim to our notice rests. The constitution of our nature is such, that whenever the pressure of the merely animal wants is removed, other and higher desires occupy their place. These are not necessarily to be regarded as modifications of the selfish principle. There is an appetency for knowledge which is not founded upon any perception of utility. Sometimes, self-reliant and alone, it exists in solitary strength; sometimes gathering support from human sympathies,

———quemcunque efferre laborem
Suadet, et inducit noctes vigilare serenas.

I have already remarked how this desire of knowledge lends an impulse to those intellectual faculties, whose province it is to educe general truths, and how the actual subjection of Nature to law affords the means, on an unlimited scale, of exercising those faculties in the most appropriate manner.

Now in these facts it seems to me to be implied, that the pursuit of knowledge, and especially of that kind of knowledge which consists in the apprehension of general truths, is a designed end of human nature. Else wherefore was that desire of knowledge implanted? Or if the feeling be derived, rather than instinctive, wherefore was our nature so contrived that the desire of knowledge should, at a certain stage of advancement, never fail to present itself? Wherefore, too,

those faculties which seem to have no other end than knowledge, and which, deprived of their fitting exercise, wither
and decline? Wherefore, lastly, that wondrous constitution
of external nature, so abounding in lessons of instruction,
suitable to our capacity, addressed to our condition? With
instances of mechanical adaptation in the works of the Divine
Architect, we are all familiar. But to the reflective mind,
there are few adaptations more manifest, there is none more
complete, than that which exists between the intellectual
faculties of man, and their scenes and occasions of exercise.
Shall we not then confess that here also design is manifest?
And shall not this manifestation of design serve in some
degree as the indication of a sphere of legitimate employment,
and, where not interfered with by other obligations, of a
duty, the neglect of which cannot be altogether innocent?

There are certain further consequences resulting from this
office of science as an exercise to our intellectual faculties,
to which it may be proper to refer. It is scarcely needful to
remark that every faculty we possess, and the intellectual
among others, is strengthened by exercise. With respect,
however, to the improvement of the individual mind by
the discipline of science, it is to be remarked that it implies
something more than a strengthening of faculties. It
involves also the power of continued attention and the habit
of application, the most difficult and most important of
mental acquisitions. That the habit is usually an acquired
one, is, I think manifest, as well as that it belongs to the
character rather than to the intellect. Furthermore, scientific studies, besides their direct influence upon the mental
habits, instruct us in the right methods of the investigation
of truth. For the discovery of truth is not commonly the
result of random effort; it is usually, as we have seen, the
reward of systematic labour, setting out from the careful
examination of facts, and proceeding by definite steps of
inductive and deductive reasoning to the evolution of
principles. And in this process we need both the precept
and the example afforded to us in those great results of
accomplished science, which we owe to the patient labours
of ages past. Finally, no small accession of intellectual force

is due to the deliverance of the mind from that dark prejudice of chance in the physical, of fate in the moral world, to which Ignorance clings with inveterate grasp.  Of all the delusions which have cast their baleful shade upon the path of human advancement, this is the most fatal.  In the one of its forms it paralyses exertion; in the other it saps the foundation of trust in that righteous appointment which assigns to our actions, even in the present life, inevitable consequences of good or evil.  I would appeal to all who have made any study of human motives, whether these are not true representations.  Let us, however, bring them to the test of facts.

Careful inquiries assure us that there is a real connexion of cause and effect between an undrained, uncleansed condition of our towns, and the prevalence of fever and a general high mortality.  I suppose that there are few conclusions better established than this.  Every now and then it receives fearful confirmation, when some epidemic disease, making head against all the resources of medical art, emerges from the dark lane or noisome alley, and sweeps away the rich and the poor in one indiscriminate destruction.  Men are, however, for the most part, so reluctant to admit the reality of that which they do not see with their eyes, that this teaching of science, and this confirmation of experience, are sometimes alike void of effect.  They cannot perceive with their bodily senses the connexion between impure air and disease, and they refuse to believe in invisible laws; or, if they acknowledge them in words, they do not give them any hearty assent.  And so the scene of desolation is renewed from year to year.

Nor much unlike the above is the moral scene.  No conclusion seems to rest upon a greater weight of cumulative evidence than that a course of life governed by a consistent regard to the principles of rectitude, is the most favourable to public and private happiness.  To carry this conviction into effect, requires that men should in some instances, do that which is contrary to their personal interest as judged by common standards.  It demands, therefore, that there should be on the part of the individual some trust in unseen principles, strong enough to resist the ever present importunity of appearances. The aspect of society does not, however, present, as its most common feature, this settled regard to principle and calm committal of the affairs of life to its direction. Now, I am very far from saying that such a course of conduct, where it is found, is solely the product of an enlightened understanding; but that this is an important element of the case, is beyond reasonable doubt. The man who has contemplated the subjection of all outward Nature to fixed laws, cannot, when he turns his gaze upon human society, think that its dispensations of good and evil are left to the strivings of self-interest or the scramble of accident. Still less, if he attend to the monitions of the internal witness, if he survey the ineradicable elements of his own being, the selfconscious Will, the authoritative Moral Perception, can he regard those dispensations as the sport of a blind fate, disposing of human affairs as if men were but the wreck and seaweed of a stormy shore. No! the discipline of true science, in disposing us to a belief in general laws, is favourable to a sound morality. If it exalts the consciousness of human power, it proportionally deepens the sense of human responsibility. If it releases us from those meshes of fatalism which bound the ancient Stoic, it is not that it may clothe us with an Epicurean liberty.

But it is not against the prejudices of ignorance alone that Science records her protest. There are dangers not less real in an over-curious spirit of speculation too much exercised in logical subtleties, too little conversant with realities. And against these dangers also, the positive results of science constitute the best preservative. The scepticism of the ancient world left no department of human belief unassailed. It took its chief stand upon the conflicting nature of the impressions of the senses, but threw the dark shade of uncertainty over the most settled convictions of the mind; over men's belief in an external world, over their consciousness of their own existence. But this form of doubt was not destined to endure. Science, in removing the contradictions of sense, and establishing the consistent uniformity of natural law, took away the main pillars of its support. The spirit, however, and the mental habits of which it was the product, still survive; but not among the votaries of science. For I cannot but regard it as the same spirit which, with whatever professions of zeal, and for whatever ends of supposed piety or obedience, strives to subvert the natural evidences of morals, and of that which is common alike to morals and to religion,—the existence of a Supreme Intelligent Cause. There is a scepticism which repudiates all belief; there is also a scepticism which seeks to escape from itself by a total abnegation of the understanding, and which, in the pride of its new-found security, would recklessly destroy every internal ground of human trust and hope. I wish it to be understood that I do not seek to identify this spirit with any party, or even personally regard it as co-extensive with any party, but speak of it abstractly as a temper and habit of the mind, which is commonly, perhaps, the result of a too partial discipline. Now to this, as to a former development of the sceptical spirit, Science stands in implied but real antagonism. And as it before vindicated the possibility of natural knowledge, so it now lends all the weight of its analogies in support of the trustworthiness of human convictions, and the reality of some deep foundation of the moral order of things, behind the changeful contradictions of the present scene.

The claims of science with which we have hitherto been occupied, are founded upon its direct relations to human nature, and it is interesting to notice further the testimonies and indications bearing upon this view of the subject, which have been left by antiquity. In any inquiry as to what human nature is, such testimony is perfectly admissible, since in the records of the thoughts and feelings of a past world, we read but another development of those principles which are common to our nature in all periods and under all circumstances.

The instinctive thirst for knowledge, its disinterested character, its beneficial tendencies, are among the most favoured topics of ancient writers. Cicero dwelt upon them with a peculiar delight, and he has invested them with more than the common charm of his eloquence. Plato made them a chief ground of his speculations concerning the just man and the well-ordered state. Aristotle gave to them the testimony of one of the most laborious of human lives. Virgil devoted the fairest passage of his best poem to the delights of a calm and meditative life, occupied in the quest of truth. Lucretius drew from philosophical speculations the matter of what some have regarded as the noblest production of the Latin muse. Sophocles made Knowledge, in its aspect of power, the theme of incomparably the finest of his choral odes. Æschylus made Knowledge, in its other aspect of patience and martyrdom, the nobler burden of his Prometheus. And there is ground for the conjecture that such influences were not unfelt by those older poets and seers with whom our own Milton felt the sympathy of a common fate, and desired to share the glory of a common renown. The early dawn too, of philosophy, not to speak of its subsequent and higher development in the schools of Athens and Alexandria, is full of suggestive indications. Some records, scattered indeed, and dim, and fragmentary, still exist of the successive attempts which were made in Ionia, in the cities of Southern Italy, in Greece, to penetrate the mystery of the Universe, to declare what it is, and whence it came. In those speculations, vague as they are, we discern the irresistible longings of the human mind for some constructive and general scheme of truth, its inability to rest satisfied with the details of a merely empirical knowledge, its desire to escape into some less confined sphere of thought, and, if it might be, to hold " converse with absolute perfection ". Nor are the efforts to which such feelings gave birth to be regarded as accidental or unmeaning. They had a prospective significance in relation to the Science that was yet to appear. They were like the prelusive touches of some great master of harmony, which serve to awaken the feeling of expectancy and preparation. I affirm, and upon deliberate examination, that the peculiar order of the development of human thought which preceded the rise and growth of modern science, was not an arbitrary thing, but is in its main features susceptible to explanation. Though for any elucidation of the phenomena of nature, it is utterly worthless, upon the human faculties it throws a light of illustration which can scarcely be valued too highly (*a*).

Beside the claims of science which are founded upon its immediate relations to human nature, there exist others of an implicit character, which nevertheless, give to it far more evident material importance. I speak of its bearing upon the arts of civilised life.

We have seen how science testifies to the fact that the material creation is governed by fixed laws. Upon this truth rests the peculiar value of science as a minister to human wants, and a subjugator of the powers of nature to the will of man. All the operations of art and mechanism, which are but applied science, presuppose this constancy of nature. *Because* the vapour of water manifests certain constant properties of elasticity and capability of condensation, the steam-engine is possible. *Because* the laws of magnetic action are fixed, the compass is available for purposes of navigation. *Because* different species of glass have different dispersive actions upon the coloured rays of light, the achromatic telescope lends its aid to our vision. *Because* electricity freely traverses metallic wires, and in so doing manifests certain properties of attraction and repulsion, we are able to communicate with the absent by the electric telegraph. In a similar spirit of reliance upon the faithfulness of nature, the husbandman commits his seed to the ground, waiting till the genial influences of sun and shower shall mature it into a harvest. And such is the multiplied industry of man. To this it may be added, that the more that industry is under the control of science, the more does it consist in simply arranging the train of natural circumstances; the inherent and impassive forces of matter ever offering themselves as substitutes for animal toil and animal suffering. To this extension of man's dominion over the inorganic world, there is no visible limit. The properties of matter, both mechanical and chemical, seem to be exhaustless in their variety, knowledge being the key to unlock their uses.

Accordingly, it has been thought by some that the results of science, conjoined with other agencies, open before the

human race a career of indefinite progression. They anticipate a period when the physical evils which afflict our present
state shall exist no longer, or exist in such measure only as is
inseparable from a condition of mortality; when painful
toil shall have been replaced by the appliances of mechanism;
when the most prolific sources of disease, as crowded cities,
undrained swamps, pernicious indulgences, shall have
disappeared before a more enlightened study of the conditions of health, and a truer appreciation of the ends of
life; when the excessive inequalities of wealth, and the
miseries which they entail, shall have yielded to a better
moral or social economy; and when the effects of those
casualties which prudence cannot avert, as earthquakes,
tempests, unfriendly seasons, shall either be reduced to a
minimum of amount, or shall be so distributed as to fall with
the least oppressive weight upon the community at large.
They anticipate that in this happy state of things to come,
relieved from the oppressive bondage of physical wants,
man shall be at liberty to accomplish, and actually shall
accomplish, the higher ends of his being; that while the
earth shall shine with more than its pristine beauty, the
human family shall not only be clothed with the fair assem-
blage of the moral virtues, but shall add to them that crown
and safeguard of knowledge which has been won from the
hard experience of ages of error and suffering.

Speculations of this kind are abused, if they only minister
to the sense of human power and pride. They have their
use when they instruct us, by the comparison of our actual
attainments in the measures of a just and happy life, with
that ideal standard to which reason and religion point. Let
us ask ourselves why that better condition of things is so
far from being realised. The probable conclusion will be,
that the impediment is not in any invincible repugnancy in
the laws of material nature, nor in any want of power and
energy in the human intellect. There seems in the present
day to be even a superfluous activity of invention, busying
itself to accomplish ends that are not valuable, and minister-
ing to a fantastic vanity. Here then, we are brought again
to that position around which all speculations concerning

the true welfare of our species seem to revolve, viz. that it essentially contains a moral element.

But to turn this discussion to some practical issue. Whether that higher state of good shall be realised upon earth or not, they who devote themselves to the pursuits of science will not err, if they keep the prospect of it before them as the scope of their practical efforts. Though contemplation is one end of knowledge, action is another; and if the spirit of science is concentrative in its individual efforts, it is generous and diffusive in its wider aims. I speak here, however, of general tendencies. To make immediate utility the sole guide of scientific research, would defeat the object in view. Let there be a liberal union of the love of truth for its own sake, and the desire to make that truth serviceable to the world, and the chief ends for which knowledge is valuable, will be secured together.

I have now endeavoured to import to you my own views of the nature and claims of Science. I have, in doing this, been careful to avoid all exaggeration, believing that the moderation and the exactness which characterise Science should be manifest in its advocacy. What I have thus sought, however, imperfectly to portray is some faint image of Truth, partly in her essential lines and features, partly in her immediate aspect and relation to ourselves. And I would now ask you if, after all deductions for the imperfection of the sketch, there is not something in the object that should command our rational esteem; something that may even justify, if I may be allowed the expression, a sober enthusiasm; not that transient blaze of feeling of which, too often, the ashes alone survive, to embitter regret, when the freshness of life's most precious years is irrecoverably gone; but that ardour of quiet and steadfast energy which addresses itself to great ends, knowing their difficulties and patiently subduing them. Such has been the feeling of all who have accomplished any eminent good, whether for their own or for a future age, of all the great masters in art and letters, in science and legislation. Such, in the more humble sphere that has been allotted to ourselves, is the feeling that we should strive to cultivate.

And if, in conclusion, I might say a few words of more special application to this country, and to present circumstances, I would remark that though to choose or to reject the offered benefits of knowledge is a point within our own election, it is an error to suppose that the conduct of any individual or of any society in this matter can affect its final issues in the world. There may be periods in which the prospects of science, and with them those of human improvement, are sufficiently discouraging. The strong tide of party may set against it. Detraction may assail its friends, misrepresentation sully and distort its beneficent aims. Nevertheless, it is not given to such principles and to such means to accomplish any permanent triumph. Calumny shall not prevail for ever. Violence and injustice shall not always usurp the place of reason. There shall be a time when men shall be judged according to their spirit and their deeds. And then shall Truth assert her rightful claims. Science shall vindicate her divine mission in the increase of the sum of human good. Obscured by the mists of prejudice, forgotten amid the strife of parties, she but the more resembles those great luminaries of heaven, which pursue their course undismayed above the rage of tempests, or amid the darkness of eclipse.

## NOTE (a)

The constant effort of philosophy in her earlier stages was to establish a basis for a purely deductive system of knowledge. This, which is the final result of united experience and science, was the first aim of speculative thought, antecedent to all true science and to all exact experience. Destitute of these aids, there seems to have been but one mode in which the human mind could proceed in its quest of philosophy, viz., by projecting its own laws and conditions upon the universe, and viewing them as external realities. Such appears to me to be the true ground upon which the earlier phases of the Greek philosophy are to be explained.

The prominent idea of the earliest schools, the Ionic, the Eleatic, &c., was that the universe was a unity. They differed in their account of this unity, variously explaining it by water, air, fire, intelligence, &c.; but the existence of some fundamental unity, comprising the whole of phaenomena, was, in perhaps all of them, an agreed point. The terms unity and universe, seem to have been almost regarded as convertible. The pantheistic language of Xenophanes, who, "casting up his eyes to the whole expanse of heaven, declared that the One was God", is a type of their most prevalent cast of thought.—Aristotle *Metaphysics*, i. 5.

In a subsequent state of philosophy—subsequent in the order of thought, and for the most part in that of time also —there was superadded to the above conception of unity as a ground of phenomena, that of a fundamental dualism in Nature. Existence was viewed as derived from the blending or the strife of opposing elements—good and evil, light and darkness, being and non-being, matter and form, &c. To the latest periods of speculation in the ancient world, these modes of thought, of which the Manichean doctrine was but the most eminent and most practical instance, prevailed; and in those modern schemes of philosophy, "falsely so called", which attempt to deduce the knowledge of Nature, *à priori*, for some purely metaphysical principle, the same influence is apparent. Now, so wide an agreement, even in what is false, must have some foundation in reality, and ought to be regarded as a misapplication of truth rather than as a fortuitous coincidence of errors. The foundation must be sought for in the ultimate laws of thought, and the positive conclusions of science serve to show its real nature.

All correct reasoning consists of mental processes conducted by laws which are partly dependent upon the nature of the subject of thought. Of that species of reasoning which is exemplified in Algebra, the *subject* is *quantity*, the *laws* are those of the elementary conceptions of quantity and of its implied operations. Of Logic, the *subject* is our conceptions of *classes* of things, represented by general names; the ultimate *laws* are those of the above conceptions and of the operations connected therewith. Let these two systems of thought be placed side by side, expressed, as they admit of being, in the common symbolical language of mathematics, but each with its own interpretations—each with its own laws; and together with much that is obviously common—so much, indeed, as to have fostered the idea that Algebra is merely an application of Logic, there will be seen to exist real differences and agreements hitherto unnoticed, but not without influence on the course of human thought. The conception of the universe in the one system will occupy the place of that of unity in the other, not through any likeness of nature, as was once supposed, but through subjection to the same formal laws. Moreover, at the root of the logical system, there will be found to exist a law, founded in the nature of the conception of " class ", to which the conceptions of quantity, as such, are not subject, and which explains the origin, though it does not furnish the justification of the dualistic tendency above adverted to. I conceive it unnecessary to show, that a law of the mind may produce its effect upon thought and speculation, without its presence being perceived. Whatever, too, may be the weight of authority to the contrary, it is simply a fact that the ultimate laws of Logic—those alone upon which it is possible to construct a science of Logic—are mathematical in their form and expression, although not belonging to the mathematics of quantity.

My apology for introducing in this place observations of a somewhat technical character is, that in discussing the relations of science to human nature, it seems necessary, or at least desirable, to consider the subject in the light of past as well as of present experience; and to this end, the study of the logical or pre-inductive stage of science is important. But there is also a great collateral interest in the inquiry. The truly scientific study of the laws of thought sets in clear view the distinctive elements of our intellectual constitution —its subjection, like external Nature, to mathematical laws—the difference of the *kind* of subjection manifest in the two cases. It would seem that this is a fundamental difference. If we strive to conceive of our nature, in its most perfect state, the intellect assenting only to what is true, the will choosing only what is good, the consciousness that

o

all this might, without any violation of our actual constitution, be otherwise, would appear to be a necessary adjunct to that conception. The view of this subject maintained in an earlier portion of the lecture, seems to me to be thus in strict accordance with the proved results of science.

# VI

## LOGIC AND REASONING *

SOME years ago I published a work in which the Science of Logic was developed in mathematical forms. This mode of expression was not founded upon any supposed relationship between the conceptions or ideas about which logicians and mathematicians are respectively conversant, but upon the fact established by actual examination that the formal laws of Thought in Logic are the same as those of Algebra or the science of Number would be if it were conversant not about all numbers but only about those which we designate as Unity and Nothing. I imagine there are few persons acquainted with the work who have not felt, as I do myself, that however curious and exact these formal analogies between the Science of Logic and that of Algebra as above limited may be, it is desirable that the former science should be developed independently. While I think it possible that but for the light of this analogy I should have failed to raise upon the basis of formal law any such structure of methods and results as is exhibited in my work, I am ready frankly to admit that in writing that work I was far too much under the dominion of mathematical ideas. And this leads me to the more immediate object of the present communication. Since the publication of the treatise above referred to, my

* [This essay is marked " E.2." in the Royal Society manuscripts. On the back of the last page of the manuscript there is a pencilled note by Mrs. Boole : " I think this was meant as the beginning of a work intended to put the principles of the Laws of Thought into non-mathematical language. Mr. Macmillan wished G.B. to write such a work and he often attempted it ; but always failed ". But there are some things which are different—or are given at least a different emphasis—here and in the *Laws of Thought*. Other fragments and manuscripts show that Boole was revising his treatment of certain questions, and this paper may belong together with them. He speaks of it on p. 214 as a " letter ", and on p. 211 as a " communication ". There are other manuscript essays, or fragments of essays, probably of the same period which he also calls " letters ". And it may be that he had in mind a series of letters to some learned periodical; just as certain of his essays on probability were written as letters to the *Philosophical Magazine*.

The manuscript has no title ; it has been supplied here.]

attention has been frequently turned to the question : What is the *logical* import of the processes there employed ? Analogies, mathematical and otherwise, being cast aside, what doctrine of the intellectual operations remains concealed beneath the forms themselves ?  I have proposed to myself to give here a brief account of the conclusions to which the study of these questions has led me.  And I wish in doing this to avoid symbolism and to present as far as I may be able to do so the thought which I shall have to express in language familiar to the logicians of Oxford.  If there is any one book to the thought and the ideas of which I should wish to bring my own into such contact as may permit of their comparison, it is Mr. Mansel's *Prolegomena Logica*—a work of which it is not needful that I should speak the praise.

First of all I would observe that there is a twofold sense of the term Logic.  The highest conception of Logic is that which is implied in the derivation of the term.  As the word λόγος signifies not only the inward thought but also its outward form or manifestation, the word Logic in its primal sense means the Science of the Laws of Thought as expressed. Considered in this light, Logic is conversant about all Thought which admits of expression; whether that expression be effected by the signs of common language or by the symbolic language of the mathematician.

But there is a secondary and narrower sense of the term Logic, according to which it is the science of the Laws of Thought as expressed by the terms of ordinary language. In contemplating a group of objects, we are perhaps impressed with the fact of their likeness to each other; we notice the several qualities in which this likeness consists, we combine them mentally in some general conception, we express this conception by a name.  The things which that name represents, separated in thought from all other things in the Universe, constitute a *class*.  Perhaps we compare this class with other classes, the notions of which have been formed by a similar process of thought.  We thus become conscious of Class-relations.  We see that one class is contained in another as a part in a whole or a species in a genus. Hence, general propositions by which such relations are expressed.  Hence, reasoning by which, from propositions thus formed, other propositions are deduced as conclusions. As the ground of all this procedure is the possibility of our forming the conception of class, the logic which determines the forms and laws of such procedure is the scientific development of the notion of a class.  We may term it the Logic of Class.

Now it is maintained by some that this Logic of Class implicitly contains all Logic.  All reasoning, it is said, is ultimately reducible to that act of the mind by which we are led to affirm of the species what has before been affirmed of the genus in which that species is contained.  Others deny this, maintaining the existence of other lines of mental suggestion in the process of inference than that which is involved in the perception of the relation between genus and species, between class and individual.  Thus it is common in geometrical demonstration to infer from the equality of two lines to a third line their equality to each other.  We suppose these to be particular and given lines, involved in a given construction.  The former contend that the reasoning is elliptical in form and consists in an application of the general axiom, things equal to the same thing are equal to each other, to the particular case under consideration.  The principle of suggestion, according to them, is the relation of the general to the particular;  the inference syllogistic.  The latter maintain that the reasoning is not elliptical, that the inference from the equality of two lines to a third line of their equality to each other is immediate, that the principle of suggestion consists in the nature of the conception of equality.  While agreeing mainly with those who hold the latter view, I would add that I think that there is an element of truth in the former one.  On the one hand, I think that we do infer the equality of two lines to each other from their known equality to a third by an act of thought which is suggested immediately by the nature of the conception of equality;  but on the other hand, the very power of forming that conception seems to me to involve an ascent from the particular to the general, or, to speak more accurately, a perception of the general in the particular.  I would say that in the reasonings of geometry, we do not deduce special conclusions from general axioms, but that we perceive the truth of the general axioms in the very act by which we deduce the special conclusions.  In this way, the conception of Class seems to be involved in all other scientific conceptions, —so involved as to constitute the ground of the possibility of reasoning by means of those conceptions,—not the determining cause of the forms and laws of the intellectual procedure when thus reasoning.  These will differ in different sciences according to the nature of the fundamental conceptions upon which they rest and the operations of thought to which those conceptions are subject.  For instance, we cannot form the conception of Number without first attributing to the things numbered that degree of likeness which constitutes them units capable of repetition.  Here the idea of likeness, which is the ground of the conception of class, is involved.  Again, the conception of Number when formed is a general conception.  It applies to all numbers.  But the forms, the laws, the procedure of the science which is conversant about number, depend not upon the fact that the conception of number is general and that the properties and affections of number thus considered are general also, but upon what these properties and affections are.  In each step of the science we may, I think, distinguish these elements : the rules and forms of inference derived from the nature of the conception of number, and the perception that these rules are general, grounded in the relation which inseparably connects the conception of number with that of class.  And what is here said of the science of number is true of all sciences in which reasoning is carried on by means of general signs.  In that the signs are general we see their connexion with the idea of class.  In that they are signs, and as such, expressions of thought, we see that their laws, and all the procedure founded upon those laws, will depend upon the nature of the thought which they express.

I proceed, however, to the more especial business of this letter, which is to state certain conclusions respecting the laws and forms of that particular Logic which is concerned about the relations of class alone, i.e. about genus and species, about whole and part,—of that Logic which finds expression in the terms of ordinary Language. And in doing this, I will endeavour to point out how these conclusions stand related to the general doctrines of logicians.

1st. It is a doctrine contained in the symbolism of my treatise of the *Laws of Thought* that the three fundamental operations of Conception, Judgment and Reasoning are subject to certain primary formal laws.

By a formal law, I mean a law determining the permitted variety of form in the expression of thought. I regard such laws as founded in the nature of thought, and as governing its outward manifestation. Suppose for instance, that an object of thought is regarded as possessing two independent attributes. We cannot give expression to our thought of it as such without expressing one of these attributes first. We think of a flower as white in colour and as fragrant in scent, and if we think of it only as such, i.e. if we add no idea of priority or of connexion, we express our thought either in the form, " white, fragrant flower ", or, " fragrant, white flower ". That we must think of these attributes in order, is a condition, I will not say of thought itself, but of thought as capable of expression,—that we may think of and express them in either of the orders which are possible is a law of such expression and in this sense, a formal law of thought. This particular law, indeed, belongs to that operation of thought which is called conception, and there exist other such laws, the entire system both determining the forms of possible conceptions and excluding forms which would represent impossible ones. Thus the so-called Principle of Contradiction forbids the formal combination of any attribute with its contradictory attribute, as of white with not-white, in the expression of a Conception. The laws of thought include, however, formal laws of judgment and formal laws of reasoning. Of these, the formal laws of judgment determine the forms of necessary propositions, i.e. of propositions true in consequence of their form alone. For instance, the proposition, " A man is a man ", is a necessary proposition, and the law of thought which it and all propositions of the same form manifest is that which Logicians term the principle of " identity ".   The propositions, " A man is either a negro or not a negro ",—" A man is either a tree or not a tree ",—are likewise necessary propositions.   Their truth is involved in their very form and is quite independent of any information we may possess as to the nature of the classes of things represented by, " man ", " negro ", " tree ".   By logicians, the law of thought involved in such propositions as " A man is a negro or not a negro ", is called the law of Excluded Middle.   The idea expressed by this term is that no middle supposition exists between the two which are specified. Of course, this supposes the conception expressed by the term " negro " to be definite and fixed.   Lastly, the formal laws of thought include formal laws of reasoning by which, from the forms of propositions given as true, the forms of other inferred as true, may be determined.   Before proceeding further, I will briefly compare the above with received doctrines.   As yet, there is not much difference to notice.

   Logicians recognise that tripartite division of thought into Conception, Judgment and Reasoning, and they do, for the most part, recognize the subjection of these operations to laws.   The chief difference which exists would have respect to the question : What are we to consider as the ultimate laws of thought?   And the answer which those in modern days who have felt the importance of the question have most generally given is, that they are the Laws of Identity of Contradiction and of the Excluded Middle. Comparing this view with that really involved in the symbolism of my work, I should say that the laws specified belong to, but do not of themselves constitute, the formal laws of thought, and that the system which regards them as alone fundamental errs by defect.   They have their formal equivalents in the system of laws upon which the rules and methods of my treatise are founded, but they form only a part of that system.

   2ndly.   It is a doctrine also contained in the symbolism of my work that the Laws of Thought constitute together a system ; that the ground of this system consists in a certain relation of dependence in which all our conceptions of things stand to two fundamental conceptions, viz. those of the existence and non-existence; and lastly, that the actual procedure of thought is governed partly by formal laws, partly by the above mentioned relation of dependence in our conceptions of things.

I do not know that there exists any doctrine of the ordinary Logic which can be directly compared with this. But there are familiar considerations which, if they do not lead to it, seem to me at least to point to it, and on these I will say a few words.

It is a familiar truth that the validity of reasoning, and of the formal processes of thought generally, does not depend upon the particular meaning of the general terms or names employed. Thus the validity of the syllogism

> Men are mortal,
> Caius is a man,
> Therefore Caius is mortal,

does not depend upon what class of things is represented by " men ", what individual by " Caius ", what attribute by " mortal ". The question then arises : If the validity of the inference does not depend upon the particular or distinctive meaning of these terms, does it depend upon some general meaning which they possess in common, or is it altogether independent of their meaning? Now the answer given to this question is that the terms must be contemplated as representing that which exists or does not exist ; in other words, that of whatsoever else we may make abstraction, not of this. I think that attentive consideration will probably confirm this view. I think it will tend to show that as it is the essence of a proposition to be true or false, so it is the essence of the terms or names between which propositions express relations to represent something which we must regard as existent or non-existent. But I am not sure that this is the view which, upon general considerations like these, will be most likely to commend itself. I think I should myself have been at first disposed to conjecture that the validity of inference depends upon the formal laws of opera-

tions alone.   I would add that it is not upon considerations
such as these the proposition as involved in the symbolism
of my treatise rests.   It is upon the fact which is established :
that the formal laws of all conceptions of class are those
which are common to the two limiting conceptions of
Universe and Nothing, i.e. to the two conceptions which
express simply the ideas of existence and non-existence.

How this common relation, in which all our conceptions of
things stand to the two ideas of existence and non-existence,
comes to be applied in the actual processes of Logic, I shall
endeavour to explain in the next section.

3rdly.   The symbolism of the *Laws of Thought* leads to a
definite answer to the old question :  What is the Universal
type of Inference ?

As I think this the most remarkable result of the entire
investigation, I shall, before stating it, make one or two
preliminary observations.

Every process of reasoning consists in deducing a legitimate conclusion from given premises.   In the Logic of Class,
which alone we are now considering, each premise is a proposition, connecting terms by means of the copula " is ",
or " are ", and these terms are either simple or complex,—
in the latter case being formed by that mental process by
which different conceptions are combined together into a
single conception.   Thus the premises consist of express
logical relations among conceptions, and any legitimate
conclusion will express a deduced relation among those
conceptions or among some of those conceptions.   In the
case of the syllogism, for instance, we have two premises
expressing relations between three conceptions, two only of
which are retained in the conclusions, the remaining one
(middle term) having been got rid of, or to speak technically,
eliminated.   The most general idea of logical inference here
suggested is that of a process of thought enabling us, 1st., to
eliminate from any given system of premises, however
complicated and however numerous, any of the conceptions
which they may involve ; 2ndly., to express the whole of the
logical relation connecting the remaining conceptions according to any legitimate order.   Now the formal laws of thought,

and chiefly those known as the principles of contradiction and excluded middle, enable us to form a necessary proposition connecting any proposed conceptions whatever in perfect independence of any relation established between them by premises.   Taking for instance, the two conceptions " men " and " rational beings ", we may at once say :—Men are either rational or not-rational, meaning thereby that every individual man belongs necessarily to one or other of two alternative classes composing the predicate term.   If we introduce another conception,  " animal ",  we have  the necessary proposition—

> Men are either rational animals,
>> or rational but not animal,
>> or not rational but animal,
>> or not rational, not animal ;

expressing that every individual man belongs of necessity to some one of the four alternative classes forming the predicate term.   If we introduce another conception, we should be able to construct a necessary proposition involving 8 alternative classes in its predicate term, and so on.   Speaking generally, we see that in these necessary propositions, the subject term expresses some given conception, and the predicate term the possible alternatives which can be formed from certain given conceptions and predicated of that subject, each individual thing in the class represented by the subject being referred to some one of the alternative classes composing the predicate.   We see further, that each of the alternative classes composing the predicate is in respect of what is called its logical quantity *indefinite*.   Thus in the necessary proposition,

> Men are either rational or irrational,

while the subject term " men " is universal, since *all* men are referred to one or other of the classes, " rational beings ", or " irrational beings ", each of those class terms is indefinite, since it is undetermined of the class of "rational beings", for instance, whether the whole or some of that class, or none, is contained in the class " men ".   As I shall have to speak of other relations of quantity beside the universal and the indefinite, I will designate all such by the general term *category*.

Now the consequences deduced from the symbolism of the *Laws of Thought* with reference to the general type of logical inference are the following :

1st.  A logical conclusion is always in the form of a necessary proposition modified by means of the premises.

2nd. The nature of the modification is the following : The alternative classes which in the predicate term of the unmodified necessary proposition were all in the category of the indefinite, are each determined under some one of the following four categories, viz.:—

1st. The universal.  When one of the alternative classes of the predicate is in this category, it is implied that all its members are contained in the class denoted by the subject.

2nd. The indefinite.  This has been already explained.

3rd. The non-existent.  When one of the alternative classes of the predicate is in this class, it is implied that none of its members are contained in the subject.

4th. The impossible.  When one of the alternative classes of the predicate term is in this category, two things are implied in the symbolism, first, that it is impossible that any of that class should exist in the class denoted by the subject ; second, the absolute non-existence of the class itself.  I suppose we may connect these two things and confine ourselves to the larger inference, viz. that the class is absolutely non-existent ;  for this implies the impossibility of finding any members of it in any other class.  But the two interpretations are separately involved in the symbolism, and it is therefore my business to state them both.

Before I proceed to illustrate this doctrine of inference, I will say a few words about the genesis of the categories of the *indefinite* and the *impossible*.  And I will do this because I think that the question very naturally arises : How can symbolic forms lead us to new ideas ?

We postulate as the very basis of our symbolism the existence of the general conception of class and of those fundamental operations of thought by which, from conceptions given, others are formed.  These, as I have stated, are

primarily the operation of composition, exemplified in the
derivation of the conception " red flower " from the component conceptions " red " and " flower ",—and the operation of addition, exemplified in the derivation of the conception " men and women " from the conception of " men ",
and the conception " women ".   To these operations there
exist two others which are respectively *inverse*, viz. as
inverse to aggregation, that process by which, from the
conception of a whole by the subtraction of one of its parts
we form the conception of the remainder, and as inverse to
composition, that by which from a given conception, we
ascend to some higher conception, from which by a given
act of composition, the conception given may be formed.
The operation commonly called abstraction is in its formal
character a particular case of this.   When from the conception " red flowers ", we ascend to that of " flowers ",
we arrive at a conception which, by composition with
" red ", gives " red flowers ".   We premise lastly, that
the conception of class has two limiting forms, viz. : the
conception of the Universe as the most comprehensive, the
conception of Nothing as the least comprehensive, of all
possible classes.

Now the processes of the Laws of Thought lead in certain
cases to a symbolic form which is inverse in character and
may be directly interpreted into the question :  What class is
that which, in composition with the conception of Nothing,
leads to the conception of Nothing ?   In other words, what
class is that from which, if we mentally separate *nothing*,
we obtain as the separated product, *nothing* ?   It is plain
that the answer to this is *any* class.   If from *any* class of
things we take nothing, we obtain nothing.   Now the
conception of *any* class is, in other words, that of an arbitrary
or indefinite class, and this is the ground of the category of
the indefinite.   If we unite by the act of composition, a
given conception as " flowers " with another conception
which may be chosen arbitrarily, i.e. if we select in thought
the individuals which are common to the two, we obtain as
the mental product the conception of all or some or none
of the class " flowers ", whose conception is given.   For

instance, if for the arbitrary conception we choose " vegetable productions ", we obtain the conception of " all flowers "—if we, for the arbitrary conception, choose " red things ", we obtain the conception of " red flowers ", and in this way we may obtain the conception of any portion of the class " flower ", i.e. " some flowers ". Lastly, if for the arbitrary conception we choose a conception which is contradictory to that of flowers, we obtain the conception of " no flowers ", or of nothing.

Again, in certain other cases, the processes of the Laws of Thought lead to a symbolic form which may be directly interpreted into the question : What class is that from which, if we mentally separate *Nothing*, we obtain as the separated mental product, the conception of the Universe? It is clear that this involves an impossibility. And this is the normal form in which the category of the impossible presents itself,—though there exist other forms of its presentation, all of which may, I think, be reduced to the requiring of an act or thought, the performance of which would be impossible unless we could identify the conception of the Universe with that of Nothing—the idea of existence with that of non-existence.

To exemplify the doctrine which I have now stated concerning the forms of inference, I will begin with the premises—

> All men are mortal.
> The Gracchi are men.

And first I observe that the Aristotelian conclusion,

> The Gracchi are mortal,

is derived from the necessary proposition,

> The Gracchi are either mortal or not mortal,

by placing the first of the alternative classes in the predicate term, viz. " mortal beings " in the category of the indefinite, and the second " not-mortal beings " in that of the non-existent. Strike out from that proposition the non-existent class, and we have,

> The Gracchi are mortal.

The portion of the class " mortals " in the category of the indefinite, strictly signifies that the Gracchi consist of, " all, some, or no mortals ",—the last alternative having reference to the possible supposition that there may be no Gracchi existing. If Gracchi do exist, the indefinite is converted into " all or some ".

If we reverse the order of the terms, and begin with the necessary proposition,

> Mortals are either Gracchi or not-Gracchi,

the premises will determine the first alternative class, viz. " the Gracchi ", in the category of the universal, and the second alternative class, viz. " not-Gracchi ", under the category of the indefinite. This implies that mortal beings include all the Gracchi and an indefinite remainder (all, some or none) of beings which are not-Gracchi.

If we choose to retain all the terms of the premises in our conclusion, and ground it upon the necessary proposition,

> Every mortal is either a man and of the Gracchi, or a man not of the Gracchi, or one of the Gracchi but not a man, or neither man nor of the Gracchi,

the first and second alternative classes will be determined in the category of the universal, the third in that of the impossible, the last in the category of the indefinite. The conclusion would be, 1st., that mortals consist of all men whether of the Gracchi or not, and an indefinite remainder of beings, which are neither men nor of the Gracchi ; 2nd., that nothing exists which is of the Gracchi, but is not man.

Lastly, if we take as our ground the necessary proposition,

> Every man is either of the Gracchi and mortal, or of the Gracchi but not mortal, or mortal but not of the Gracchi, or neither mortal nor of the Gracchi,

the first alternative class, " of the Gracchi and mortal ", will be in the category of the universal ; the second, " of the Gracchi but not mortal ", in that of the impossible ; the third, " mortal but not of the Gracchi ", in that of the indefinite ; the fourth, " neither mortal nor of the Gracchi ", in that of the non-existent. The conclusion would be, 1st.,

Men consist of all beings which are of the Gracchi and mortal, and an indefinite remainder of mortals which are not of the Gracchi; 2nd., To be of the Gracchi and not mortal is impossible.

And thus every necessary proposition that we can form becomes the ground of a form of inference.

A resemblance which stops far short, however, of agreement, will be observed between the categories whose origin and use have just been explained and certain parallel divisions of the well-known Table of Categories given by Kant. His categories of quantity, the division which may most directly be compared with the above, are—

The Universal, The Particular, The Singular.

I would observe upon this triad, that if it is meant to denote those affections of quantity which give rise to distinctions in logical form, it is redundant, in including both the Universal and the Singular. Wallis has shown that these are not distinct as to logical form. On the other hand, as compared with the scheme which I have described, it is deficient in that it takes no account of the two categories of the non-existent and the impossible. Lastly, I think it an error, though nearly universal among logicians, that the particular is made to take the place of the indefinite.

Confining ourselves to the notion expressed by the word " some ", it seems to me that this is a notion of the indefinite and not of the particular. Taking the conception of " flowers " as universal, the conceptions of " red flowers ", " white flowers ", etc., are particular, since they involve particular determinations of the general conception, but the conception, " some flowers ", which is not limited to one of these conceptions more than to another, is definite.

But a more important question than any involved in the mere comparison of the scheme of categories which I have given with others is, whether the scheme can be established independently of the interpretation of symbolic forms. I will not venture to answer this question positively, and the answer which I shall give will, in fact, be little more than an analysis of the scheme itself. I suppose, then, it is legitimate

to inquire what possible relation may be established between
a proposed conception and a given conception by virtue of
logical premises in which those conceptions, if simple, and
the elementary conceptions from which they are formed, if
complex, are involved. Now first of all, it may be that the
proposed conception is that of something, the existence of
which is forbidden by the premises. In this case, it not
only does not actually co-exist with the other conception,
but it is impossible that it should co-exist with it. Here
we have the category of the impossible. Secondly, the
proposed conception may be that of something, the existence
of which is not forbidden by the premises. In this case it
may, considered as a mark or attribute, enable us either to
affirm, to deny, or to doubt, the existence of that which is
the subject of the other or given conception. It can only
enable us to affirm it when we know that all the cases of
its occurrence are associated with the latter; to deny it
when we know that none are associated therewith; to doubt
it when we are ignorant of the nature of the connection between them. The two first of these suppositions lead us to
the categories of the Universal and the Non-existent; the
last, if we suppose the ignorance complete, leads us to that
of the Indefinite. But though I think that general considerations such as these may conduct us to the above as a
very probable scheme of logical affections of quantity, I
doubt whether they will carry us to that further point of
view from which we can perceive that it is precisely this
scheme which governs the possible forms of inference.

4thly. The conclusions which I have now stated relate to
the forms of Logic as occupied about our conceptions of
things. But the very same series of forms exists in the Logic
of that reflex thought which is occupied not about things,
but about propositions. This is that division of Logic
which, in the ordinary treatment of the subject, is called the
Logic of hypotheticals. As it has the same series of forms, it
exhibits a corresponding series of categories,—for categories
are not mere forms, but also involve interpretation. Thus
in the science of Logic, completed in both its divisions, there
exist two parallel series, each of four categories. And these

P

categories, though in their general character they resemble the well-known categories of Immanuel Kant, differ from them in that they have a real and scientific, not a merely imagined, relation to the possibilities of logical thought. There is no part of Kant's speculations which is, at first sight, more striking than his systematical table of categories. It is, however, the appearance of scientific order without the reality.

I began with speaking of that higher Logic, the conception of which is implied in the derivation of the term,—the Science of all Thought as expressed. I have since been speaking of the subordinate Logic of Class. It is impossible to arrive at any adequate conception of Logic in its higher sense except through the study of its particular forms and manifestations. I said, in speaking of the axiomatic truths of Geometry, that they were general truths which were first seen, and could only be seen, in the particular application. And a similar observation applies here. The general principles of Logic considered as the Science of all Thought that admits of expression, can only be apprehended through the particular manifestations of them which are founded in the Logic of Class, the Logic of Number and the other sciences into which it may be developed.

And now let us state some of the general conclusions respecting this higher Logic, which the results we have arrived at warrant or suggest.

1st. The basis of all Logic is the possibility of apprehending the laws of general conceptions. The conceptions themselves may be only the unattainable limits of processes of abstraction. We may be unable to picture them to ourselves in their separate essence. They are νοητά, not αἰσθητά; but νοητά which we can only comprehend in and through the αἰσθητά. But we can study and contemplate their laws. And these laws contemplated and applied constitute the immediate subject matter of all Logic.

2ndly. These conceptions are expressed by signs, the sign itself, as consisting in some material act or shape, taking the place of the αἰσθητόν or sensuous element, without which the conception could not have been thought, and the laws of the sign taking the place of, and expressing the laws of the conception.

Hence it follows that the sign is arbitrary as to its material character, fixed as to its interpretation and its laws.

3rdly. As concerns the nature of the laws of thought, the intellectual procedure may in all Logic be represented as consisting in elementary operations of thought, by which conceptions are combined so as to form new conceptions, are compared so as to give rise to judgments expressed by propositions, or by which, from propositions given, others are inferred. And this being premised, the laws of thought are the laws which determine either what operations are equivalent, or what judgments are in themselves necessary. One case in which operations are equivalent, is when they merely differ in some adjunct which does not affect the nature of the equivalence, and which may be removed by abstraction. Thus the principle of supposition in Geometry is nothing more than an expression of the right to abstract unessential differences as to position in the comparison of magnitudes.

4thly. Every intellectual operation implies a *subject* upon which it is performed, and a *result* to which it leads. When the subject and the operation are given, the determination of the result depends only upon formal laws; the procedure is direct. When the result is given, the operation defined and the subject sought, the procedure is inverse. The determination of the subject depends upon two things, viz. 1st., our knowledge of the general nature of the subject conception; 2ndly., the specification of this knowledge through a knowledge of the general results of the direct procedure.

5thly. Operations may be subject to conditions of possibility, as well as to formal laws, when possible. But the same formal laws may belong to different sets of operations, and in the one set, the conditions of possibility may be wider than in the other. In this case, we may conduct our reasonings about the sphere of the one by transferring them to the sphere of the other.

6thly. The question whether the intellectual procedure of thought is entirely dependent upon formal laws,—so that we may not only neglect the conditions of possibility of the operations in the actual sphere of the reasoning, but also the consideration whether there exist any other sphere in which operations subject to the same laws exist, but not limited by the same conditions of possibility,—still remains. But as I do not propose to express any opinions which cannot be brought to some kind of external test of their accuracy, I will only say that whatever *à priori* ground there may be for the principle asserted in the last section, there seems to be the same for the one now under consideration.

In reviewing what has been said on the subject of the general nature of reasoning, one observation of importance presents itself. It has been much disputed what are the limits of the human faculties in their commerce with such ideas as those of the Infinite, the Absolute, some thinking that we really can conceive them, others that we are entirely limited to the phenomenal and the finite. Now I do not think that the views of the nature of thought which have been described in this essay bring us directly into contact with the above question, but they do, I think, contain this doctrine, viz. that the processes of formal thought have an extra-phenomenal ground. We cannot, I think, contemplate apart from all admixture of phenomenal elements derived ultimately from sense, the idea of *existence*. I am not sure that we can picture to ourselves absolute non-existence, the non-existence not only of the external world, but of ourselves, —of the *ego* and the *non-ego* together. And yet the *intellectual* ideas of existence and non-existence are seen to form the basis of all our formal thought, and to determine its processes,—for they not only are the ground of the laws of those direct operations to which our finite conceptions are subject, and which we can perform without stepping beyond the finite, but they are the sources of the logical relations which I have termed the categories of quantity and which determine *à priori* the possible forms of all inference. I suppose that what we ought to say is, that while in those faculties of our minds, the office of which is to reproduce or to combine the images of sense, we are limited by the conditions which sensuous perception imposes, so that the soarings of imagination are confined to the phenomenal and the finite, yet, in the laws of our intellectual constitution itself, we are compelled to acknowledge something which is not phenomenal and not finite.   We think and reason about the finite, but we do so because our reasoning faculties have a relation to the infinite.   On the one hand, the infinite is to us the unattainable limit of abstraction ; on the other hand, it is the ground of the exactness of the formal processes of thought.   It seems, indeed, a mystery to say that where imagination fails, there science begins, but if so, it is not the only one which the study of the relations of thought presents, and it is, at least, not a contradiction.   We do not feel it to be such even in the physical world, when we say that the truths of Astronomy in their absolute strictness relate to ideal heavens.

## EXTRACTS FROM A PAPER ENTITLED "ON THE MATHEMATICAL THEORY OF LOGIC AND ON THE PHILOSOPHICAL INTERPRETATION OF ITS METHODS AND PROCESSES "*

IT may be necessary to inform the reader that the mathematical theory of which some illustrations will be given in the following Essay is one which I have developed in a treatise published about two years ago and entitled "An Investigation into the Laws of Thought, on which are founded the Mathematical Theories of Logic and Probabilities." ... As, moreover, this paper is in some measure introductory to another containing a special application of its principles, I deem it right to state circumstances in which it originated. Some time after the publication of the *Laws of Thought* my attention was directed by the Bishop of Edinburgh to a question in the theory of probabilities, not noticed in the above work, upon which conflicting opinions had been formed by different writers, and the fallacious character of the reasonings which had been employed was at the same time pointed out. In the course of the correspondence which followed, I was led to express a hope that Bishop Terrot would publish his observations upon the subject, and I placed at his disposal such results as I had myself obtained. Without entering further into the details of this correspondence, let it suffice to say that it was finally agreed that the publication of an analysis of the question in accordance with the principles developed in the *Laws of Thought* should be

* [The paper consists of the Royal Society manuscripts "B 2" and "C 42". There is a note on the back of the second one : "Later than 1855—M.B." The essay was evidently written at the time Boole was preparing his paper on "The Application of the Theory of Probabilities to the Question of the Combination of Testimonies or Judgments", printed below, p. 308 f. Much of it, especially the first half, covers similar ground to that of the paper on "Logic and Reasoning" above. And although the present paper is fuller and in some ways more thorough, it is also more diffuse; and Boole might think it a less satisfactory statement.]

undertaken by myself. As this analysis involved the application of the Mathematical Theory of Logic, I found it
necessary, after an unsatisfactory attempt to combine that
application with a philosophical statement, to divide the
task. The present essay contains, therefore, an account,
freed as far as possible from the language of symbols, of the
grounds upon which the mathematical development of the
Science of Logic rests. It is proposed in a subsequent paper
to publish the solution of the question in the theory of
probabilities to which reference has been made....

...The following principles may, I conceive, be regarded
as of general application, viz :

That Conception has to do with the object of thought only
as it falls under some general scientific notion; e.g. in
Arithmetic under the general notion of Number with its
affections, in Geometry under that of Figured Space with
its affections, in Logic under that general notion of Class
of which genus and species may be considered as affections.
—That the analysis of the laws of Conception must consciously or unconsciously precede the analysis of the laws
of Judgment and Reasoning.—That none of their laws can
be determined *à priori*, that is independently of the nature
of the concepts involved.—That Judgment consists essentially in a perception of the agreement of concepts, but that
the nature of this agreement depends upon the nature of
the concepts to which it relates; in Geometry, for instance,
it is usually agreement in magnitude supposed capable of
being ultimately tested by superposition, in Arithmetic it
is that agreement in respect to number which is termed
equality, in Logic the fundamental agreement is, as will
hereafter be shewn, that of identity.—That Reasoning
consists in the inferential succession of the propositions by
which Judgment is expressed, its fundamental principle
being that of substitution, viz. that two concepts, between
which an agreement has been established in our premises,
may in any proposition expressive of the same kind of
agreement be substituted for one another.—That there are
two fundamentally distinct methods in which this principle
is applied, viz. the method of synthesis and the method of

analysis; in the former of which we begin with the premises or given propositions, and by successive applications of the principle of substitution, arrive by a direct process at the conclusion, while in the latter we begin by expressing the conclusion in the form of a necessary proposition, involving arbitrary elements to be determined, and apply the principle of substitution so as to determine these elements in accordance with the premises.—Finally, that the intellectual operations generally conducted by means of their instrument, language, are formal, not concerned with the individual nature of the object of thought, but only with the scientific notion under which that object is apprehended, and with such notions only as they are of influence in determining the laws of thought. . . .

When mental concepts and mental operations are expressed by signs, the laws of those concepts and operations become the laws of the signs themselves. But the laws of the mental procedure are independent of the special meaning or content of the concepts involved, and depend only upon the general notion of class, under which those concepts fall. Hence, therefore, the laws of the signs by which that procedure is symbolized are equally general in their application.

Perhaps there is no single principle in the Science of Logic which has been avowed more generally or in a manner apparently more unequivocal than the above. Aristotle, in expressing the terms of propositions by letters, set an example of its adoption which nearly all subsequent writers have followed. It is on the ground of this same principle, too, that modern authorities have described the validity or conclusiveness of arguments regularly expressed as " made evident from the mere form of the expression, independently of any regard to the meaning of the words ". It seems doubtful, however, whether to its full extent the above principle has really been admitted or even understood by logicians. Its illustrations seem to have been almost exclusively borrowed from the syllogism. Neither am I aware that it has been noted, in connexion with such statements as have been quoted, that the meaning of words is not always wholly independent of the form of expression in which they occur. Thus the formula " X's and Y's " does not express an intelligible concept unless the symbols connected by the conjunction " and " be interpreted to signify classes of things wholly distinct. If by the term " X's " we agree to mean " mammalia ", we cannot interpret the term " Y's " by " marine animals ", because cetacea, which are marine, are included in the class of mammalia, and the expression " mammalia and marine animals " taken in strictness would be unmeaning. But the condition, that " X's " and " Y's " must represent distinct classes, being attended to, the interpretation of these terms is in all other respects arbitrary. If we trace to its origin the principle of which the above is not the only kind of example, we shall see that the intellectual operations connected with the faculty of Conception do in certain cases impose conditions upon the otherwise arbitrary concepts which are submitted to them. And hence it is that the forms of language, which is but the outward expression of thought, impose conditions of *interpretability* upon the symbols which they connect.

This leads us to the threshold of perhaps the deepest question in the Philosophy of Logic, viz : Are we bound when conducting the processes of reasoning by means of language to keep constantly in mind the conditions of interpretability, and therefore to employ forms which impose such conditions then only when those conditions are actually satisfied? Is Logic necessarily ostensive in its character? Or is the intellectual procedure in Logic governed solely by a reference to abstract forms and laws? If the latter view be adopted, Logic might be described (to use a term which has already been employed) as a noetic, not an ostensive science.

I hold, as will be evident . . , the latter view. And the investigation of the laws of the faculties of Conception, Judgment and Reasoning to which I shall shortly proceed will tend, I hope, to throw that view in a clearer light than has yet been shed upon it. For I shall, while investigating the laws of the intellectual operations, determine at the same time the conditions of their interpretability, and then shew that the application of the formal laws as a completed system does implicitly and in a very remarkable manner supply the place of that direct consideration of the conditions of interpretability which the ostensive view of the subject would render necessary.  At the same time, it is to be observed that whether we adopt the *ostensive* or what I have termed the *noetic* view of the Science of Logic, the foundations of that science must equally be laid in an analysis of the laws of the intellectual operations....

[In the discussion of the Laws of Conception, which comes soon after this passage, Boole emphasizes particularly the special conditions to which the four different operations of Conception—Addition, Subtraction, Composition and Abstraction—are subject.  After that comes the analysis of Judgment, and then the section on Reasoning.]

### *Analysis of Reasoning as exercised within the sphere of Formal Logic*

The office of Reason is to determine the inferential succession of propositions.  Moreover, a proposition is in Formal Logic an affirmation of identity; it asserts that it is to the same object—to the same individual *things*—that two concepts in thought, or two terms (properly limited) in language, refer.  Logical Reasoning, therefore, is specially concerned with the notion of identity; and it might with propriety be said to consist in the operations which arise from the development of that notion.  But as the identity with which logical reasoning is concerned is the identity of *things*, which, as represented by the terms of the proposition, have become the subjects of Conception, under the general notion of Class and in subjection to the formal laws and relations therewith connected, we are ultimately conducted to the following definition, viz : Logical reasoning is a process of *formal* inference applied to propositions considered as affirmations of the *identity* of the things which, as conceived by us under the notion of Class, are expressed in the connected terms of propositions.  We shall, in speaking of the connexion of the terms of propositions, or of the relation between the concepts which those terms express, describe that connexion or relation as one of equality,—equality of two terms or concepts corresponding to identity in the objects which they represent.

The elements in the above description to which it is most important to attend, and from which the laws of reasoning as a process are derived, are the following, viz :

1st. Reasoning (in Logic) is a process founded upon the notion of identity.

2nd. Reasoning is a formal process.

Now the fundamental law of Reasoning as developed from the notion of identity, is the following :

"*Two concepts which in the sense above explained are equal to a third concept are equal to each other.*"

And the rule or principle regulative of the process of reasoning founded upon this law is the following, viz :

*Terms or concepts which are equal may be substituted the one for the other in any process of logical inference.*

As an example of the application of this principle, which may be termed the principle of substitution, suppose the following premises * given :

"Similar triangles = triangles which have their respective sides proportional."

Then it follows from the principle of substitution that,

"Triangles which have their respective angles equal = triangles which have their respective sides proportional."

The order of the process followed in the above example consists in substituting for the concept "similar triangles", in the second premiss, the equal concept "triangles which have their respective angles equal" derived from the first. There exists a distinct definition of "similar figures", which involves consideration neither of angles nor of sides. Neither is the reasoning, though it relates to a geometrical subject, geometrical reasoning.

There are three applications of the direct law of substitution which admit of distinct exhibition in the form of subsidiary or derived laws of reasoning. They are as follows.

* [The first premise should be here : "Similar triangles = triangles which have their respective angles equal".]

Law A. *If to equal concepts the same or equal concepts be added, the resulting concepts are equal.*

Law B. *If from equal concepts the same or equal concepts be subtracted, the remaining concepts are equal.*

Law C. *If equal concepts be compounded with the same or equal concepts, the resulting concepts are equal.*

In the *Laws of Thought* these laws appear as primary. I believe that if carefully examined it will be seen that the ground of the intellectual assent to their truth is founded in the perception that they are direct applications of the law of substitution, a perception which becomes the stronger from the comparison of the different laws with each other.

Thus suppose it given that,

" Philosophers = lovers of wisdom."

An example of Law C would be furnished by the inference that " Philosophers who are poets = lovers of wisdom who are poets ", and it is plain at least that this *may* be obtained by the substitution of its first * member, or subject of the term " lovers of wisdom ", for the term " philosophers ", the equality of those conceptions being guaranteed by the premises.

Again, if we had the premises,

" Practical men = men who value the ideal only for the sake of the real ",

" Speculative men = men who value the real only for the sake of the ideal ",

we should have as an illustration of Law A :

" Practical men and speculative men = men who value the ideal only for the sake of the real and men who value the real only for the sake of the ideal."

It is manifest that this is, equally with the last illustration, an example of direct substitution; and if we compare the two examples together, it will appear that this is the only element in which they agree. The operations by which the first members are formed are quite distinct. The one is formed by Composition, the other by Addition. Now the

* [Second ?]

nature of the operation no further affects the reasoning than as such operation furnishes a ground for the application of the principle of substitution.   The syllogism, as it perhaps most readily presents itself to the common sense of mankind, seems to rest on a similar basis.   Take for example the syllogism,

> " Men are mortal beings,
>     Kings are men,
>         Therefore kings are mortal beings."

Reducing the premises to the form of identities,

> " Men = some mortal beings,
>     Kings = some men."

Therefore, by substitution,

> " Kings = some mortal beings ";

that is to say, " Kings = some taken out of some mortal beings ", and this is perceived to be the equivalent of saying, " Kings = some mortal beings ", or " Kings are mortal ".

If we carefully examine the above process of inference, we shall see that it involves two distinct steps, viz : the act of substitution, leading to the formal conclusion, " Kings = some out of some mortal beings "; and the further process dependent upon Conception, by which this conclusion is brought to the form, " Kings are mortal ".   It is apparent even from this example that the principle of substitution is not of itself sufficient for the conducting of an argument. It must be employed in combination with other intellectual acts dependent upon the faculties of Judgment and Conception, and it is in such combination that it is actually employed in the ordinary reasoning of mankind.   To these conditions of its application it may be added that it of necessity fails us when, as in all the more difficult forms of logical reasoning, we have to call in the aid of Abstraction. For the operation of Abstraction is, as it has been seen,* purely inverse, and therefore dependent, in its character, and essentially involves the employment of those faculties of the mind by which necessary propositions are formed.   And

* [The passage has been omitted here.   But compare p. 221 above.]

hence, while we are able by the principle of substitution alone to combine the premises together through operations of Addition, Subtraction and Composition, we are compelled to have recourse to those canons of abstract thought which enable us to add to the premises whose truth is only assumed, other propositions whose truth is not assumed but necessary. In other words, we must adopt the analytical and not the synthetical method before we can apply the same principle of substitution in connexion with the operation of Abstraction.  The application of the analytical method is, however, so dependent upon language, and its exposition is so much facilitated by the employment of a proper system of notation, that it becomes if not necessary at least highly important to introduce such a system, and avail ourselves of its aid in expression, before proceeding further into the analysis of Logical Reasoning. . . .

[A fairly long section follows " on systems of notation " and on " symbolical expression of the formal laws of logic ". He shows " that there exists a perfect formal identity between Logic represented by symbols in the scheme above explained " and what he calls " the dual Algebra ", i.e. an Algebra admitting only the quantities 1 and 0.* " Upon this identity the methods developed in the *Laws of Thought* are founded.  I have not, however, in that treatise so fully considered the grounds of the relation upon which its methods rest."  The logical symbolism is the same as in the *Laws of Thought*.  He then returns to the analysis of Reasoning.]

The distinction of reasoning as synthetical and analytical has already been noticed.  As the synthetical form consists in the direct application of the laws of thought, with or without the aid of a symbolical language, to the premises, and as those laws have already been investigated, there is little more to be said upon the subject.  It remains, then, to explain more fully the nature of the analytical method of reasoning, and to shew how it is developed by means of symbolical forms.

It must be remarked, then, that this method always has reference to a proposed end.  It begins with some such

* [See Note in Editing, pp. 20–22.]

question as the following : What unknown concept do we seek explicitly to determine, and by means of what other concepts is its explicit determination sought ?

I say *explicit determination*, because it is the office of a conclusion not to present to us new truth, but only to bring into explicit form and statement some portion of that truth which was implicitly involved in the premises. And having determined what kind of conclusion is sought, we proceed, 2ndly, to express the most general form which that conclusion, in accordance with the necessary laws of Judgment, and in perfect independence of the particular information conveyed in the premises, must have. This being done, we proceed, 3rdly, to determine by means of the premises whatever is arbitrary in the general form, so far as such determination is possible. It is in the last step, chiefly, that the principle of substitution is employed.

The two orders of procedure which have been described, viz. the synthetical and the analytical, are clearly inverse to each other; and they rest upon fundamentally different, but perfectly consistent, views of the nature of a conclusion. For we may regard a conclusion either, 1st, as a consequence following directly from the premises, or 2ndly, as a condition necessary in order that the premises may be thought as true. There is no difference in point of validity between the methods. In comparing them we should say that the method of synthesis is the more simple in theory, that it is necessarily ostensive, not demanding even a recognition of the formal character of the processes of inference; to counterbalance all which advantages it must be added that it is necessarily limited in application. The method of analysis, on the other hand, rests upon a deeper basis of theory, it regards the processes of inference as essentially formal, it is perfectly general in its application.

Now what is the most general problem which Formal Logic can propose ? In considering this question I confine myself to the class of propositions each of which expresses a relation between two concepts. Each again of the two concepts thus connected is either an elementary concept expressed by a single name or description, or it is formed by the com-

bination of elementary concepts according to the laws of
the faculty of Conception already investigated. Ultimately,
therefore, we may say that the premises of an argument
consist of propositions expressing relations among elementary
concepts.

The conclusion which we seek must also be a proposition,
and express a relation connecting all or some of the elementary
concepts involved in the premises. If it involve only some
of them, the others must have been eliminated. And
hence an essential part of a general method in Logic must
be a process of elimination, i.e. a process by which we may
get rid of those concepts which we do not wish to retain in
the conclusion, and which we may view as only deserving
of consideration in so far as they help to establish relations
among the other concepts.

Again, it may be required to determine the conclusion
either, 1st, as a direct expression of existence or non-
existence, or 2ndly, as an expression of the relation in which
a given concept, whether elementary or formed by a combination, stands to the other concepts retained. For
example, if the premises expressed certain relations between
the concepts " coals ", " minerals " and any other concepts,
and if it were required to determine the explicit relation
thereby established between coal and minerals, a definite
process of inference might lead to that conclusion in the form,

" Coals that are not minerals do not exist " ;

and another process of inference, or the same carried still
further, might lead to an equivalent conclusion in the form,

" Coals are minerals " ;

and this latter might be arrived at as an answer to the
question, " How far is it possible to define the object *coals*
by means of the concept *minerals*? ". Of these forms of
the conclusion, the former is simply an expression of non-
existence, the latter is an expression of the relation in which
a given concept stands to another concept.

The general problem of Formal Logic, in reference at least
to catagorical propositions, is therefore the following.

Given any set of propositions expressing logical relations

among concepts, required to express by a single proposition the whole of the relation connecting either, 1st, all these concepts, or 2ndly, any of them chosen at liberty. Required, moreover, to express such relation either, 1st, as an expression of existence, or 2ndly, as an expression of the relation in which some given subject formed by the elementary concepts stands to other concepts.

This problem under its most general form, the symbolical calculus enables us to solve. The formal laws, whose naked expression has been given in the previous section, furnish us with the requisite methods. For the fundamental processes which these methods involve, viz. Development, Elimination and Reduction, I must refer to the *Laws of Thought*. But I will say a few words here on the philosophy of the most important of these processes, viz. that of Development,— more especially as it is in this process that the analytical method of reasoning finds expression.

Resuming the example just considered, in which from supposed premises it was required to express " coals " in terms of " minerals ", we may remark that it is possible antecedently to any knowledge of the meaning of the terms, or to any information conveyed in the premises, to posit the necessary proposition,

" Coals are either minerals or not-minerals ".

If there were another term required to be taken into account, e.g. " vegetable origin ", we might, quite as independently, form the necessary proposition,

" Coals are either minerals of vegetable origin,
          or not-minerals of vegetable origin,
          or minerals not of vegetable origin,
          or not-minerals not of vegetable origin ".

The only effect of a knowledge of the premises would be to enable us to limit in some more definite manner these necessary propositions. They might, for example, enable us to reject in the first form of conclusion the alternative " not-minerals ", and to affirm, " Coals are minerals ". They might possibly enable us to say, " Coals are all minerals ". And in like manner the four alternatives involved in the

Q

second form of conclusion might severally be affected or placed under different categories of thought by means of the premises.  All such modifications presuppose the existence of necessary and *à priori* forms of judgment.

He who in ordinary reasoning adopts this mode, reasons analytically.  He begins with a necessary proposition, and imposes upon it special limitations so as to make it accord with the premises.

Now the method of Development furnished by the symbolical calculus is in reality but the same process presented in a purely scientific form, and in connexion with and dependence upon the laws of thought.  It virtually begins with presenting the conclusion in the form of a necessary proposition, but it derives that necessary proposition from the fundamental law of thought expressed by the equation

$$x(1 - x) = 0.$$

It proceeds by a general method to determine what I have called above the categories or general relations under which the several terms or elements involved in the necessary proposition must be contemplated by the mind in accordance with the premises.  This determination proceeds essentially upon the principle that Logic is formal in its character,— that those relations do not depend upon the meaning or nature of the concepts involved in the premises, but only upon the relations in which they stand.  I will endeavour to illustrate these positions by one or two simple examples, first giving the symbolical solution according to the method of the dual algebra in the *Laws of Thought*, and interpreting the several steps in the solution.

Suppose that from the proposition " Men are rational animals " it were required to find explicitly a definition of " rational beings " in terms of " men " and " animals ".

If we represent the concept " men " by $x$, " rational beings " by $y$ and " animals " by $z$, we have the equation,

$$x = yz. \quad (1)$$

Hence $$y = \frac{x}{z}, \quad (2)$$

and developing the second member,

$$y = 1zx + 0z(1 - x) + \frac{1}{0}(1 - z)x + \frac{0}{0}(1 - z)(1 - x). \quad (3)$$

The interpretation of which is the following :

1st. Rational beings consist of all animals that are men, no animals that are not men and an indefinite remainder (some, none or all) of beings that are neither animals nor men.

2ndly. Men that are not animals do not exist.

I will first make a few observations upon the symbolical equations (1), (2), (3), in order.

In (1), which is the symbolical expression of the premiss, the concept $y$ whose explicit definition is sought appears in *composition* with $z$. From this connexion it is freed by the inverse operation of abstraction. The equation (2) expresses this fact, and shews that it is by abstraction of the concept $z$ from the concept $x$ that the definition of $y$ must be obtained. Equation (3) exhibits the result of the abstraction as obtained by the process of development, that process depending not upon the meaning of the symbols $z$, $x$, but only upon their formal laws.

We may distinguish in the resulting expression for $y$ two classes of elements, viz. 1st, the terms $zx$, $z(1 - x)$, $(1 - x)z$, $(1 - z)(1 - x)$ ; 2ndly, the coefficients, $1$, $0$, $\frac{1}{0}$, $\frac{0}{0}$, with which those terms are affected. The former class are quite independent of the manner in which $z$ and $x$ enter into the original equation (1). The explicit definition of the logical concept $y$ in terms of the logical concepts $x$ and $z$, whatever the given relation among those concepts may be, must in its ultimate state of resolution involve those elements, not because the concepts $x, y, z$ are logical, but in virtue of the law of thought, $x(1 - x) = 0$. The second class of elements, viz. the coefficients, are, however, dependent upon the premiss. They shew under what logical categories the several terms of the necessary proposition must be thought in connexion with the premises.*....

* [Cf. the discussion of the categories in the previous paper.]

...It is a remarkable circumstance that however numerous the terms of a conclusion those terms appear under no other relations or categories than the above. The categories do not, however, necessarily all present themselves in every conclusion, nor in fact is there any other general observation to be noted than that the above are all which do appear. We may therefore with propriety term them logical categories. A similar system, with corresponding interpretations, results from the application of the method of development to hypothetical propositions.

I will endeavour to illustrate the above process, and subsequently that of elimination, without the introduction of mathematical forms. ...

[The illustration is long, and will not be given here.* At the end of it Boole remarks :]

...Cumbrous as this method will doubtless appear, it may serve to explain the nature of a logical conclusion as formed by the limitations of a necessary proposition, and also to shew in what way the two limiting concepts of Nothing and Universe may be employed to effect the necessary reduction. But this employment would scarcely occur to any mind unacquainted with the researches upon which the method is founded; nor can it be employed with even tolerable convenience except in connexion with a symbolical calculus.

Much more remarkable is the method of elimination. It reduces to a single rule or principle the elimination of any concept from any proposition, however complex, or from any system of propositions. And the rule, though perfectly general, is such that it would seem in the highest degree improbable that it should have been discovered without an explicit study of the formal laws upon which it is founded. I will state the rule as applicable to single propositions, and briefly illustrate it by an example.

The law is the following : If any proposition be reduced to a form in which it expresses the non-existence of a class, the elimination of any single concept involved in the expression of that class will be effected by substituting for that concept in the given expression the limiting concepts " Uni-

* [Note in Editing, pp. 29–32, is partly a paraphrase of it.]

verse " and " Nothing "; successively compounding the expressions thus obtained; and affirming by a proposition that the class so defined is non-existent.

Let us apply the rule, without intervention of mathematics, to the proposition, " Men = rational beings that are animals "; and suppose it required to eliminate the concept " rational beings ". We have

" Men, except rational beings that are animals, do not exist ",

in which form it expresses the non-existence of a class. In that class substituting for " rational beings ", " Universe ", we obtain " men except animals "; substituting for " rational beings ", " Nothing ", we obtain " men "; compounding these results we have the expression, " men, except men that are animals " or " men that are not animals "; and lastly, affirming by a proposition the non-existence of the class so defined,

" Men that are not animals do not exist ",

a proposition in which the concept " rational " no longer appears. The method of development applied to this result would bring it to the form, " Men are animals ".

Lastly, I will apply this rule, in combination with reduction, to the premises of the syllogism considered above, viz :

" Men are mortal,
Kings are men ".

These may be reduced to propositions expressive of non-existence, in the form,

" Men not-mortal exist not,
Kings not-men exist not ".

And hence we have the single proposition,

" Men not-mortal and kings not-men exist not ".

I stop to remark that this proposition is really and truly a single proposition. We can form the concept of a single group or collection of individuals composed of two parts, viz. " kings not-men " and " men not-mortal ", these parts being from the very form of expression mutually exclusive and therefore admitting of addition. And of the collective group thus formed we can affirm non-existence. It is in the oneness of this affirmation that the singleness of the proposition consists. The reduction of complex systems of propositions to single propositions constitutes one of the three great processes of the Calculus of Logic,—the converse resolution of single propositions into systems of propositions being a particular application of the method of development.

In the class whose non-existence is declared, let us substitute for " men " the concepts " Universe " and " Nothing " in succession. The results are, " things not-mortal " and " kings ". Hence, compounding these and affirming by a proposition the non-existence of the resulting class,

" Kings not-mortal exist not ",

a proposition which development would reduce to the form,

" Kings are mortal ".

It will be noted that in the above applications, reductions of various kinds are employed of which no account has been given; e.g. the reduction of the proposition, " Men are mortal ", to the form, " Men not-mortal exist not ". In the symbolical methods no such adventitious aid is required or admitted, all transformations whatever being resolved into applications of the three general methods of Development, Elimination and Reduction, the basis of which consists entirely in the *formal* laws of thought. These methods are the same, without any difference, in the dual Algebra, whose formal identity with Logic has been demonstrated.

[The manuscript ends here.

In a set of notes in preparation for this essay, Boole wrote :]

Objection that we do not actually reason thus.

Reply : It is a mistake to suppose that the actual performances of our nature in any case fully answer to its faculties and capacities.

We are in all things constituted with reference to an ideal standard.

# VIII

## ON THE THEORY OF PROBABILITIES, AND IN PARTICULAR ON MITCHELL'S PROBLEM OF THE DISTRIBUTION OF FIXED STARS *

*To the Editors of the Philosophical Magazine and Journal.*

Gentlemen,

My attention has lately been directed to a communication by Professor Forbes, in the Philosophical Magazine for December 1850, entitled " On the alleged Evidence for a Physical Connexion between Stars forming Binary or Multiple Groups, deduced from the Doctrine of Chances ". I have read Professor Forbes's observations with great care and interest; and desire, both because the subject of them is important, and because it is closely related to a class of speculations in the pursuit of which I have long been engaged, to offer a few remarks which have been suggested to me by the perusal of the paper.

I agree with Professor Forbes in thinking that " any abuse of the mathematical sciences, such as to give definite demonstrations and results when no such demonstrations and results can, in the nature of things, be legitimately obtained, tends to weaken our confidence in mathematical conclusions generally "; and I also agree with him that the evidence for final causes is of such a nature that " all attempts to base the proof of design on strictly *à priori* and geometrical ground should be received with scrupulous caution ". May I add, that in calling the attention of mathematicians to a supposed, and I think also real discrepancy between an alleged result of their science and the conclusions of common sense, Professor Forbes appears to me to have deserved their thanks? No one who values the science of mathematics upon the only just ground of estimation, as an instru-

---

* [*The Philosophical Magazine*, Series 4, vol. i, June, 1851.]

ment for the discovery of truth, can desire to shield its conclusions from the severest scrutiny of reason. To endeavour to do this would either be to set the means above the end, or it would be to confess (by implication) that there is some essential want of harmony among the intellectual powers. Upon either of these grounds, and more especially upon the latter, this whole question appears to me to deserve the most careful examination. It would be no rash assertion to say, that it is of far less importance to know whether an *à priori* argument for the physical connexion of the double stars is valid, than it is to know whether the human mind is so constituted as to become of necessity the sport of its own inconsistencies.

Let us consider first, what is the proper statement of the problem considered by Mr. Mitchell *; secondly, whether that problem admits of solution on the principles of the theory of probabilities.

Mr. Mitchell assumes it as a fit expression of the idea of a distribution of the stars over the sky " by mere chance ", that any star is as likely to be found in any one spot of the heavens as in any other. Supposing then, that there are 230 stars equal in brightness to $\beta$ Capricorni, he estimates the probability, that upon the above principle of distribution, no such double star would appear in the heavens as $\beta$ Capricorni to be about 80 to 1. From this, and from similar calculations relating to the Pleiades, and from the extension of " the same argument to the smaller stars as well as those which are collected together in clusters, such as the Præsepe Cancri, the nebula in the hilt of Perseus's Sword, &c., as to those stars which appear double, treble, &c., when seen through telescopes ", he thinks it may be concluded with " the highest probability (the odds against the contrary opinion being many million millions to one) that the stars are really collected in clusters in some places where they form a kind of system, while in others there are either few or none of them ; to whatever cause this may be owing,

* [" An Inquiry into the probable Magnitude and Parallax of the Fixed Stars, from the quantity of light which they afford to us, and the particular circumstances of their situation." By the Rev. J. Mitchell. Philosophical Transactions of the Royal Society for 1767.]

whether to their mutual gravitation, or to some other law or appointment of the Creator ''.

It is impossible to reason upon chance. With reference to the phænomena of material nature, the idea of universal causation seems to be interwoven in the very texture of our minds. Dismissing the idea of chance, let us then consider the meaning of the assumption that it is as likely that a particular star will be found in one spot of the sky as in another. Such a principle would, as implied by Prof. Forbes, be a legitimate expression of the hypothesis, that the distribution of the stars has been effected according to a law or manner, of the consequences of which we should be unable to form any opinion. The proper statement of Mr. Mitchell's problem, as relates to $\beta$ Capricorni, would therefore, be the following :—

1. Upon the hypothesis that a given number of stars have been distributed over the heavens according to a law or manner whose consequences we should be altogether unable to foretell, what is the probability that such a star as $\beta$ Capricorni would nowhere be found ?

2. Such a star as $\beta$ Capricorni having been found, what is the probability that the law or manner of distribution was not one whose consequences we should be altogether unable to foretell?

The first of the above questions certainly admits of a perfectly definite numerical answer. Let the value of the probability in question be $p$. It has then generally been maintained that the answer to the second question is also $p$, and against this view Prof. Forbes justly contends. I am not sure that the abstract of Mitchell's paper which I have consulted, warrants the conclusion that he held precisely this opinion; but it has been a prevalent one, and to Prof. Forbes belongs the honour of having first called it in question. Although the source of the fallacy is not a matter of much importance, I will venture to offer an explanation of it somewhat different from that of Prof. Forbes.

Let us state Mr. Mitchell's problem, as we may now do, in the following manner :—There is a calculated probability $p$ in favour of the truth in a particular instance of the proposition, If a condition A has prevailed, a consequence B has not occurred.   Required the similar probability for the proposition, If a consequence B has occurred, the condition A has not prevailed.

Now, the two propositions are logically connected.   The one is the "negative conversion" of the other; and hence, if either is *true* universally, the other is so.   It seems hence to have been inferred, that if there is a probability $p$ in a special instance in favour of the former, there is the same probability $p$ in favour of the latter.   But this inference would be quite erroneous.   It would be an error of the same kind as to assert that whatever probability there is that a stone arbitrarily selected is a mineral, there is the same probability that a mineral arbitrarily selected is a stone. But that these probabilities are different will be evident from their fractional expressions, which are—

1. $$\frac{\textit{Number of stones which are minerals}}{\textit{Number of stones}}.$$

2. $$\frac{\textit{Number of non-minerals which are not stones}}{\textit{Number of non-minerals}}.$$

It is true that if either of these fractions rises to 1, the other does also; but otherwise, they will, in general, differ in value.

Does then the problem, as above stated, admit of solution? I do not say of such solution as will throw light upon the constitution of the heavens, but of such solution as will relieve from all suspicion of inconsistency the theory of probabilities.

In reply to this question, I shall give some account of a method of which I have been in possession for a considerable period, and which appears to me to answer all the requirements of a *general method*.   Of the particular question which is more immediately before us, I shall present a solution to which that method conducted me about two years ago, and from which I was led to take that view of the nature of the fallacies exposed in the preceding pages which I have endeavoured to exhibit.

Although the immediate business of the theory of probabilities is with the frequency of the occurrence of events, and although it therefore borrows some of its elements from the science of number, yet as the expression of the occurrence of those events, and also of the relations, of whatever kind, which connect them, is the office of language, the common instrument of reason, so the theory of probabilities must bear some definite relation to logic. The events of which it takes account are expressed by propositions; their relations are involved in the relations of propositions. Regarded in this light, the object of the theory of probabilities may be thus stated :—Given the separate probabilities of any propositions to find the probability of another proposition. By the probability of a proposition, I here mean, according to previous definition, the probability that in any particular instance, arbitrarily chosen, the event or condition which it affirms will come to pass.

In confirmation of this view, let it be remarked, that as simple events are expressed by simple propositions, so combinations of events are expressed by compound propositions, i.e. by propositions expressing some logical connexion among the simple propositions which they involve. Upon the *nature* of that connexion depends the *mode* in which the probability of the compound event represented is derived from the probabilities of the simple events. The relation of cause and effect may, in like manner, be resolved into the relation of the terms of a *conditional* proposition. With any metaphysical inquiries into the nature and the source of that relation we are not concerned. The above and similar instances justify the assertion, that the subject of the theory of probabilities is coextensive with that of logic, and that it recognises no relations among events but such as are capable of being expressed by propositions. We may carry this reasoning one step further. Our data are the probabilities of propositions. That which we seek to determine is also the probability of a proposition. Now, every proposition may be considered with reference either to its matter or to its form. With the matter of propositions however, we have no concern, for it imports not what kinds of events they are whose occurrence is asserted in the given premises. There remains then, but the form to be considered, the mere logical connexion. Hence it may be inferred that the dependence of the numerical value of the probability sought upon the numerical values of the probabilities given, is founded solely on the logical connexion of the propositions. Or the principle may be thus stated :— The probability sought is a *function* of the probabilities given ; but the *form of that function* depends only upon the logical connexion of the proposition whose probability is sought with those propositions whose probabilities are given. There are then, two conditions necessary toward the construction of a perfect method for the calculus of probabilities :—

1. The prior construction of a general method for determining the logical dependence of any proposition upon another given proposition, or set of propositions.

2. The deduction from that expression of the corresponding relation among their probabilities.

Let us consider these objects in succession.

1. In a hasty and (for this reason) regretted publication, entitled " The Mathematical Analysis of Logic ", and in a paper published in the Cambridge Mathematical Journal, entitled, " The Calculus of Logic ", I have stated certain general laws of thought, mathematical in their expression, and constituting, as I believe, the true basis of formal logic. The actual development of those laws in the works referred to is far too imperfect to meet the requirements of the case now under our consideration. But that imperfection does not apply to the laws themselves. The results of subsequent investigations authorise me to say that there exists a general method, enabling us not only to educe any of the consequences of a system of propositions, but also to express in a scientific form and order the connexion which any proposed proposition bears to any other proposition, or system of propositions. It is not needful that I should here fully explain how it is that a logical dependence of this nature can exist where propositions appear to be wholly or quite unconnected. But I may remark that by the very conditions of thought, there arise certain relations necessary *à priori*, e.g. the so-called principle of contradiction, " Πασῶν

βεβαιοτάτη τῶν ἀρχῶν ",* the principle that a proposition is
true or false, &c., that these are implicitly involved in the
fundamental laws of the method, and that they render
possible the expression of the relation sought.  By the solution thus obtained, the first object which we have in view may
in all cases be accomplished.

2. The result at which we shall thus have arrived will
express the logical dependence of our final proposition upon
those which are involved in the premises of the inquiry.  It
is, as has been said, an equation whose symbols are logical—
they relate to *events*, not to *numerical magnitudes*.  But
at the same time, they are subject to most of the laws of
the symbols of arithmetical quantity, satisfying however a
peculiar law, to which the symbols of quantity, as such, are
not subject.  Now I have ascertained that in the formal
relations which thus assimilate the laws of thought in logic
with the laws of thought in arithmetic, lies the basis of a new
and general theory of probabilities.  Accordingly, from the
purely *logical* equation to which the present application of
our analysis has conducted us, there results a system of
*algebraic* equations determining the numerical value of the
probability sought.

To give some idea of the generality of this method, I shall
add a brief account of some of the results to which I have
been led by its application.

The received theory of probabilities is, so far as it is a
general theory, essentially based upon the hypothesis that
the probabilities given are those of independent simple
events.  To meet a few of the cases in which this hypothesis
is not realised, Laplace has stated, partly as his own and
partly as the result of the investigations of others, certain
supplementary principles, of which he also makes frequent
use.  These relate to such questions as the following :
viz. the relative probabilities of causes deduced from the
probabilities of an observed event upon the several hypotheses of the different causes operating separately;  the
probability of a future event deduced from the probabilities
of its separate possible causes, and the probabilities of its

* Arist. *Met.* iii. 3.

following those separate causes, &c. I have verified the whole of Laplace's general principles of this nature by the application of the method above referred to.

I have applied it to a considerable number of questions, to which, as it appears to me, the received theory is in its present state inapplicable. The necessity for a more general theory is, I conceive, founded on this circumstance; that observation, especially of social phænomena, does not in general present to us the probabilities of simple events, but of events occurring, in particular connexions, whether of causation or of coincidence. To such cases the method I am describing is peculiarly applicable, inasmuch as it imposes no restriction upon either the number or the nature of the data. If the data are insufficient for the definite numerical determination of the probability sought, the solution involves arbitrary constants. These express certain unknown probabilities, which are to be determined from further experience. Their interpretation is given, and hence the nature of that experience determined, by referring to the final step of the logical solution. But it does not hence follow that, when the experience cannot be obtained, the solution is useless; for by giving to the constants their extreme values 0 and 1, we obtain two definite limits, within which the probability sought *must* lie independently of all further results of experience. The extreme case is that in which the proposition, whose probability is sought, has no logical connexion whatever with the premises. Even then the method does not fail. The final expression consists of a series of terms, each multiplied by an arbitrary constant, and the nature of the experience by which the constants are to be determined is assigned; but in the absence of that experience, the limiting values of the series are 0 and 1. As a general example of the method, I will take the following case. I suppose that, from observations made upon the health of a district during a period of sickness, it appeared that a portion of the houses represented by the fraction $p$ were visited by fever; a portion represented by the fraction $q$ by cholera; and a portion represented by the fraction $r$ were free from both these diseases, and at the same time in a proper sanitary condition as respects cleanliness and ventilation : required the probability that any house taken at random was in a defective sanitary condition.

The solution of this problem would be sufficiently simple if we were permitted to assume that the three events represented by the presence of fever in a house, the presence of cholera, and the prevalence of a defective sanitary condition, were independent of each other. This, however, we have no right to assume. The solution must be sought for on other principles. The following is the result to which the general method conducts me.

Probability sought

$$= \frac{(1 - p - r)(1 - q - r)}{1 - r} + cp + c' \cdot \frac{q(1 - p - r)}{1 - r},$$

$c$ and $c'$ being arbitrary constants. Assigning them the extreme values 0 and 1, we get

$$\frac{(1 - p - r)(1 - q - r)}{1 - r},$$

and $1 - r$ for the limits of its value. The interpretation of the arbitrary constants afforded by the final logical equation is, that $c$ is the probability that if a house is visited by fever its sanitary condition is defective, $c'$ the probability that if a house is visited by cholera without fever, its sanitary condition is defective. These elements must be determined by further experience. It may be further remarked, that for the application of the general method, it is perfectly indifferent whether the number of our data is equal to the number of simple events or not, and that the mode of their combination is equally unimportant. The case above given is a very simple one; but for this reason its verification by common sense, to those who may choose to undertake the task, will be the more easy.

I will now exhibit the results to which this method conducts us when applied to Mr. Mitchell's problem. That problem, under a somewhat more general aspect, may be thus stated.

Given the probability ($p$) of the truth of the proposition, If the condition A is satisfied, the event B will not happen.

Required the probability P of the proposition, If the event B does happen, the condition A has not been satisfied. The result which I obtain is

$$P = \frac{c(1-a)}{c(1-a) + a(1-p)},$$

where $c$ and $a$ are arbitrary constants, whose interpretation is as follows : viz. $a$ is the probability of the fulfilment of the condition A, $c$ is the probability that the event B would happen if the condition A were not satisfied.

Let us apply this solution to Mr. Mitchell's problem, and test its agreement with common sense. The condition A is, that the stars have been so distributed, that it is as likely that any star will be found in one spot of the sky as another. Let us term this a "random distribution", meaning thereby a distribution according to some law or manner, of the consequences of which we should be totally ignorant; so that it would appear to us as likely that a star should occupy one spot of the sky as another. Let us term any other principle of distribution an *indicative* one.

The event B is the occurrence somewhere in the heavens of a double star as close as $\beta$ Capricorni. Hence $p$ is the given probability that, on the principle of random distribution, there will not exist such a double star. Its numerical value appears to be $\frac{159}{160}$, not $\frac{80}{81}$.

P is the required probability, drawn from the existence of $\beta$ Capricorni, that the principle of random distribution did not prevail; $a$ is the unknown probability of a random distribution, $c$ is the unknown probability, that, if the principle of random distribution had not prevailed, such a star as $\beta$ Capricorni would have existed.

If $c$ and $a$ could be determined in addition to $p$, the value of P would be definitely given by the formula.*

* A candid mind will not object to this solution, the impossibility of determining the unknown constants $a$ and $c$ by any actual experience; but I can imagine such a mind as hesitating under the difficulty of conceiving what *kind* of experience, could it be had, would suffice for their determination. Perhaps the proper answer would be, that such experience ought to extend to different acts of the Creative Power; that it ought to enable us to say with reference to each of them, whether the connexion of effect

We have then

$$P = \frac{c(1-a)}{c(1-a) + a(1-p)}.$$

First suppose that we had $p = 1$, then

$$P = \frac{c(1-a)}{c(1-a)} = 1.$$

If, then, it were certain that such a combination as $\beta$ Capricorni could not exist upon the principle of random distribution, it would be certain from its existence that the principles of random distribution did not hold. This is agreeable to common sense.

Suppose, in the second place, that there was a high *à priori* probability in favour of the principle of random distribution. Then $a$ approaches to unity, and the value of P diminishes. Hence the probability afforded by the existence of $\beta$ Capricorni *against* the principle of random distribution diminishes also. And it is perfectly evident from the value of P, that the *à priori* probability in favour of the principle of random distribution might be so great as to outweigh altogether the influence of the observations made upon $\beta$ Capricorni. This appears also to be quite agreeable to reason.

3. Suppose that there is but a very small probability that $\beta$ Capricorni could result under any other condition than that of random distribution; the value of $c$ is then very small, and the probability against the hypothesis of random distribution diminishes. If $c$ were 0, i.e. if it were certain that $\beta$ Capricorni could not appear under any other circumstance than that of a random distribution of the stars, then the expression would vanish, however near $p$ might approach to unity. However unlikely, then, the principle of random distribution

with cause was manifest in the phænomena of stellar distribution; and that it should make known to us in how many of the particular instances in which such connexion was *perceived*, the occurrence of double stars was an attendant result. There are, however, cases, and perhaps the above is one, in which we may with some confidence proceed upon other grounds than direct experience, e.g. upon the *reasonableness* of an hypothesis viewed in the light of that general analogy of nature which experience tends daily to confirm. Data derived from this source may properly be said to be *à priori* in relation to problems such as the above, and it is thus that I have referred to them in the concluding portion of the paper.

R

may be, it becomes certain whenever it is known that no other cause can produce the effect observed.

Let us investigate the conditions under which P is greater than $p$. If P is greater than $p$, we have

$$\frac{c(1-a)}{c(1-a)+a(1-p)} > p \sim$$

$c(1-a) > c(1-a)p + ap(1-p)$, or $c(1-a)(1-p) > ap(1-p)$, or $c(1-a) > ap$. Now $1-a$ is the probability that the principle of random distribution did not prevail, and $c$ is the probability on this hypothesis that such a double star as $\beta$ Capricorni should exist. Hence $c(1-a)$ is the probability of the whole hypothesis, that the distribution of the stars was not a random one, and that double stars should exist. In like manner, $ap$ is the probability that the principle of random distribution did prevail, and that a double star like $\beta$ Capricorni should not exist.

Hence we have the following conclusion :—If the probability of an indicative law of distribution, and the consequent existence of a double star, is greater than the probability in favour of a random distribution, and a consequent absence of double stars, then the probability in favour of an indicative law of distribution, granting the existence of a double star, is stronger than the probability against a double star, granting the hypothesis of a distribution at random.

If $c$ and $a$ were each equal to $\frac{1}{2}$, i.e. if it were à priori just as likely as not that the stars are scattered at random, and also just as likely as not that, if they were not scattered at random, $\beta$ Capricorni would exist, we should find

$$P = \frac{\frac{1}{4}}{\frac{1}{4} + \frac{1}{2} \times \frac{1}{160}} = \frac{80}{81}.$$

I had intended to append to this paper an investigation of the probability of the occurrence of triple stars of determinate closeness in the heavens, assuming Mr. Mitchell's law of distribution. But the paper has already extended beyond its due limits, nor would the investigation proposed at all service the purpose of the main argument.

I trust that the design of this communication will not be misunderstood. It is commonly the business of scientific methods to teach us that which we could not learn without them; but to give us confidence in their results, it is also required that they should, in those cases upon which un-assisted reason pronounces a decision, not contravene her verdict.   In the present instance that confirmation has not been easy; but it will, I trust, be considered to have been complete.

I am, Gentlemen,

Your obedient Servant,

GEORGE BOOLE.

Queen's College,
Cork.
March 11th, 1851.

## IX

# FURTHER OBSERVATIONS ON THE
# THEORY OF PROBABILITIES *

*To the Editors of the Philosophical Magazine and Journal.*

Gentlemen,

Some communications which I have received since the publication of my letter on the Theory of Probabilities in the last Number of your Journal, have led me to think that a little further explanation of certain points involved in it may be desirable. This explanation I the more readily offer, because it appears to me that upon one of the points in question, viz. the prevalent doctrine among mathematicians concerning the investigation of the probabilities of causes, I have made a statement which a more careful survey of authorities does not fully warrant. As the question lies at the foundation of some of the most interesting applications of the theory of probabilities, I am desirous of stating how it has really been viewed by eminent writers; and I shall subsequently notice certain other points suggested to me in the correspondence above referred to.

The problem under discussion was the following :—Given the probability $p$ of the truth of the proposition : If the condition A has been satisfied, the event B has not happened. Required the probability P of the truth of the proposition : If the event B has happened, the condition A has not been satisfied. And its correct solution, as given in my letter, is

$$P = \frac{c(1-a)}{c(1-a) + a(1-p)}, \quad \cdot \quad \cdot \quad \cdot \quad (1)$$

$c$ and $a$ being arbitrary constants whose interpretation is assigned. I have remarked that it has generally been erroneously held, that the solution of the above question is $P = p$. It is to this point that I desire first to refer.

The doctrine that $P = p$ is expressly taught in the Edin-

* [*The Philosophical Magazine*, Series 4, vol. ii, August 1851.]

burgh Review (Quetelet on Probabilities). Speaking of a certain combination of phaenomena observed in rock-crystal, the Reviewer says, " The chances against such a coincidence happening thirteen times in succession by mere accident are more than 8000 to 1 ; and this therefore was the probability that some law of nature, some cause was concerned ".

The same doctrine seems to me to be strongly implied by Laplace in the Introduction to his great work on Probabilities. Discussing the question of a primitive cause, fixing the direction of rotation of the planets in their orbits, he introduces the object of his inquiry in the words, " pour avoir la probabilité avec laquelle cette cause est indiquée ". And then having determined, on the hypothesis of the absence of such determining cause, the probability *against* the phaeno-menon of rotation in one uniform direction, he says, " Nous devons donc croire au moins avec la même confiance qu'une cause primitive a dirigé les mouvements planétaires, surtout si nous considérons que l'inclinaison du plus grand nombre de ces mouvements a l'équateur solaire est fort petite ". Laplace does not indeed expressly affirm the principle under consideration, but it appears to me that his language does in some degree give it sanction.

Mr. De Morgan, in investigating the probability that there is a cause for the observed phaenomenon that the sum of the inclinations of 10 of the planetary orbits is less than $92°$, reasons in the following manner. Having found a calculated probability ·00000012, say $q$, that the sum of the inclinations would be less than $92°$ on the assumption that all inclinations are equally possible in each orbit, he says, " If there be a reason for the inclinations being as described, the probability of the event is 1. Consequently it is 1 : ·00000012 (i.e. 1 : $q$) that there was a necessary cause in the formation of the solar system for the inclinations being what they are." The probability of the existence of such a cause is thus expressed by the fraction

$$\frac{1}{1+q}.$$

I at one time thought that this reasoning involved an error very nearly equivalent to that which I have adverted to in the previous remarks. But upon examination it appears that Mr. De Morgan's result is really a limitation of the general formula (1) obtained by assigning particular values to the constants $a$ and $c$. For in order to apply that formula to the case considered by Mr. De Morgan, let us assume A to represent the absence of any determining cause of the phaenomenon B, viz. of the phaenomenon that the sum of the planetary inclinations is less than 92°, then will $a$ represent the *à priori* probability of the absence of a determining cause, and $c$ the probability that on the assumption of its existence, the phaenomenon B would result. Mr. De Morgan's reasoning then involves the hypothesis that $a = \frac{1}{2}$ and that $c = 1$. Also $p = 1 - q$. If we make these substitutions in the general value of P, we find

$$P = \frac{\frac{1}{2}}{\frac{1}{2} + \frac{1}{2}q} = \frac{1}{1 + q}.$$

There is, therefore, I conceive, no error in the *reasoning* adopted; although there may be, as it seems to me (but I state this merely as an opinion), a serious doubt as to the determination of the constant $a$. We are not, I think, at liberty to assume that it is *à priori* as likely as not that a sufficient ground for a determinate phaenomenon should exist in nature. All that we can infer from the general solution is, that unless the existence of such a ground is *à priori* highly improbable, then, after frequent experience of the phaenomenon, there exists a high probability in favour of the existence of that ground.

I have not at present the opportunity of making further references; but I think the most just inference from what has been adduced, to be, that while the doctrine objected to has really been put forth, it has not been held uniformly or universally. I would suggest also the consideration, that even the passage quoted from the Edinburgh Review, although certainly conveying the erroneous notion adverted to, might by the omission of the word *therefore* be understood as expressing the result of a train of reasoning similar to that which Mr. De Morgan has adopted. For if we granted in that case Mr. De Morgan's determination of the constants, the numerical result obtained would be extremely near to that which the Reviewer has assigned. It seems to me to be the part of justice, to give to such considerations as these their full share in estimating the opinions which a writer has expressed. While on the one hand we ought to bring every statement into comparison with the standard of what is absolutely true and right, we ought on the other hand, to be willing to take into account those possible hypotheses upon which there may be reason to think that an author has proceeded, even though no mention of them be retained in his conclusions.

Upon the whole, I conceive that the following is the true theory of that class of questions which has been under consideration :—

1st. That it is not in any case a question whether a particular phaenomenon which has come under our notice is an effect of causation or not, but whether or not it is an effect of some single predominant cause, or simple combination of causes, the consequences of which are in some measure within the reach of our intelligence.

2nd. That upon the supposition of the absence of such cause, or simple combination of causes, certain results appearing to us equally probable, the probability of that definite combination of those results which constitutes the effect observed may be definitely calculated.

3rd. That if the value thus obtained be expressed by $p$, then the formula (1) will represent the probability of the existence of such predominant cause or combination of causes. That in that formula we may, following Mr. De Morgan, justly assume $c = 1$, but that there appear to be no grounds further than the analogy of Nature for determining $a$. (The difficulty here is not that we are choosing among causes equally probable, but that we are attempting to assign the à priori probability of the existence of a condition of things, or in other words, to compare the probabilities of its presence and its absence. Now this is a question, the conjectural solution of which will vary with our varying knowledge of the

constitution of Nature. Unless, however, we have reason
to suppose that the value in question is very small, the general
formula will still be available for our general guidance, if not
for definite numerical evaluation.)

Quitting this problem, I shall now notice two others, of
which solutions have been given, that appear to me to be
defective in generality from the same cause, viz. the non-
recognition of the requisite arbitrary constants.

1st. Given $p$ the probability of an event X, and $q$ the
probability of the joint concurrence of the events X and Y :
required the probability of the event Y.

The solution of this problem afforded by the general method
described in my last letter is

$$\text{Prob. of Y} = q + c(1 - p),$$

where $c$ represents the unknown probability, that if the
event X does not take place the event Y will take place.
Hence, it appears that the limiting probabilities of the event
Y are $q$ and $1 + q - p$. The result is easily verified.

The only published solution of this problem with which
I am acquainted is

$$\text{Prob. of Y} = \frac{q}{p},$$

a result which involves the supposition that the events X
and Y are independent. This supposition is, however, only
legitimate when the distinct probabilities of X and Y are
afforded in the data of the question.

Given the probabilities $p$ and $q$ of the two premises of the
syllogism,

All Ys are Xs
All Zs are Ys.

Required the probability P of the conclusion

All Zs are Xs.

Here, by the probability $p$ of the premiss all Ys are Xs, is
meant the probability that any individual of the class
represented by Y, taken at random, is a member of the class
X, and so in the other cases. The resulting probability of
the conclusion afforded by the general method is then

$$P = pq + c(1 - q),$$

where $c$ is an arbitrary constant expressing the unknown probability, that if the minor premiss is false the conclusion is true.   The limiting probabilities of the conclusion are thus

$$pq \text{ and } pq + 1 - q.$$

The only published solution of the above problem with which I am acquainted is $P = pq$, a result which manifestly involves the hypothesis that the conclusion cannot be true on any other grounds than are supplied by the premises.

There are also, I have reason to think, other cases than the above in which definite numerical results have been assigned, either by neglecting the arbitrary constants, or by determining them upon grounds not sufficiently explained. I do not, however, purpose to enter into the further consideration of this subject here, nor do I offer the above remarks with any view to depreciate the eminent labours of those from whose writings my illustrations have been drawn. Indeed, the results which I have deduced from the new method might all have been obtained by the principles of the received theory, with this principal difference, that the constants, which with their interpretations are given by the one method, would require to be assumed in the other. While I think it right to make this acknowledgment, I feel it to be just also to say, that it is only to the simpler kind of problems that the remark appears to me to be applicable. Granting even a proper assumption of the arbitrary constants, I do not see how a solution is to be obtained by the received methods when the data are much involved; not to mention those cases in which the number of the data exceeds or falls short of the number of simple events combined in them, and in the solution of which cases nevertheless arbitrary constants may not be required. Restricting our attention to the ordinary theory, it appears to me to be certain that the problems which fall under our notice may be resolved into two great classes; viz. 1st, those in which definite numerical solution is attainable from the data alone, without any determination of arbitrary constants; 2nd, those in which the data do not suffice to this end, but in which we must either introduce arbitrary constants, as has been done in this paper, or implicitly determine them as Mr. De Morgan has done.  And I can conceive of nothing as more likely to inspire a rational confidence in the theory of probabilities, than a clear and well-marked distinction between these cases, accompanied by a distinct statement of the grounds upon which, whenever constants are determined, their determination is effected.

The question has been suggested to me by a correspondent,* to whom I am indebted for some valuable remarks, whether the general method described in my last paper involves any fundamentally different idea of probability from that which is commonly accepted.  He observes that the results which I have given are in accordance with the principles of the established theory.  As the same question may present itself to other minds, I would remark that the theory of probabilities has, in the view which I have been led to take of it, two distinct but accordant sources.  From whichsoever of these it may be derived, it would be found to involve the idea of numerical magnitude; but in the one case that idea will have reference simply to the relative frequency of the occurrence of events, being in fact the received ground of the theory; in the other, to the persistency of certain forms of thought, which are manifested equally in the operations of the science of number, and in the reasonings and discourses of common life.  Setting out from either of these grounds, we may, I conceive, without difficulty attain to a knowledge of the other.  Now it appears to me to be perfectly in accordance with the nature of probability that this should be the case; for its relation to number is not more essential than its relation to the manner in which events are combined.  But while the expression of the former relation belongs to arithmetic, or more generally to algebra, that of the latter belongs to logic.

I design, as soon as leisure and opportunity shall permit, to publish the general theory to which reference has been made in this and the previous paper.  Had it been possible for me to offer in the space which they have afforded a satisfactory statement of its principles, I should have gladly availed

* W. F. Donkin, M.A., Savilian Professor of Astronomy, Oxford.

myself of the opportunity of doing so.   But for the particular ends here in view, this has been the less necessary to be done, as the result actually exhibited admit of verification by known methods.   Still I trust that the collateral discussions into which I have entered have not been altogether without interest or profit, even with reference to established doctrines.

I remain, Gentlemen,

Your obedient Servant,

GEORGE BOOLE.

Lincoln, June 17th, 1851.

# X

## PROPOSED QUESTION IN THE THEORY OF PROBABILITIES *

OF those rigorous consequences of the first principles of the theory of probabilities the general utility of which has caused them to be ranked by Laplace among the great secondary principles of the science, none is more important than the following :—If an event $E$ can only happen as the result of some one of certain conflicting causes $A_1$, $A_2$, ... $A_n$, then if $c_i$ represent the probability of $A_i$, and $p_i$ the probability that if $A_i$ happen $E$ will happen, the total probability of the event $E$ will be represented by the sum $\Sigma c_i p_i$.

I am desirous of calling the attention of mathematicians to a question closely analogous to that of which the answer is conveyed in the above theorem; like it also, admitting of rigorous solution and susceptible of wide application. The question is the following :—If an event $E$ can only happen as a consequence of some one or more of certain causes $A_1$, $A_2$, ... $A_n$, and if generally $c_i$ represent the probability of the cause $A_i$, and $p_i$ the probability that if the cause $A_i$ exist the event $E$ will exist, then the series of values $c_1$, $c_2$, ... $c_n$, $p_1$, $p_2$, ... $p_n$, being given, required the probability of the event $E$.

It is to be noted that in this question the quantity $c_i$ represents the total probability of the existence of the cause $A_i$, not the probability of its exclusive existence; and $p_i$ the total probability of the existence of the event $E$ when $A_i$ is known to exist, not the probability of $E$'s existing as a *consequence* of $A_i$. By the cause $A_i$ is indeed meant the event $A_i$ with which in a proportion $p_i$ of the cases of its occurrence the event $E$ has been associated.

The motives which have led me, after much consideration,

* [*The Cambridge and Dublin Mathematical Journal*, vol. vi, November 1851.]

to adopt with reference to this question a course unusual in the present day, and not upon slight grounds to be revived, are the following. First, I propose the question as a test of the sufficiency of received methods. Secondly, I anticipate that its discussion will in some measure add to our knowledge of an important branch of pure analysis. However, it is upon the former of these grounds alone that I desire to rest my apology.

While hoping that some may be found who, without departing from the line of their previous studies, may deem this question worthy of their attention, I wholly disclaim the notion of its being offered as a trial of personal skill or knowledge, but desire that it may be viewed solely with reference to those public and scientific ends for the sake of which alone it is proposed.

## SOLUTION OF A QUESTION IN THE
## THEORY OF PROBABILITIES *

THE question considered by Mr. Cayley in the *Philosophical Magazine* for October 1853, p. 259, is a particular case of a problem proposed by me in the *Cambridge and Dublin Mathematical Journal* in the month of November 1851. This may justify my offering a few remarks upon the subject.

The problem as considered by Mr. Cayley is thus stated.

Given the probability $\alpha$ that a cause A will act, and the probability $p$ that A acting the effect will happen; also the probability $\beta$ that a cause B will act, and the probability $q$ that B acting the effect will happen; required the total probability of the effect, supposed impossible in the absence of both the causes. The solution given by Mr. Cayley is as follows. Let $\lambda$ be the probability that the cause A acting will act efficaciously, $\mu$ the probability that the cause B acting will act efficaciously. Then

$$p = \lambda + (1 - \lambda)\mu\beta \quad . \quad . \quad . \quad . \quad (1)$$
$$q = \mu + (1 - \mu)\lambda\alpha, \quad . \quad . \quad . \quad (2)$$

which determines $\lambda$, $\mu$, and the total probability $u$ of the effect will be given by

$$u = \lambda\alpha + \mu\beta - \lambda\mu\alpha\beta \quad . \quad . \quad . \quad (3)$$

Mr. Cayley shows that this leads to a correct result when $\alpha = 1$. He further remarks, that the problem presents no difficulty.

I think it to be one of the peculiar difficulties of the theory of probabilities, that its difficulties sometimes are not seen. The solution of a problem may appear to be conducted according to the principles of the theory as usually stated; it may lead to a result susceptible of verification in particular instances; and yet it may be an erroneous solution. The

* [*The Philosophical Magazine*, Series 4, vol. vii, January 1854.]

problem which Mr. Cayley has considered seems to me to afford a good illustration of this remark. Several attempts at its solution have been forwarded to me, all of them by mathematicians of great eminence, all of them admitting of particular verification, yet differing from each other and from the truth. Mr. Cayley's solution is the only published one I have seen, and I feel I must extend to it the same observations. But in doing this, I willingly add that I have two or three times attempted to solve the problem by the same kind of reasoning, and have not approached so near the truth as Mr. Cayley has done. To illustrate these remarks, I will first complete Mr. Cayley's solution, and give one or two apparent verifications, then exhibit the true solution; and lastly, make a few observations upon the general subject.

1st. To complete Mr. Cayley's solution, eliminate $\lambda$ and $\mu$ from (1), (2), and (3) : the result is

$$\frac{[1 - \alpha(1 - p) - u][1 - \beta(1 - q) - u]}{1 - u} = (1 - \alpha)(1 - \beta), (4)$$

a quadratic equation from which $u$ must be determined. Suppose that $p = 1$ and $q = 1$, the above equation gives

$$1 - u = (1 - \alpha)(1 - \beta),$$
$$\therefore \quad u = 1 - (1 - \alpha)(1 - \beta),$$

a result obviously correct. For if either cause necessarily produces the effect, the probability of the effect is equal to the probability that both the causes will not be absent.

Again, suppose that $\alpha$ and $\beta$ are very small, so that their product may be neglected, then the solution gives

$$(1 - u)^2 - [\alpha(1 - p) + \beta(1 - q)](1 - u)$$
$$= (1 - \alpha)(1 - \beta)(1 - u),$$

whence we find

$$u = \alpha p + \beta q.$$

Now this is the known form of the solution when the causes are mutually exclusive, so that they cannot coincide. But the smaller their separate probabilities, the smaller is the probability of their coincidence. And in the limit the two probabilities correspond.

I suppose that few persons, after reading Mr. Cayley's solution and noticing the above verifications, would feel any doubt of its correctness; and yet it is certainly erroneous. Take the particular cases of $p = 1$ and $q = 0$. It is evident that the probability of the effect ought then to be $\alpha$. If the cause A always produced the effect, and the cause B never, the probability of the effect, there being no other causes to which it can be ascribed, will be equal to that of the cause A. The equation (4), however, becomes in clearing of fractions,

$$(1 - u)(1 - \beta - \alpha) = (1 - \alpha)(1 - \beta)(1 - u),$$

whence either $u = 1$, or

$$1 - \beta - u = (1 - \alpha)(1 - \beta),$$

wherefore

$$u = (1 - \beta) - (1 - \alpha)(1 - \beta)$$
$$= \alpha(1 - \beta).$$

But neither of these results is correct.

2nd. I will now exhibit the true solution of the problem. Representing, as before, by $u$ the probability of the effect, the value of that quantity will be determined by the solution of the quadratic equation

$$\frac{[1 - \alpha(1 - p) - u][1 - \beta(1 - q) - u]}{1 - u} = \frac{(u - \alpha p)(u - \beta q)}{\alpha p + \beta q - u} \quad (5)$$

Of this equation that root must be taken which is at the same time not less than each of the two quantities

$$\alpha p \text{ and } \beta q, \quad \cdots \quad \cdots \quad (6)$$

and not greater than any one of the three quantities

$$1 - \alpha(1 - p), 1 - \beta(1 - q), \alpha p + \beta q \quad \cdot \quad (7)$$

Moreover, whenever the data of the problem are real, i.e. represent a possible experience, there will exist one root, and only one root, of the above equation satisfying the conditions described. The conditions of a possible experience are, that each of the three quantities in (7) exceeds each of the two in (6).

The above solution may readily be verified in the case

considered by Mr. Cayley, and in the three cases discussed in this paper.   Of these I will here confine myself to the last.

Clearing the equation of fractions, and making $p = 1$, $q = 0$, we have

$$(1 - u)(1 - \beta - u)(\alpha - u) = (1 - u)(u - \alpha)u.$$

This equation is satisfied by the values

$$u = \alpha \quad u = 1;$$

but the conditions above stated restrict our choice to the first, which we have before seen to be the true one.

3rd. Upon the nature of the errors which are most to be apprehended in the solution of questions in the theory of probabilities, I will only remark that they are not usually mathematical, in the ordinary sense of that term, but arise from the necessity of employing a logic of a peculiarly subtle or highly complex character.   When the data are the probabilities of independent simple events, the method of procedure is sufficiently easy; but if those data relate to events occurring in combinations, or connected by casual relations, the principles which suffice for the former case become either inadequate or inapplicable.   Laplace has to some extent investigated the additional new principles (derivable from the prior definitions and axioms of the new science) of which it is then necessary to take account.   But all these aids carry us but a short way in advance; and of this I am fully assured, that no *general* method for the solution of questions in the theory of probabilities can be established which does not explicitly recognise, not only the special numerical bases of the science, but also those universal laws of thought which are the basis of all reasoning, and which, whatever they may be as to their essence, are at least mathematical as to their form.   Such a method I have exhibited in a treatise now on the eve of publication, and to which I must refer for the investigation of the problem, the solution of which has been exemplified in this paper.

5 Grenville Place, Cork,
    Nov. 30th, 1853.


S

## REPLY TO SOME OBSERVATIONS BY MR.
## WILBRAHAM ON THE THEORY OF CHANCES *

*To the Editors of the Philosophical Magazine and Journal.*

Gentlemen,

Controversy is in every way so disagreeable to me, that it is with the most unfeigned reluctance I feel myself called upon to reply to the observations of Mr. Wilbraham inserted in the last Number of your Journal.

Mr. Wilbraham states that it is his object " to show that Professor Boole does in the greater number of questions relating to chances solvable by his method (or at least in those which are most difficult to treat by other methods), tacitly assume certain conditions expressible by algebraical equations, over and above the conditions expressed by the data of the problem, and to show how these conditions may be algebraically expressed ". And in a subsequent passage he describes the procedure of that part of my work on the Laws of Thought which relates to the theory of probabilities, thus :—" In cases not determinable by the ordinary algebra, his (Professor Boole's) system is this; he takes a general indeterminate problem, applies to it particular assumptions not definitely stated in his book, but which may be shown, as I have done, to be implied in his method, and with these assumptions solves it; that is to say, he solves a particular determinate case of an indeterminate problem, while his book may mislead the reader by making him suppose that it is the general problem which is being treated of." (*Phil. Mag.* vol. vii, pp. 465, 475.) †

I fear that the impression produced upon the mind of any person not acquainted with my work by such statements as the above would be, that I have introduced in a covert

---

* [*The Philosophical Magazine*, Series 4, vol. viii, August 1854.]
† [See pp. 473, 486 of this volume.]

manner assumptions of the existence of which I was ignorant, or of the recognition of which I was afraid. It may be therefore right for me to state that I have, in the chapter containing the demonstration of the general method for the solution of questions in probabilities (*Laws of Thought*, Chap. XVII), explicitly stated the principles upon which that demonstration proceeds, and with equal explicitness deduced from them the algebraical equations upon which the solution depends. In the practical examples which are contained in the subsequent chapters, the rule to which the above-mentioned principles have led is applied without any reserve or addition whatever. To prove that particular assumptions not definitely stated in my book are employed, it ought, I conceive, to have been shown that the principles which I have expressly stated are insufficient for the conclusions which are drawn from them. But though I might, I think, justly complain of the representations which Mr. Wilbraham has made, I very gladly dismiss this part of the question, and desire to consider simply whether Mr. Wilbraham's strictures affect in any way the validity of the method which I have published. Before entering upon this inquiry, I would beg permission to state what is the view which I have been led to take of the theory of probabilities as a science.

It cannot, I think, be doubtful that the theory of probabilities belongs to that class of sciences which are termed pure sciences. Its fundamental idea or conception is that of probability. From this idea, from the definition of the *measure* of probability by which it becomes associated with number, and from the laws of thought with which it is connected through its having to do with events capable of logical expression, flow the axioms and first principles of the science. I would refer in partial illustration of this view, to a remarkable paper by Professor Donkin, published in this Journal (May 1851). He has there announced the following principle, and has shown that it leads at once to (I believe) all the principles before recognized. " If there be any number of mutually exclusive hypotheses, $h_1, h_2, \ldots h_n$, of which the probabilities relative to a particular state of information are $p_1, p_2, \ldots p_n$, and if new information be given which changes the probabilities of some of them, suppose of *h* and all that follow, without having otherwise *any reference to the rest*, then the probabilities of these latter have the same ratio to one another, after the new information, that they had before ; that is,

$$p'_1 : p'_2 \ldots : p'_m = p_1 : p_2 \ldots : p_m,$$

where the accented letters denote the values after the new information has been acquired." I am not at present going to discuss this principle, but I adduce it as an instance of the general position maintained, viz. that the ordinary doctrines and principles of the theory of probabilities do run up into some more general ones, the truth of which, when they are once stated, the mind can hardly refuse to acknowledge, and which seem to be involved in the very nature of expectation and of thought. I go on to observe, that such principles, if truly axiomatic, lead in every pure science, and therefore in the theory of probabilities, to a developed system of truth, or of methods for the attainment of truth, which possess certain *invariable* characteristics never found unimpaired where error has been permitted to enter. These are, mutual consistency, the property of verification wherever verification is possible, continuity, and perhaps some other qualities to which I cannot refer. Now I propose to show, before I have done, that the theory of probabilities does actually admit of this kind of statement, progression and results. At present I merely offer these observations as preliminary to the question which I am called upon now to consider.

Mr. Wilbraham's remarks chiefly apply to two solutions of the following problem respectively published in this Journal by Mr. Cayley and myself. " The probabilities of two events $A_1$, $A_2$ are $c_1$ and $c_2$ respectively. The probability that if $A_1$ present itself another event E will accompany it $p_1$. The event E cannot happen in the absence of $A_1$ and $A_2$, but of the connexion of the latter events nothing is known. Required the probability of E." (See also *Laws of Thought*, p. 321.*) Representing $A_1$, $A_2$, and E by $x$, $y$, $z$ respectively,

* [1916 edition, p. 338.]

the data of this problem are

Prob. $x = c_1$    Prob. $y = c_2$    Prob. $xz = c_1 p_1$
Prob. $yz = c_2 p_2$    Prob. $z(1 - x)(1 - y) = 0$.

Mr. Wilbraham shows that both Mr. Cayley's solution and my own introduce two equations. To this I remark in passing, that there can be no objection so long as the equations in question are consequences of the laws of thought and expectation as applied to the actual data. Respecting the equations involved in my own solution, Mr. Wilbraham remarks :—" The second of these two assumed equations, though perfectly arbitrary, is perhaps not an unreasonable one. . . . I do not, however, see that it is a more reasonable or probable hypothesis than others that might be framed; for instance, than those assumed by Mr. Cayley in his memoir in this Magazine. But the first of these equations appear to me not only arbitrary but eminently anomalous." After this he deduces the equations which represent in a similar manner Mr. Cayley's hypotheses.

I should be reluctant to enter into any comparison of Mr. Cayley's hypothesis and my own if the above remarks did not render it necessary in the interests of truth. It cannot be doubted that Mr. Cayley's solution is erroneous. Granting for a moment that both solutions involve hypotheses, there is this difference between them (a difference passed over in silence by Mr. Wilbraham), that Mr. Cayley's hypotheses lead to results absolutely inconsistent with the data—that my own hypotheses do not. One case easily tested is when we have $p_1 = 1$, and at the same time $p_2 = 0$. Another and more general case is when the constants are so related that we have either

$$c_1 p_1 + c_2 (1 - p_2) = 1,$$

or

$$c_2 p_2 + c_1 (1 - p_1) = 1.$$

I would refer on these points to a paper " On the conditions by which the Solutions of Questions in the Theory of Probabilities are limited ", * which I forward for publication with this letter. On the other hand, there are no cases whatever

* [See pp. 280–288 of this volume.]

in which the problem is solvable by other methods, which do not furnish a verification of the solution I have given. Now I cannot but think that a cautious inquirer after truth, seeing that two hypotheses (still adopting Mr. Wilbraham's language), one of which appears to him "eminently anomalous", conduct to a solution which cannot by any known test be proved erroneous, while two other hypotheses, which appear to him "perhaps not unreasonable" (for this, Mr. Wilbraham's language already quoted implies with reference to Mr. Cayley's hypotheses), conduct to a solution which will not bear the test of examination, would be led to suspect that he had been judging of the reasonableness and of the anomalous character of hypotheses by some false standard. Of course if a solution is erroneous, it need not be argued that there must be error in the hypotheses by which it was obtained. But it is easy to show this directly. If we apply the second of the equations representing Mr. Cayley's hypotheses to the particular case in which $p_1 = 1$, $p_2 = 0$, a case perfectly consistent with the character of the original data, it will be found to lead to the equation $c_1c_2 = 0$, an equation *not* implied by those data in the particular case contemplated. On the other hand, I affirm without hesitation that there is no case in which the equations deduced by Mr. Wilbraham from my method of solution can be proved to be erroneous. They do not, indeed, represent "hypotheses", but they are legitimate deductions from the general principles upon which that method is founded, and it is to those principles directly that attention ought to be directed.

I would request your readers to observe that I do not offer the above remarks as affording any proof that the principles upon which my method is established are true, but only as conclusive that Mr. Wilbraham's objections against them, drawn from what to him appears to be the anomalous character of an equation to which they lead, are of no value whatever. Nor is it difficult to see what is the source of the erroneous judgments, for erroneous I cannot but term them, which Mr. Wilbraham has been led to form. It is in a principle, the influence of which appears to me to tinge the whole course of his speculations, that those events which in the language of the data appear as *simple events*, are the ultimate elements of consideration in the problem. These are the elements in terms of which he expresses his equations, overlooking the fact that it is by mere *convention* that such elements are presented as simple, and that the problem might have been expressed quite otherwise. It cannot be too often repeated that the distinction of simple and compound is wholly relative—that there is not and cannot be any kind of pre-eminence among events founded merely upon the mode of their expression. The neglect of this consideration makes truth to be not merely the creature of language, but the creature of the merest *accidents* of language.

The paper which I forward on the Conditions by which the Solutions of Questions in the Theory of Probabilities are limited, will be followed, should circumstances permit, by two others; one containing a statement of the principles upon which my method is founded, the other an analysis of its results considered especially with reference to the question of the conditions of limitation. It was my design to publish all these researches in a single memoir. I have now determined to send them forth at once, in the hope that when I shall have calmly stated my views, I may with propriety leave the further discussion of them to others.

I am, Gentlemen,

Your most obedient Servant,

Lincoln, July 5th, 1854. George Boole.

# XIII

## ON THE CONDITIONS BY WHICH THE SOLUTIONS OF QUESTIONS IN THE THEORY OF PROBABILITIES ARE LIMITED *

Suppose the following question in the theory of probabilities to be given : " The probability that it rains on a given day is $p$, the probability that it both rains and hails is $q$; required the probability $w$ that it neither rains nor hails ". We know that the data of this problem cannot represent a possible experience unless $p$ is equal to or greater than $q$. The absolute probability of an event " rain ", cannot be less than the probability of the joint occurrence of that event and of another event " hail ". Again, we know that the probability $w$ which we have to seek cannot exceed $1 - p$. The probability that it neither rains nor hails cannot exceed the probability that it does not rain. Hence the data of the problem are limited by the conditions

$$p \gtrless q;$$

and the probability sought, viz. $w$, by the condition

$$w \gtrless 1 - p.$$

If the former condition is not satisfied in the data, the problem is not a *real* one. If the latter is not satisfied in the solution, that solution may at once be pronounced to be incorrect. Conditions of this nature are involved in almost every problem on chances in which the data are not the probabilities of simple independent events. I propose in this paper, to develop an easy and general method of determining such conditions. This object has been attempted in Chapter XIX. of my treatise on the *Laws of Thought*. But the method there developed is somewhat difficult of application, and I am not sure that it is equally general with the one which I am now about to explain. I premise the following proposition.

* [*The Philosophical Magazine*, Series 4, vol. viii, August 1854.]

*Proposition.*—To eliminate any symbol of quantity $x$ from any system of inequations in the expression of which it is involved.

The general method will be best explained by an example. Suppose it required to eliminate $x$ from the inequations

$$x + y - z \gtrless 0$$
$$3y - x - z \gtrless 0$$
$$x - 2y + z \gtrless 0.$$

Reducing each of these inequations to a form in which the first member shall be $x$, we have

$$x \gtrless z - y$$
$$x \lessgtr 3y - z$$
$$x \gtrless 2y - z.$$

From these equations it appears that $x$ has for a superior limit $3y - z$, and for inferior limits $z - y$ and $2y - z$. As the superior limit must in general exceed each of the inferior limits, we have

$$3y - z \gtrless z - y, \ 3y - z \gtrless 2y - z,$$

whence $\qquad 2y \gtrless z \ y \gtrless 0.$

And these are the only conditions which are independent of $x$.

The general rule would therefore be *to seek from the several inequations the superior and inferior limits of* x, *and then to express by new inequations the conditions that each superior limit shall be equal to, or greater than, every inferior limit.*

If it is a condition that $x$ is a positive quantity, then must each superior limit be made $\gtrless 0$; or we might add to the system of inequations the inequation $x \gtrless 0$, and apply the general rule.

When several quantities, as $x$, $y$, &c., are to be eliminated, we can proceed by first eliminating $x$, then from all the inequations which either result or remain eliminating $y$, and so on.

It is obvious that the number of inequations obtained by the elimination of a symbol may greatly exceed that of the inequations from which the elimination has been effected.

*General proposition.*—The probabilities of any events whose logical expression is known being represented by $p$, $q$, $r$.. respectively, required the conditions to which those quantities are subject.

Here it also may be well to commence with a particular case. I will take the problem already discussed in this Journal (Oct. 1853, Jan. 1854 *) by Mr. Cayley and myself. The elements of that problem may be thus expressed, $w$ being the element sought in that discussion.

$$\text{Prob. } x = c_1, \text{ Prob. } y = c_2, \text{ Prob. } xz = c_1 p_1, \text{ Prob. } yz = c_2 p_2,$$
$$\text{Prob. } z = w, \text{ Prob. } z(1 - x)(1 - y) = 0 \quad . \quad (1)$$

Here, according to the notation of the calculus of logic, Prob. $xz$ denotes the probability of the occurrence of the events $x$ and $z$ together. Prob. $z(1 - x)(1 - y)$ denotes the probability of the occurrence of $z$ conjointly with the absence of $x$ and $y$, &c.

The events whose probabilities are given may all be resolved by logical development into disjunctive combinations of events, which do not admit of further resolution with reference to the same elements of distinction $x$, $y$, $z$. Thus

$$xz = xzy + xz(1 - y)$$
$$x = xyz + xy(1 - z) + x(1 - y)z + (1 - x)(1 - y)(1 - z).$$

And hence we have

$$\text{Prob. } xz = \text{Prob. } xyz + \text{Prob. } x(1 - y)z, \quad . \quad (2)$$

and so on. Now assume

$$\text{Prob. } xyz = \lambda, \text{ Prob. } xy(1 - z) = \mu, \text{ Prob. } x(1 - y)z = \nu,$$
$$\text{Prob. } x(1 - y)(1 - z) = \rho, \text{ Prob. } (1 - x)yz = \sigma$$
$$\text{Prob. } (1 - x)y(1 - z) = \tau, \text{ Prob. } (1 - x)(1 - y)(1 - z) = v.$$

These represent all the possible combinations of $x$, $y$ and $z$, except $z(1 - x)(1 - y)$, which by the data is excluded.

The equation (2) gives, by virtue of (1),

$$\lambda + \nu = c_1 p_1;$$

* [See above, p. 270.]

and forming all similar equations furnished by the data, we have

$$\left.\begin{array}{l} \lambda + \mu + \nu + \rho = c_1 \\ \lambda + \mu + \sigma + \tau = c_2 \\ \lambda + \nu \qquad\quad = c_1 p_1 \\ \lambda + \sigma \qquad\quad = c_2 p_2 \\ \lambda + \nu + \sigma \quad = w \end{array}\right\} \qquad \cdots \quad (3)$$

to which we may add the necessary condition

$$\lambda + \mu + \rho + \sigma + \tau + \upsilon = 1 \qquad \cdots \quad (4)$$

Now the quantities $\lambda$, $\mu$, $\nu$, &c. are individually $\lessgtr 0$. Moreover, they are subject to no other relations than the above. Our object then, is to seek the relations among $w$, $c_1$, $c_2$, $c_1 p_1$, $c_2 p_2$, which are necessary in order that the above conditions may be satisfied.

For this purpose we must, and the rule is of general application, determine as many of the quantities $\lambda$, $\mu$, $\nu$, &c. as we can in terms of $w$, $c_1$, $c_2$, &c., and make their expressions $\lessgtr 0$. These will furnish a part of the conditions sought. We must substitute the above expressions in the equations of the system (3) (4) which remain, and, supposing those residual equations to be $n$ in number, find from them the expressions of $n$ more of the quantities $\lambda$, $\mu$, $\nu$ in terms of the quantities which remain, and of the known quantities $w$, $c_1$, $c_2$, &c. We must make these expressions also $\lessgtr 0$, and from the inequations thus formed, eliminate by the previous proposition such of the positive quantities $\lambda$, $\mu$, $\nu$ as are still left. This will furnish the remaining conditions among the constants $w$, $c_1$, $c_2$, &c. In the steps of this process we shall have successively introduced all the conditions $\lambda \lessgtr 0$, $\mu \lessgtr 0 \ldots \upsilon \lessgtr 0$, and shall therefore have obtained all the equations connecting the elements $w$, $c_1$, $c_2$, $c_1 p_1$ and $c_2 p_2$.

Thus, from the third, fourth, and fifth equations of (3), we find

$$\sigma = w - c_1 p_1, \quad \nu = w - c_2 p_2, \quad \lambda = c_1 p_1 + c_2 p_2 - w,$$

furnishing the conditions

$$w - c_1 p_1 \lessgtr 0, \quad w - c_2 p_2 \lessgtr 0, \quad c_1 p_1 - c_2 p_2 - w \lessgtr 0 \quad (5)$$

Substituting the values of $\sigma$, $\nu$, and $\lambda$ in the remaining equations of (3) and (4), we find on transposition,

$$\mu + \rho = c_1(1 - p_1)$$
$$\mu + \tau = c_2(1 - p_2)$$
$$\mu + \rho + \tau + \upsilon = 1 - w.$$

Hence, selecting $\rho$, $\tau$, and $\upsilon$ as the quantities to be determined, we have

$$\rho = c_1(1 - p_1) - \mu$$
$$\tau = c_2(1 - p_2) - \mu$$
$$\upsilon = 1 - w - c_1(1 - p_1) - c_2(1 - p_2) + \mu;$$

whence, therefore,

$$c_1(1 - p_1) - \mu \gtreqless 0, \; c_2(1 - p_2) - \mu \gtreqless 0$$
$$1 - w - c_1(1 - p_1) - c_2(1 - p_2) + \mu \gtreqless 0.$$

Or, in order to eliminate $\mu$,

$$\mu \lesseqgtr c_1(1 - p_1), \; \mu \lesseqgtr c_2(1 - p_2)$$
$$\mu \gtreqless c_1(1 - p_1) + c_2(1 - p_2) - 1 + w.$$

And hence

$$c_1(1 - p_1) \gtreqless c_1(1 - p_1) + c_2(1 - p_2) - 1 + w$$
$$c_2(1 - p_2) \gtreqless c_1(1 - p_1) + c_2(1 - p_2) - 1 + w;$$

or

$$\left. \begin{array}{c} w \lesseqgtr 1 - c_2(1 - p_2) \\ w \lesseqgtr 1 - c_1(1 - p_1) \end{array} \right\} \quad . \quad . \quad . \quad (6)$$

From the conditions (5) and (6), we see that $w$ has for its lower limits, the expressions

$$c_1 p_1 \text{ and } c_2 p_2 \quad . \quad . \quad . \quad . \quad (7)$$

and for its upper limits, the expressions

$$c_1 p_1 + c_2 p_2, \; 1 - c_1(1 - p_1) \text{ and } 1 - c_2(1 - p_2) \quad (8)$$

These are the conditions assigned in my treatise on the *Laws of Thought*, p. 325. They show, that if it is our object to determine Prob. $z$ or $w$, the solution, to be a correct one, must lead us to a value of that quantity which shall exceed each of the values assigned in (7), and fall short of each of those assigned in (8). They show also that the data of the problem will only represent a possible experience when each of the values in (7) shall fall short of, or not exceed each of those in (8).

There is a class of problems characterized by the circumstance that the quantities $\lambda, \mu, \nu$.. are fewer in number than the equations in which they enter, which, treated by this method, lead to equations as well as inequations connecting the data with each other and with the probability sought. Whenever, too, the probability sought can be expressed as a linear function of the probabilities which are given, its actual expression will be determined by the above method, and it will agree with the result which would be assigned by the general method in probabilities (*Laws of Thought*, Chap. XVII.).   To exemplify this, let us take the following problem (Ibid. p. 279).

Given Prob. $x = p$, Prob. $y = q$, Prob. $[x(1 - y) + y(1 - x)] = r$, to find the limits of Prob. $xy$ or $w$.

Assume

Prob. $xy = \lambda$, Prob. $x(1 - y) = \mu$, Prob. $(1 - x)y = \nu$,
Prob. $(1 - x)(1 - y) = \rho$.

Then we have as the conditions furnished by the data,

$$\left. \begin{array}{r} \lambda + \mu = p \\ \lambda + \nu = q \\ \mu + \nu = r \\ \lambda = w \\ \lambda + \mu + \nu + \rho = 1 \end{array} \right\} \quad . \quad . \quad . \quad (9)$$

From the three first equations and the last we find

$$\lambda = \frac{p + q - r}{2}, \mu = \frac{p + r - q}{2}, \nu = \frac{q + r - p}{2},$$

$$\rho = \frac{2 - p - q - r}{2},$$

furnishing the conditions

$$p + q \gtrless r, p + r \gtrless q, q + r \gtrless p, p + q + r \lessgtr 2.$$

There still remains the fourth equation of the system (9), in the first member of which, substituting for $\lambda$ its value, we find

$$w = \frac{p + q - r}{2},$$

the value of Prob. $xy$ sought (*Laws of Thought*, p. 280).

There is a peculiarity in these " determinate " solutions to which I desire to advert. It is, that if in any series of observations, the events referred to in the data occur with a frequency exactly proportional to their assigned probability, the event whose probability is sought will occur in the same series with a frequency exactly proportionate to its determined probability. For instance, in the problem just solved, if in $n$ observations the events $x$, $y$ and $x(1-y)+y(1-x)$ occur exactly $np$, $nq$, and $nr$ times respectively, the event $xy$ will in the course of the same observations occur exactly $n\dfrac{p+q-r}{2}$ times. This is easily shown by substituting throughout the demonstration contained in Prop. 2, $Nx$ for Prob. $x$, $Ny$ for Prob. $y$, N applied to the expression of any class denoting the number of individuals contained in that class; and generally substituting *numbers* for *probabilities*. This change will not affect the truth of the equations. For instance, if we have

$$Nx = a \quad Nxy = b,$$

we shall have

$$Nx - Nxy = a - b,$$

or

$$Nx(1-y) = a - b,$$

and so on. I remark that this is a *peculiarity* of the above determinate solutions. If the probabilities of two independent events $x$ and $y$ are $p$ and $q$ respectively, the probability of their concurrence is $pq$; but we are not permitted to affirm that if in $n$ observations $x$ occurs $np$ times, and $y$ occurs $nq$ times, their concurrence will be observed exactly $npq$ times.

When by the method of this chapter we have found the conditions of limitation of the solution of a question in the theory of probabilities, we can at once ascertain from those conditions in what cases the problem becomes *determinate* in the sense above explained. Thus in the particular problem discussed in Proposition 2, since we have

$$w \gtrless c_1 p_1 + c_2 p_2, \quad w \gtrless 1 - c_1(1-p_1), \left.\begin{matrix}\\\\\end{matrix}\right\} \quad . \quad (10)$$
$$w \gtrless 1 - c_2(1\ p_2), \quad w \lessgtr c_1 p_1, \quad w \lessgtr c_2 p_2 \left.\begin{matrix}\\\\\end{matrix}\right.$$

it follows that whenever one of the upper limits of $w$ becomes equal to one of the lower, the other conditions remaining satisfied, the problem becomes determinate. Thus, if we have $p_2 = 0$, we find from the above,

$$w \lessgtr c_1 p_1, \ w \lessgtr 1 - c_1(1 - p_1), \ w \lessgtr 1 - c_2, \ w \gtrless c_1 p_1.$$

Now as $w$ cannot at the same time be both greater and less than $c_1 p_1$, it must be equal to $c_1 p_1$; the other conditions simply reducing to $1 - c_2 \gtrless c_1 p_1$. The solution, therefore, is

$$w = c_1 p_1,$$

the data being necessarily connected by the condition

$$1 - c_2 \gtrless c_1 p_1.$$

Let us apply to this case the solutions of the general question in probabilities respectively given by Mr. Cayley and myself. Mr. Cayley's solution is expressed by the quadratic equation

$$[1 - c_1(1 - p_1) - w][1 - c_2(1 - p_2) - w]$$
$$= (1 - c_1)(1 - c_2)(1 - w) . \quad . \quad (11)$$

If we make $p_2 = 0$, it becomes

$$[1 - c_1(1 - p_1) - w](1 - c_2 - w) = (1 - c_1)(1 - c_2)(1 - w),$$

and this equation is *not* satisfied when we make $w = c_1 p_1$. The solution which I have given is contained in the quadratic equation

$$(w - c_1 p_1)(w - c_2 p_2)(1 - w) = [1 - c_1(1 - p_1) - w]$$
$$[1 - c_2(1 - p_2) - w](c_1 p_1 + c_2 p_2 - w) \quad . \quad (12)$$

and this equation, on making $p_2 = 0$, is satisfied by the value $w = c_1 p_1$. The reader may examine for himself, and with exactly similar results, the class of cases in which the data happen to be connected by the relation

$$c_1 p_1 + c_2(1 - p_2) = 1,$$

or by the relation

$$c_2 p_2 + c_1(1 - p_1) = 1.$$

But there is another and more remarkable distinction to which I would advert. I have shown (*Laws of Thought*, p. 324) that in all cases in which the data of the above general problem are possible, the quadratic equation (12) furnishes one root, and only one, falling within the limits assigned by the method of this chapter. It is needless to remark that Mr. Cayley's equation does not possess this characteristic. It may readily be shown that that equation will always furnish a single root satisfying the two conditions

$$w \lesssim 1 - c_1(1 - p_1),\ w \lesssim 1 - c_2(1 - p_2)\ ;$$

but that the remaining three conditions assigned in (10) will not be satisfied by it unless certain other conditions, distinct from the conditions of possible experience, obtain.

And this leads me to notice, in the last place, a remarkable distinction, *à posteriori*, between unwarranted hypotheses in the solution of questions in the theory of probabilities, and axiomatic principles flowing out of the very idea and definition of probability, or sanctioned by the laws of thought. It is that the latter never impose, either upon the data or upon the solution, any limitations but those under which alone experience is possible, while the former do in general (always, I think, when the equation of a solution rises above the first degree) impose such limitations.

But these considerations only conduct us again to that general view of the theory of probabilities which is contained in my reply to the strictures of Mr. Wilbraham. They confirm, so far as they go, the doctrine already advanced, that its claim to rank among the pure sciences must rest upon the degree in which it satisfies the following conditions :—

1st. That the principles upon which its methods are founded should be of an axiomatic nature.

2nd. That they should lead to results capable of exact verification, wherever verification is possible.

3rd. That they should be capable of a systematic development consistent in all its parts and processes, and neither acknowledging nor imposing any limitations but those which exist in the nature of things.

Lincoln, July 6th, 1854.

# FURTHER OBSERVATIONS RELATING TO THE THEORY OF PROBABILITIES IN REPLY TO MR. WILBRAHAM*

SEVERE domestic affliction prevents me from forwarding this month the papers mentioned in the conclusion of my letter just published in the *Philosophical Magazine*. That letter, and the paper by which it was accompanied, have, I trust, in some degree prepared the way for the more fundamental questions to which I hope shortly to be able to proceed. A careful inquiry into the conditions which a true method must satisfy, may greatly narrow the field of discussion, by entitling us to set aside methods which do not satisfy those conditions, and enabling us to estimate at their just value objections drawn from any assumed advantage of such methods, or, in fact, from assumptions of any kind the information of which such conditions have been neglected.

And I conceive that it may thus narrow the field of inquiry in the present instance, if, having already examined Mr. Wilbraham's comparison of the solutions of a certain problem given by Mr. Cayley and myself, I should offer a few remarks, and suggest a question with reference to the method proposed by Mr. Wilbraham himself in the conclusion of his letter (*Phil. Mag.* vol. vii, p. 476). Mr. Wilbraham's observations are as follows :—" If, being in ignorance what system of assumptions ought to be made to render the problem determinate, we were to wish to give a definite answer to the problem, it might be in the following form : ascertain the chance of the required event happening on any one system of assumptions, and the chance of that system representing the true connexion among the simple events, and multiply the values of these chances together; the sum of a series of these products comprising every possible system of assumptions would be the true chance of the event. But

* [*The Philosophical Magazine*, Series 4, vol. viii, September 1854.]

Prof. Boole's method evidently does not attempt to solve any question of this nature." Now I make no objection against the truth of the principle here enunciated, though I may doubt its efficiency. It is a principle well known to all who are acquainted with the elementary treatises on the theory of probabilities. Moreover, I think that the principle is *not* opposed to the method which I have employed, because I have never seen any other method which leads to "assumptions" (adopting Mr. Wilbraham's language) accordant with those conditions which, as we have seen, *must* be satisfied. Leaving such considerations, however, I trust that the following proposal will not be deemed an unreasonable one.

If Mr. Wilbraham's method is both *correct* and *sufficient*, while mine is *false*, there must surely be some case in which the two would lead to different results, and in which, from the comparison of those results, my own may be proved to be erroneous. I would therefore request Mr. Wilbraham to endeavour to furnish an instance of this kind. Of course I refer only to problems of the kind discussed in my work, viz., those in which the data are the probabilities of events, simple or compound, with or without information respecting the connexion of such events. Should any method, even of limited application, be discovered which should lead to solutions satisfying the conditions to which I have referred, and yet different from those furnished by my own method, which is *not* of limited application, and which *always* causes those conditions to be satisfied, I should regard it as a very interesting and remarkable circumstance. But at present I am, as I have said, wholly ignorant of the existence of any such method.

I trust to be able in another month to forward a demonstration of the general method in probabilities exemplified in the *Laws of Thought*; and I am anxious to do this, because the demonstration may, I think, be presented in a more simple and satisfactory form than it there possesses and because an important addition, (not correction) justified by recent researches, may be made to the rule there given.

Lincoln, August 5th, 1854.

# XV

## ON A GENERAL METHOD IN THE THEORY OF PROBABILITIES *

### *Preliminary Statement of Principles*

1. The class of question which I propose to consider here is that of which the data consist of—

1st. Probabilities of events, or of combinations of events, capable of being expressed by the signs of ordinary language;

2nd. Absolute connexions or conditions among events capable of similar expression;

and of which the quæsitum or element sought is also the probability of some event or combination of events whose expression is known. Thus the elements of the question considered in my paper (On the Conditions by which the Solutions of Questions in the Theory of Probabilities are limited, *Philosophical Magazine*, vol. viii. p. 91), are,

### *Data*

Probabilities, Prob. $x = c_1$, Prob. $y = c_2$,
$$\left. \begin{array}{l} \text{Prob. } x = c_1, \text{ Prob. } y = c_2, \\ \text{Prob. } xz = c_1 p_1, \text{ Prob. } yz = c_2 p_2 \end{array} \right\} \quad . \quad (1)$$

Absolute connexion,
$$z(1 - x)(1 - y) = 0 \quad . \quad . \quad . \quad . \quad (2)$$

### *Quæsitum*

### Prob. $z$

Here, beside the probabilities of the several events whose logical expressions are $x$, $y$, $xz$, and $yz$, we have given the absolute connexion $z(1 - x)(1 - y) = 0$, denoting (in the language of the calculus of Logic) that the event $z$ cannot happen in the absence of the events $x$ and $y$. The quæsitum is the probability of the event whose expression is $z$. I design to investigate a general method of solving problems of this kind. Such a method, viewed through the range

* [*The Philosophical Magazine*, Series 4, vol. viii, December 1854.]

of its consequences, is entitled to be regarded as a general method in probabilities, because all solvable questions may be referred either directly, or through some intermediate principle, to the above class. And the hope which moves me to repeat here without substantial change the demonstration of such a method contained in my treatise on the Laws of Thought, is that of being able to set forth with greater fulness the distinctive principles upon which the demonstration depends, and of annexing to the final statement of the rule to which it leads, an important addition.

2. Probability I conceive to be not so much expectation, as a rational ground of expectation, and its numerical measure I define with mathematicians generally * as follows.

*Definition.* If, respecting any event, the mind is only able to form a number $n$ of similar and mutually exclusive hypotheses, to none of which it is entitled to give any preference over any other, and if $m$ of those hypotheses are favourable to the event, i.e. such that any one of them being realised, the event will happen, while the remaining hypotheses are unfavourable to it, i.e. favourable in the above sense to its *not* happening, the probability of the event is measured by the fraction $\frac{m}{n}$.

It does not, I think, need proof that the principles of the theory of probabilities must be derived either—1st, from the nature of probability as set forth in its measure; or 2ndly, from its connexion with logic and language. Commencing with the former source, I remark that it is implied in the definition that probability is always relative to our actual state of information and varies with that state of information. Laplace illustrates this principle by supposing the following case. Let there be three urns, A, B, C, of which we are only informed that one contains black and the two others white

---

* To quote, for example, Laplace's definition, " La théorie des hasards consiste à réduire tous les évènements du même genre a un certain nombre de cas également possibles, c'est à dire, tels que nous soyons également indécis sur leur existence ; et à déterminer le nombre de cas favorables à l'évènement dont on cherche la probabilité. Le rapport de ce nombre à celui de tous les cas possibles est la mesure de cette probabilité, &c."— *Essai philosophique sur les Probabilités*, p. 7. Subsequently, Laplace speaks of the different " cases " as " hypotheses ", which, indeed they are.

balls; then, a ball being drawn from C, required the probability that the ball is black. As we are ignorant which of the urns contains black balls, so that we have no reason to suppose it to be the urn C rather than the urn A or the urn B, these three hypotheses will appear equally worthy of credit; but as the first of the three hypotheses alone is favourable to the drawing of a black ball from C, the probability of that event is $\frac{1}{3}$. Suppose, now, that in addition to the previous data it is known that the urn A contains only white balls, then our state of indecision has reference only to the urns B and C, and the probability that a ball drawn from C will be black is $\frac{1}{2}$. Lastly, if we are assured that both A and B contain white balls only, the probability that a black ball will issue from C rises into certitude. (*Essai Philosophique sur les Probabilités*, p. 9.) Here it is seen that our estimate of the probability of an event varies with our *knowledge* of the circumstances by which it is affected. In this sense it is that probability may be said to be relative to our actual state of information.

Let us, in further illustration of this principle, consider the following problem. The probability of an event $x$ is measured by the fraction $\frac{a}{m}$, that of an event $y$ by the fraction $\frac{b}{n}$, but of the connexion of the events $x$ and $y$ absolutely nothing is known. Required the probability of the event $xy$, *i.e.* of the conjunction of the events $x$ and $y$.

There are (see definition) $a$ cases in which $x$ happens, to $m$ cases in which it happens or fails; and concerning these cases the mind is in a state of perfect indecision. To no one of them is it entitled to give any preference over any other. There are, in like manner, $b$ cases in which $y$ happens, to $n$ cases in which it happens or fails; and these cases are in the same sense equally balanced. Now the event $xy$ can only happen through the combination of some one of the $a$ cases in which $x$ happens, with some one of the $b$ cases in which $y$ happens, while nothing prevents us from supposing any one of the $m$ cases in which $x$ happens or fails from combining with any one of the $n$ cases in which $y$ happens or fails. There are thus *ab* cases in which the event *xy* happens, to *mn* cases which are either favourable or unfavourable to its occurrence. Nor have we any reason to assign a preference to any one of those cases over any other.

Wherefore the probability of the event *xy* is $\frac{ab}{mn}$. Or if we represent the probability of the event *x* by *p*, that of the event *y* by *q*, the probability of the combination *xy* is *pq*.

It cannot be disputed that the above is a rigorous consequence of the definition adopted. That new information might alter the value of Prob. *xy* is only in accordance with the principle (already exemplified from Laplace) of the *relative* character of probability. It is only so far forth as they are *known*, that the connexions, casual or otherwise, of events can affect expectation. Let it be added, that the particular result to which we have been led is perfectly consistent with the well-known theorem, that if *x* and *y* are known to be *independent* events, the probability of the event *xy* is *pq*. The difference between the two cases consists not in the numerical value of Prob. *xy*, but in this, that if we are sure that the events *x* and *y* are independent, then are we sure that there exists between them no hidden connexion, the knowledge of which would affect the value of Prob. *xy*; whereas if we are not sure of their independence, we are sensible that such connexions may exist. Again, it is perfectly consistent with the known theorem, that if the probability of *x* is *p*, and the probability that if *x* happen *y* will happen is *q*, then the probability of the combination *xy* is *pq*. For if we know nothing of the connexion of *x* and *y*, the occurrence of *x* will not affect our expectation of the occurrence of *y*, so that the probability that if *x* happen *y* will happen will, in the actual state of our information, be the same as the simple probability of *y*, i.e. as *q*.

4. As from the simple data Prob. $x = p$, Prob. $y = q$ we deduce Prob. $xy = pq$, so from the same data we should have Prob. $x(1 - y) = p(1 - q)$, Prob. $(1 - x)(1 - y) = (1 - p)(1 - q)$ &c. And generally, it may be shewn that if the probabilities of any events *x*, *y*, *z* are simply given, the probability of any combination of them expressed by

F $(x, y, z . .)$ will be found by substituting in that expression for $x, y, z . .$ their given probabilities.

The general principle involved in the above deductions may be thus stated.

*Principle I.*—Probability is always relative to our actual state of information. Upon the actual connexions of events it depends no further than as such connexions are known to us.

This doctrine of the nature of probability, it may be added, has been fully recognized by acute and thoughtful minds approaching the subject from a point of view different from the mathematical one.*

I proceed to the statement of an important principle founded on the nature of language as an instrument of expression. It is, that in the theory of probabilities, as in every other branch of science, the solution of a question ought to depend upon the *information* conveyed in the data, and not upon the special elements or constructions of the language which may serve as the vehicle of that information. Now one very important point in which languages are observed to differ, is the selection of the objects or events to which simple terms are appropriated. In the rude infancy of nations, the number of such terms is small, and their application is confined within the limits of daily experience. With the progress of society, the need of a wider vocabulary is felt, not merely for the expression of things unknown to former experience, but also for the purpose of abbreviation. Simple terms are invented, not solely for the representation of things wholly new, but for the more simple expression of things which it was before possible to express by a combination of terms. Whensoever in this gradual advance of language the combination of two simple terms is replaced by a new simple term, a definition or an equivalent series of ordinary propositions is introduced. Thus, if every combination of rain with snow becomes represented, for abbreviation, by the simple term " sleet ", we virtually

---

* For instance, it is stated with great clearness in an extract from the commonplace book of Bishop Copleston, recently published by Archbishop Whately.

carry with us, whenever we use that term, the definition
" Sleet is rain with snow ", or the equivalent train of propositions, " If there is sleet, there is rain with snow ",
" If there is rain with snow, there is sleet " ; and that definition, or its equivalent propositions, we must, if need be,
*express* as well as assume.   Now it is manifest that there is
no limit to this invention of simple terms, and consequent
implication of propositions.   In a language possessed of an
infinite copiousness of diction, every object of experience,
every combination of events, might thus be expressed by a
simple term.   Supposing that we had such a language at
command, it is evident that we might in various ways
express the data and the object of a question in the theory
of probabilities.   The events whose probabilities are given
might, according to one mode of expression, appear as
compound events expressed by combinations of simple
events; according to another mode, as simple events
connected together by *definitions* or by implied *propositions*.
Now the principle which I wish to assert is, that it is wholly
indifferent which mode of expression we employ, provided
that it be adequate to convey all the information we possess.
Perhaps that principle may be more definitely stated as
follows.

*Principle II.*—Any events which suffice simply, or by
combination, for the expression of the data may be assumed
as simple events and symbolized accordingly, provided that
we explicitly determine the whole of the relations which
implicitly connect them.   To make plain my meaning, let
it be supposed that observation has furnished the following
elements of a problem :—

Probability of rain $= p$,
Probability of rain with snow $= q$ ;

the quæsitum of that problem being

Probability of rain without snow.

The expression of this problem by an observer in whose
language there should exist no word for " snow ", but in

which every combination of rain with snow should be termed
" sleet ", would be as follows :—

  1st. Probability of rain $= p$,
  2nd. Probability of sleet $= q$, $\Big\}$ Data.
  3rd. Sleet always implies rain

Required probability of rain without sleet.

It is then affirmed that these two statements are equivalent.  The expectation of a phænomenon cannot be affected
by the mere mode of statement of it, and of the circumstances
upon which it depends.  As respects the two modes of
statement in the above instance, it will be seen that in the
former of them, one of the given probabilities is that of a
compound event; in the latter, both the given probabilities
are those of simple events between which an absolute
relation (3rd) is affirmed to exist and in terms of which the
event whose probability is sought is directly expressed.

Now, beside that it is the most obvious course of procedure
to determine *directly* the event whose probability is sought
in terms of those whose probabilities are given, an object
which we can always effect by the Calculus of Logic, there
is a special reason why we should take this course.  Consider
the problem employed for the purpose of illustration in the
first section of this paper.  Representing the events $xz$ and
$yz$, since their probabilities are *given*, by $s$ and $t$ respectively,
its data become

$$\text{Prob. } x = c_1, \text{ Prob. } y = c_2, \text{ Prob. } s = c_1 p_1,$$
$$\text{Prob. } t = c_2 p_2 \quad . \quad (3)$$

the elements $x$, $y$, $s$ and $t$, here assumed (Principle II.) as
simple events, being connected by the relation

$$xyst + x(1-y)s(1-t) + (1-x)y(1-s)t$$
$$+ xy(1-s)(1-t) + x(1-y)(1-s)(1-t)$$
$$+ (1-x)y(1-s)(1-t)$$
$$+ (1-x)(1-y)(1-s)(1-t) = 1 \quad . \quad . \quad . \quad (4)$$

and the event whose probability $w$ is *sought* being under the
same conditions

$$xyst + x(1-y)s(1-t) + (1-x)y(1-s)t \quad . \quad (5)$$

These results (4) and (5) are both given by the development (*Laws of Thought*, p. 322). The probabilities (3), together with the relation (4), are equivalent to the data of the problem as expressed in terms of $x$, $y$, and $z$ in the section referred to. Now I remark that the mere probabilities (3) do not of themselves furnish any relations connecting $x$, $y$, $s$, and $t$. The whole of the relation connecting those elements is given by (4), and it is given in the form of a logical equation, i.e. of an equation interpretable into a *proposition*. We possess of that relation an *explicit* and *available* knowledge. But it is not so with the relation connecting the elements $x$, $y$, $z$, when, as in the primary statement of the problem, these are assumed as simple events. We are explicitly informed that these elements are connected by the relation $z(1 - x)(1 - y) = 0$; but beside this, they are connected with each other in a complex manner through the data

Prob. $x = c_1$, Prob. $y = c_2$, Prob. $xz = c_1p_1$, Prob. $yz = c_2p_2$.

These data exhibit both $x$ and $y$ as connected with $z$, and thereby also connected with each other. But that connexion is not of a kind which can be exhibited in an explicit form by means of propositions. And our consequent inability to express by any distinct and intelligible formula the implied relations among the elements $x$, $y$, $z$, renders it difficult to judge of the " reasonableness ", or of the " anomalous " character of results in the expression of which these elements are employed.*

---

\* I need scarcely remark, that the statement of the problem furnished by (3), (4) and (5) will lead and by the same method, to the conditions connecting $c_1$, $c_2$, $c_1p_1$, $c_2p_2$, and $w$, investigated in my former paper (vol. viii. p. 91). If we assume

Prob. $xyst = \lambda$          Prob. $x(1 - y)s(1 - t) = \mu$
Prob. $(1 - x)y(1 - s)t = \nu$      Prob. $xy(1 - s)(1 - t) = \rho$
Prob. $x(1 - y)(1 - s)(1 - t) = \sigma$    Prob. $(1 - x)y(1 - s)(1 - t) = \tau$
Prob. $(1 - x)(1 - y)(1 - s)(1 - t) = \upsilon$

we shall have the following equations :

$$\lambda + \mu + \rho + \sigma = c_1$$
$$\lambda + \nu + \rho + \tau = c_2$$
$$\lambda + \mu = c_1p_1$$
$$\lambda + \nu = c_2p_2$$
$$\lambda + \mu + \nu = w$$
$$\lambda + \mu + \nu + \rho + \sigma + \tau + \upsilon = 1.$$

whence the conditions in question may be deduced.

The above, together with the general principles of symbolical algebra, suffice for the ground of the following demonstration, which differs from that contained in the *Laws of Thought* only in applying throughout the familiar illustration of the urn.

## Demonstration

Let those events, which in the actual language of the problem appear as simple events, be represented by the logical symbols $x$, $y$, $z$.. Any event whose probability is given or sought may then be represented upon the principles of the calculus of Logic by a *function* of those symbols. Thus the event which consists in the concurrence of $x$ and $y$ jointly with the absence of $z$ will be represented by $xy(1 - z)$; and the event which consists in the happening of some one alone of the events $x$, $y$, $z$, will be represented by the function

$$x(1 - y)(1 - z) + y(1 - x)(1 - z) + z(1 - x)(1 - y);$$

of which function, it is to be observed, that the several terms connected by the sign $+$ are called constituents. If we express generally functions of the above description by the ordinary functional symbols $\phi$, $\psi$, $\theta$, F, &c., we may thus express the problem which we have to consider in the following manner.

Probabilities given :—

$$\text{Prob. } \phi(x, y, z) = p, \text{ Prob. } \psi(x, y, z) = q, \text{ \&c. } . \quad (1)$$

Annexed absolute conditions :—

$$\theta(x, y, z..) = 0, \text{ \&c. } . \quad . \quad . \quad . \quad (2)$$

Quæsitum, or probability sought :—

$$\text{Prob. F } (x, y, z..) \quad . \quad . \quad . \quad . \quad (3)$$

Now the most obvious mode of procedure is to seek to express the event whose probability is sought, explicitly in terms of the events whose probabilities are given. To do this, we must, in accordance with Principle II., regard all these as simple events, expressing them by new logical symbols $w$, $s$, $t$, &c. Let then

$$\phi(x, y, z..) = s, \psi(x, y, z..) = t, \text{F}(x, y, z..) = w \quad . \quad (4)$$

From the logical equations (2) and (4) we can now determine $w$ in terms of $s$, $t$, &c. The solution will be of the form

$$w = A + 0B + \frac{0}{0}C + \frac{1}{0}D \quad . \quad . \quad . \quad (5)$$

Here, A, B, C, D, are functions of $s$, $t$, &c., and the several terms of the development are, by means of their coefficients, thus interpretable.

1st. A represents those combinations of the events $s$, $t$, &c. which must happen if $w$ happen.

2nd. B those combinations which cannot happen if $w$ happen, but may otherwise happen.

3rd. C those combinations which may or may not happen if $w$ happen.

4th. D those combinations which cannot happen at all.

And the above representing all possible combinations, we have

$$A + B + C + D = 1 \quad . \quad . \quad . \quad (6)$$

Now there are many problems in which the combination denoted by C does not present itself. Such is the one considered by Mr. Cayley and myself, and commented on by Mr. Wilbraham. As the principle of solution is the same in this as in the more general class of problems in which C does appear, I shall, for simplicity, confine myself to the simpler case. The event $w$, then, consists solely of that combination of the simple events $s$, $t$, &c. which is denoted by A, and the sole condition to which those events are subject is

$$D = 0, \text{ or } A + B = 1 \quad . \quad . \quad . \quad (7)$$

these logical equations being, by virtue of the *necessary* equation (6), strictly equivalent when C does not make its appearance in the development.

The problem may now be briefly stated as follows. The events $s$, $t$, &c. are subject to the condition (7), and at the same time their respective probabilities are

$$\text{Prob. } s = p, \text{ Prob. } t = q, \text{ &c.}$$

Required the value of Prob. A.

Now let us consider whether upon the familiar notion of an urn containing balls, we can construct a problem whose expressed data shall be in all respects the same as the above, and which shall, at the same time, admit of definite solution.

And, in the first place, it is manifest that any event or combination of events, may be represented by the issuing of a ball possessing a particular quality, or combination of qualities from an urn. Thus the event $s$ may be represented by the issuing of a ball possessing a particular quality which we will term the $s$-quality, the event $t$ by that of a ball possessing the $t$-quality, and so on. In like manner, the event $st$, or the combination of the events $s$ and $t$, may be represented by the issuing of a ball possessing at once the qualities $s$ and $t$. And generally, the events A, B, D, whatever combinations of the symbols $s$, $t$.. these letters may stand for, may be represented by the issuing of balls possessing the corresponding qualities or combinations of qualities.

And as every species of events can thus be represented by the issuing of a ball of a particular species from an urn, so every problem relating to events may be represented by a corresponding problem relating to the issuing of balls from an urn. If, in such imagined problem, any events $s$, $t$, &c. so enter as that nothing is known or can be inferred respecting their connexion, they must be treated (Principle I.) as if they were *independent*, and therefore the balls by whose issue they are represented must be regarded as free from any *nexus* affecting their issue. On the other hand, if the events $s$, $t$, &c. are subject to any condition as D = 0, such condition must be introduced by the supposition of a *nexus* simply forbidding the issue of balls of the species D, without affecting the freedom of the other balls. Such a *nexus* we may suppose to be established by the attachment of every ball of the species D by a thread to the walls of the urn. All possible issues are thus restricted to balls of the species A or B, so that the condition D = 0 is equivalent, as we have before seen, to the condition A + B = 1.

The general problem may therefore be represented as follows :—

An urn contains balls whose species are expressed by means of the qualities $s$, $t$, &c. and their opposites, concerning the connexion of which qualities nothing is known. Suddenly all balls of the species D are attached by threads to the walls of the urn, and this being done, there is a probability $p$ that any ball drawn is of the species $s$, a probability $q$ that it is of the species $t$, and so on.    What is the probability that it is of the species A, supposing that A and D denote mutually exclusive species of balls, each defined by means of the properties $s$, $t$, and their opposites?

Let us, for simplicity, represent A $+$ B by V, and let us represent by $V_s$ the aggregate of constituents in V of which $s$ is a factor by $V_t$ the aggregate of constituents of which $t$ is a factor, and so on.    Then, according to the principles of the calculus of Logic, we shall have the following interpretations, viz.,—

V $=$ that event which consists in the drawing of a ball which is not of the species D.

$V_s$ $=$ that event which consists in the drawing of a ball which is of the species $s$ and is not of the species D.

$V_t$ $=$ that event which consists in the drawing of a ball which is of the species $t$ and is not of the species D.

Now, let the total number of balls in the urn be N, and let S be the number which are of the species $s$, T the number which are of the species $t$, &c.    Hitherto $s$ and $t$ have been used only as *logical* symbols expressing *events*.    Let us now introduce a new set of symbols, $s$, $t$, &c. to be used in a *quantitative* acceptation, to denote the numerical ratios $\dfrac{S}{N}$, $\dfrac{T}{N}$, &c.    Then we have

$s$(quantitative) $=$ probability, before the nexus, of the event $s$,

$t$(quantitative) $=$ probability, before the nexus, of the event $t$,

and so on.    And hence V, $V_s$, $V_t$, &c. *quantitative*, representing what the same expressions *logical* become when we change, as above, the signification of $s$, $t$, &c., we have the following derived probabilities (Principle I.).

Probabilities before the nexus :—

V(quantitative) $=$ probability of the drawing of a ball not of the species D.

$V_s$(quantitative) = probability of the drawing of a ball of the species $s$ but not of the species D.

$V_t$(quantitative) = probability of the drawing of a ball of the species $t$ but not of the species D.

A(quantitative) = probability of the drawing of a ball of the species A.

Now, after the *nexus*, the probability of the drawing of a ball of the species $s$ is obviously the same as the probability before the nexus, that if a ball not of the species D be drawn, it will be of the species $s$.   Hence

$$p = \frac{\text{Prob. (before nexus) of } s \text{ not D}}{\text{Prob. (before nexus) of not D}} = \frac{V_s}{V} \quad . \quad . \quad (8)$$

And thus we form the series of *quantitative* equations,

$$\frac{V_s}{V} = p, \ \frac{V_t}{V} = q, \ \&c. \ . \quad . \quad . \quad . \quad (9)$$

Again, the probability after the nexus, of the event A, is equal to the probability before the nexus, that if a ball not of the species D be drawn it will be of the species A,

$$= \frac{\text{Prob. (before nexus) of A not D}}{\text{Prob. (before nexus) of not D}}$$

$$= \frac{\text{Prob. (before nexus) of A}}{\text{Prob. (before nexus) of not D}}.$$

Since the events A and D are mutually exclusive,

$$= \frac{A}{V}.$$

Hence representing Prob. $w$ by $u$, we have

$$u = \frac{A}{V} \quad . \quad . \quad . \quad . \quad . \quad (10)$$

The solution of the problem is now completed.   The values of the ratios $s$, $t$, &c. being found from (9), must be substituted in (10).   These ratios being positive fractions, we must employ a set of values of $s$, $t$, &c., which consists solely of positive fractions.   It will hereafter be shown, that when the problem is a *real* one, the system (9) furnishes one, and only one set of values answering the required description : that set must therefore be taken.   This is the only addition required to the general rule as given in the *Laws of Thought*.

The combined systems (9) and (10) may be elegantly deduced by the following method, originally communicated to me by Professor Donkin.

The probabilities, before the nexus, of the events $V$, $V_s$, $V_t$.. and $A$ are the corresponding *quantitative* functions $V$, $V_s$, $V_t$.. and $A$. The probabilities of the same events after the nexus are $1$, $p$, $q$.. and $u$ respectively. Now the only effect of the nexus is to exclude a number of hypotheses unfavourable to the happening of the above events, without affecting the cases favourable to their happening. Hence the several probabilities have to each other the same ratio before the nexus as after, and therefore

$$V : V_s : V_t .. : A = 1 : p : q : ... : u;$$

or

$$\frac{V_s}{p} = \frac{V_t}{q} .. = \frac{A}{u} = V,$$

a system equivalent to the system (9) and (10).

The investigation is conducted in the same manner when the function $C$ presents itself in the final logical development (5), and the general rule thus established is the following :—

*Rule.*—Form the symbolical expressions of the events whose probabilities are given or sought, and equate such of them as relate to compound events to a new set of logical symbols, $s$, $t$, &c. Express also any absolute conditions which may be given in the data. From the combined system determine by the calculus of Logic, $w$, the event whose probability is sought in terms of all the events $s$, $t$, &c. whose probabilities are given, and let the result be

$$w = A + 0B + \frac{0}{0} C + \frac{1}{0} D.$$

Then representing the aggregate $A + B + C$ by $V$, and the sum of those constituents in $V$ of which $s$ is a factor by $V_s$, and so on, form the algebraic system of equations

$$\frac{V_s}{p} = \frac{V_t}{q} .. = V \quad . \quad . \quad . \quad \text{(I.)}$$

$$\text{Prob. } w = \frac{A + cC}{V} \quad . \quad . \quad . \quad . \quad \text{(II.)}$$

wherein $p$, $q$, &c. are the given probabilities of $s$, $t$, &c.

*If the problem be a real one, the system* (I.) *will furnish one set, and only one set, of positive fractional values of* s, t, *&c., which, substituted in* (II.), *will determine Prob. w.*

The interpretation of *c*, when it appears in the solution, is

$$\frac{\text{Prob. C}w}{\text{Prob. C}}$$

and it indicates the new experience requisite to complete the solution of the problem.

*If the system* (I.) *does not furnish a single system of positive fractional values of* s, t, *&c., the problem is not a real one, and does not in its statement represent a possible experience.*

The passages in italics contain the additions to the rule as it is presented in the *Laws of Thought.*

In concluding this paper, I shall briefly consider the only two objections which have at any time occurred to my own mind as likely to occasion a difficulty in the reception of the above results.

1st. It may be, and indeed it has been urged that the logical calculus upon which the investigation proceeds does not constitute a science or represent " reality ", being only based upon a system of " substituted ratios ".

To this it is replied, that pure science, as such, is concerned only with ratios or relations.   To know things as they are in themselves, is the professed but unattainable object of a so-called philosophy proper.   It is, however, here maintained that the logical calculus does represent reality and constitute science, inasmuch,—1st, as the laws of thought upon which it is founded, and which it expresses by the fundamental equations $xy = yx$, $x^2 = x$, &c. are not fictitious, but are derived from a real analysis of the intellectual operations; 2nd, as it is a fact, and not an assumption, that the laws thus determined are formally identical with the laws of a certain properly defined species of arithmetic; 3rd, as it accords with the catholic objects of science to avail itself of all discovered laws and relations, without regard to the fashion of the schools or the prescription of ancient usage.

2nd. It may be objected that, although in the representa-

U

tive problem of the urn we can readily pass in thought from a system of balls having an actual physical nexus to the same system free from that nexus, we cannot, in the represented problem in which the events $s$, $t$, &c. are subject to the logical and therefore necessary connexion $D = 0$, interpret to ourselves the same events as freed from that connexion; and therefore the problem of the urn does not completely and adequately represent the problem for which it is substituted, inasmuch as in the one case the nexus or condition implied by the equation $D = 0$ is merely actual, while in the other case it is not only actual but necessary.

It is replied, that this necessity may be regarded as merely posterior to some act of limitation by which the events $s$, $t$, &c., previously of larger comprehension, became restricted to that particular interpretation in terms of $x$, $y$, &c. which they bear in the problem, and which is the foundation of the logical necessity referred to. What that larger comprehension is, it is wholly unnecessary to attempt to define. It suffices, upon the general grounds of symbolical algebra, to apply to the inverse process of the removal of a nexus, the formal laws which are derived from the direct and always interpretable case of its imposition. I regard this as a principle which, though capable of verification in innumerable instances, does not rest simply upon the cumulative evidence afforded by such instances, but has a real foundation in the intellectual constitution.

Finally, as respects the mode in which the aforesaid logical necessity has been represented in the example of the urn, it may be remarked that it involves no more than is implied in the various figures by which, in different languages, the idea of necessity has been symbolised. For in each of those figures we have presented to us the notion of something which has once been free, but has ceased to be so through a material act, or a positive determination.* And any one

---

* Witness the supposed derivation of the Latin *necesse* from *nexus*, of the Greek εἱμαρμένη, from a verb signifying division by the casting of lots, of the word *fate*, &c. The higher limitation implied by the addition of such terms as *absolute* (*e.g.* absolute necessity) is curiously derived, not from the direct idea of physical restraint, but from the converse one of the removal of all restraint upon the restraining power.

of these modes of illustration might with equal propriety have been adopted.

The verification of these results will be considered in my next paper*.

Lincoln, Sept. 30th, 1854.

* [Not printed here; but cf. pp. 374–382, 400–421 below.]

# XVI

## ON THE APPLICATION OF THE THEORY OF PROBABILITIES TO THE QUESTION OF THE COMBINATION OF TESTIMONIES OR JUDGMENTS *

1. The method for the solution of questions in the theory of probabilities applied in this paper, is that which was developed by the author in a treatise entitled, " An Investigation of the Laws of Thought, on which are founded the Mathematical Theories of Logic and Probabilities." The practical object of the paper is to deduce from that method certain conclusions relating to the combination of testimonies or judgments. Beside this, however, it will have a speculative reference to some more general questions connected with the theory of probabilities; and especially to the following question, viz. : To what extent the different modes in which the human mind proceeds, in the estimation of probability, may be considered as mutually confirming each other,—as manifestations of a central unity of thought amid the diversity of the forms in which that unity is developed.

The special problems relating to the combination of testimonies or judgments which are considered in this paper are the following : 1st, That in which the testimonies to be combined are merely differing numerical measures of a physical magnitude, as the elevation of a star, furnished by different observations taken simultaneously; 2ndly, That in which the testimonies or judgments to be combined relate not to a numerical measure, but to some fact or hypothesis of which it is sought to determine the probability,—the probabilities furnished by the separate testimonies or judgments constituting our data.

* [_Transactions of the Royal Society of Edinburgh_, vol. xxi, 1857. Communicated by Bishop Terrot. Read January 19th, 1857. For this paper Boole was awarded the Keith Medal for the period 1855–1857. Compare Bishop Terrot's own paper, read 10 months earlier, and printed as an appendix to this volume, pp. 487–496.]

2. I have, in the treatise to which reference has been made, described the method which will be practically applied in this paper as a general one. It will, I think, ultimately appear that there is a true and real sense in which the propriety of the description may be maintained. But at present I am anxious to qualify the appellation, and to speak of the method as general only with respect to problems which have been resolved into purely logical elements, or which are capable of such resolution. A more thorough analysis of the mental phenomena of expectation will, I think, tend to establish the position that all questions of probability, in the mathematical sense, admit of being resolved into primary elements of this nature, or, to speak more strictly, admit of being adequately represented by other problems whose elements are logical only. Postponing the consideration of this question, I will first endeavour to explain what is meant by the logical elements of a problem, and how the consideration of such elements affects the mode of its solution.

I regard the elements of a problem relating to probability as logical, when its data and its quæsitum are the probabilities of *events*. The reason for this appellation will shortly be seen. In *expression*, events may be distinguished as simple or compound. A simple event, i.e. an event simple in expression, is one which is expressed by a single term or predication; a compound event, one which is formed by combining the expressions of simple events. " It rains,"— " it thunders," would be simple events; " it rains and thunders,"—" it either rains or thunders," &c., would be compound events. The constructions by which such combinations are expressed, although they belong to language, have their foundations in Logic. Thus the conjunctions *and, either, or*, &c., express merely certain operations of the faculty of Conception, the entire theory of which belongs to the science of Logic. The calculus of Logic, to which I shall have occasion to refer, is a development of that science in mathematical forms, in which letters represent things or events, as subjects of Conception, and signs connecting those letters represent the operations of that faculty, the laws of the signs being the expressed laws of the operations signified. It is simply a mistake to regard that calculus as an attempt to reduce the ideas of Logic under the dominion of number. Such are the grounds upon which the class of problems to which I have referred are said to involve logical elements. The description is, however, not entirely appropriate, for the problems, as they are concerned with probabilities, in the mathematical acceptation of that term, involve numerical as well as logical elements; but it is by the latter that they are distinguished, and of them only is account taken in the nomenclature.

Thus, as an illustration of what has been said, that problem would be composed of logical elements, which, assigning for its numerical data the probabilities of the throwing an ace or six with each single die, should propose to determine the probability that the issue of a throw with two dice should be two aces, or that it should be an ace and a six, or that it should be either two aces or an ace and a six; and so on for any conceivable throw with any number of dice.

3. In the above example, the events whose numerical probabilities are given are simple events, of which the event whose probability is sought is a logical combination. But it might happen that the former events were themselves combinations of simple events. For instance, the data might be the probabilities that certain meteorological phaenomena, as rain, thunder, hail, &c., would occur in certain definite combinations, and the object sought might be the probability that they would occur in certain other combinations; all these combinations being, such as it is within the province of language to express by means of conjunctions, and of the adverb *not*. Now this would still be a problem whose elements are logical.

4. But there are questions universally recognised as belonging to the theory of probabilities, whose elements cannot, in their direct significance, be regarded as logical. The problem of the reduction of astronomical observations belongs to this class. Two observers, equally trustworthy, take an observation at the same place and time of the altitude of a star. One of them declares that it is 50° 20′, the other

that it is 50° 22'. From these data, what shall we regard as the most probable altitude? We cannot, in this case, directly affirm that the numerical data are measures of probability at all. They are conflicting measures of a physical magnitude. And that which is sought is not the measure of a probability, but the most probable measure of the same magnitude. This is a problem evidently of a different kind from the one which we last considered. And accordingly it will be found that the principles of solution which have been actually applied to it are different from, perhaps we ought rather to say supplementary to, those which have sufficed for the solution of the others. In the problem of the dice, we have only to apply, and that directly, such principles as the following, viz., that when the probability of the occurrence of an event is $p$, that of its non-occurrence is $1 - p$; that if the probabilities of two independent events are $p$ and $q$, that of their concurrence is $pq$, and so on. In the reduction of the conflicting elements of the observers' problem, another and quite distinct principle is usually employed, viz., the principle of the arithmetical mean, which affirms that if two different values are, on equal authority, assigned to a magnitude which is in itself single and definite, the mind is led to consider the arithmetical mean of those values as more likely to be its true measure than any other value. This is not the only principle which has been employed for the reduction in question. We shall refer to others. But it may justly be regarded as the most obvious of all which have been employed; and there is ground for considering it, as some eminent writers have expressly done, as primary and axiomatic in its nature.

5. The following is the typical form of problems whose elements are logical. If we represent the simple events involved in their expression by $x, y, z$, &c., then may all their data (we will suppose the number of data to be $n$) be expressed in accordance with the principles of the calculus of Logic, under the general forms

$$\text{Prob. } \phi_1(x, y, z \ldots) = p_1, \text{ Prob. } \phi_2(x, y, z \ldots) = p_2, \ldots$$
$$\text{Prob. } \phi_n(x, y, z \ldots) = p_n,$$

and the quæsitum, or object sought, will be the value of

$$\text{Prob. } \psi(x, y, z \ldots),$$

where $\phi_1$, $\phi_2$, $\ldots \phi_n$ and $\psi$ denote different but given logical functions of $x, y, z$.

Although the method for the solution of questions in the Theory of Probabilities whose elements are logical has been developed at considerable length in a special chapter of the *Laws of Thought*, yet much that is essential for its proper and distinctive exhibition, has only been discovered since the publication of that work. For this reason it will be proper to offer some account here of the principles upon which the method rests.

6. I define the mathematical probability of an event as the ratio which the number of distinct cases or hypotheses favourable to that event bears to the whole number of distinct cases possible, supposing that to none of those cases the mind is entitled to give any preference over any other. Fundamentally, this definition agrees with that of Laplace. "La théorie des hazards consiste," he remarks, "à réduire tous les évènements du même genre a un certain nombre de cas également possibles c'est à dire tels que nous soyons également indécis sur leur existence ; et à déterminer le nombre de cas favorables à l'évènement dont on cherche la probabilité. Le rapport de ce nombre à celui de tous les cas possibles est la mesure de cette probabilité."—*Essai Philosophique sur les Probabilités.*

It is implied in this definition, that probability is relative to our actual state of information, and varies with that information. Of this principle, Laplace gives the following illustration :—" Let there be three urns, A, B, C, of which we are only informed that one contains black and the other white balls ; then, a ball being drawn from C, required the probability that the ball is black. As we are ignorant which of the urns contains black balls, so that we have no reason to suppose it to be the urn C rather than the urn A or the urn B, these three hypotheses will appear equally worthy of credit, but as the first of the three hypotheses alone is favourable to the drawing of a black ball from C, the probability of that event is $\frac{1}{3}$.  Suppose now that, in addition to the previous data, it is known that the urn A contains only white balls, then our state of indecision has reference only to the urns B and C, and the probability that a ball drawn from C will be black is $\frac{1}{2}$.  Lastly, if we are assured that both A and B contain white balls only, the probability that a black ball will issue from C rises into certitude."—*Essai Philosophique sur les Probabilités*, p. 9.  (*Phil. Mag.*, p. 433.)  Our estimate of the probability of an event varies not absolutely with the circumstances which actually affect its occurrence, but with our knowledge of those circumstances.

7. When the probabilities of simple events constitute our only data, we can by virtue of the above definition, determine the probability of any logical combination of those events, and this either, 1*st*, absolutely; or, 2*ndly*, conditionally.   The reason why we can, in this case, more immediately apply the definition is, that not only is no connexion expressed among the events whose probabilities are given, but none is implied, nor is any restraint imposed upon their possible combinations.   This, as we shall see, is not the case when the data are the probabilities of compound events.

As an example, let us suppose that the probability of the conjunction of two events, $x$ and $y$, is required, the data being simply that the probability of the event $x$ is $p$, and that of the event $y$ is $q$.  Or, to express the problem in a form which we shall hereafter generally employ :

Given           Prob. $x = p$, Prob. $y = q$
Required                Prob. $xy$.

Let $a$ be the number of distinct cases favourable to the event $x$, out of $m$ distinct cases equally possible, from the comparison of which the probability $p$ has been assigned to the event $x$.   In like manner let $b$ be the number of distinct cases favourable to the event $y$, out of $n$ distinct cases equally possible, from the comparison of which the probability $q$ has been assigned to the event $y$.   Then,

$$\frac{a}{m} = p \text{ and } \frac{b}{n} = q.$$

Now the conjunction $xy$ can only come to pass through the combination of some one of the $a$ cases in which $x$ happens, with some one of the $b$ cases in which $y$ happens, at the same time that we have an equal right to suppose that any one of the $m$ cases in which $x$ happens or fails may combine with any one of the $n$ cases in which $y$ happens or fails. To none of these combinations is the mind entitled to attach any preference over any other. Hence, there exist $ab$ distinct cases favourable to the conjunction of $x$ and $y$ out of a total of $mn$ distinct and equally possible cases. Thus, by definition, the probability of the conjunction of $x$ and $y$ will be presented by the product $\dfrac{ab}{mn}$ or $pq$.

Here the question may be asked,—Does then, no difference exist between the case in which the events $x$ and $y$ are known to be independent, and that in which we are simply ignorant of the existence of any connexion between them? I reply that there is none, so far as the numerical estimation of probability is concerned. There is, however, an important difference as respects the practical value of the numerical result. If the events $x$ and $y$ are known to be independent, and to have probabilities $p$ and $q$, we know that, in the long run, the conjunction $xy$ will tend to recur with a frequency which will be proportional to the magnitude of the fraction $pq$. We do not know that this will be the case if we are simply ignorant of any connexion between $x$ and $y$. This is the difference referred to, and it is an important one. But it does not affect the calculation of probability as flowing from the definition of its numerical measure.

8. As from the data Prob. $x = p$, Prob. $y = q$, we deduce Prob. $xy = pq$, so from the same data we should have, adopting the language of the calculus of Logic,

$$\text{Prob. } x(1 - y) = p(1 - q)$$
$$\text{Prob. } (1 - x)(1 - y) = (1 - p)(1 - q),$$

and so on. Here $x(1 - y)$ denotes the compound event which consists in the occurrence of $x$ conjointly with the non-occurrence of $y$; $(1 - x)(1 - y)$, the compound event which consists in the joint non-occurrence of both $x$ and $y$.

$$\text{Prob. } \phi(x, y, z\,..) = \phi(p, q, r\,..) \quad . \quad . \quad (1)$$

where $x$, $y$, $z$, &c., denote any simple events whose probabilities (our only data) are $p$, $q$, $r\,..$, and $\phi(x, y, z\,..)$ denotes any event which can be expressed by means of the simple events $x$, $y$, $z$, &c., in accordance with the notation of the calculus of Logic.

By the above theorem the probability of any compound event is determined absolutely, when the probabilities of its simple components are given.

9. And by the same mode of investigation, the probability of any combination may be determined conditionally, i.e. the probability which the combination will have under a given condition consisting in the happening of some other combination.   Thus, if our data are as before,

$$\text{Prob. } x = p, \text{ Prob. } y = q, \text{ Prob. } z = r, \&c.$$

and if we require the probability that if the event $\phi(x, y, z\,..)$ present itself, the event $\psi(x, y, z\,..)$ will be present at the same time, we may demonstrate the following result, viz.,

Prob. that if $\phi(x, y, z\,..)$ happen, $\psi(x, y, z\,..)$ will be present also

$$= \frac{\chi(p, q, r\,..)}{\phi(p, q, r\,..)} \quad . \quad . \quad . \quad . \quad . \quad (2)$$

where the form of the function $\chi$ is determined by multiplying together, according to the principles of the calculus of Logic, the functions $\phi(x, y, z\,..)$ and $\psi(x, y, z\,..)$ and representing the result by $\chi(x, y, z\,..)$—(*Laws of Thought*, p. 258, Prop. I.)

10. I postulate that when the data are not the probabilities of simple events, we must, in order to apply them to the calculation of probability, regard them not as primary, but as derived from some anterior hypothesis, which presents the probabilities of simple events as its system of data, and exhibits our actual data as flowing out of that system, in accordance with those principles which have already been shown to be involved in the very definition of probability.

The ground of this postulate is, that to begin with the simple and proceed to the complex, seems to be, in all questions involving combinations such as we are here concerned with, a necessary procedure of the understanding. The calculation of probability depends upon combinations subject to a peculiar condition, viz., that they shall always present to us a series of cases or hypotheses, to none of which the mind is entitled to attach any preference over any other. We cannot, in endeavouring to ascend from the complex to the simple, secure the maintenance of this condition; but we can do so in descending from the simple to the complex. We have had an illustration of this truth in the reasoning by which we deduced the expression for the probability of the complex event $xy$ from the probabilities of the simple events $x$ and $y$, supposed to be given. And the methods which have been actually employed in the solution of problems whose immediate data were not the probabilities of simple events, have in fact rested upon the postulate above referred to. Thus in questions relating to juries, the immediate data are the probabilities, founded upon continued observation, that a decision will be unanimous, or that it will be pronounced by a given majority, &c. But it is usual, in solving these problems, to regard such events as compound, and to derive them from a hypothesis which presents as its scheme or system of data, the probabilities of individual correctness of judgment in the members of the jury; the correctness of judgment in any such members being regarded as simple event. And this mode of procedure is a very natural and very obvious one. For the degree of unanimity of a decision will so far depend upon the correctness of judgment in the members that, if we knew what the probability of correctness in each member was, we could determine *à priori* the probability of any proposed measure of agreement in the body.

The only question which arises indeed, is not concerning the necessity of the postulate, but concerning the mode in which it may be lawfully applied. How shall we lawfully construct the hypotheses by which the solution of a problem shall be made to depend upon the consideration of simple events? In answering this question, I will endeavour to show, 1*st*, upon what the construction of the hypotheses does not depend; 2*ndly*, upon what it does depend.

11. The legitimate construction of the hypothesis in question cannot depend upon the accidents of language, or causes deeper than accident, which have led us to express particular things or events by simple terms, thus regarding them as simple events; and other events by combinations of these simple terms, thus presenting them as compound. The solution of a question in the theory of probabilities must depend upon the *information* conveyed in the data, not upon the peculiar elements and constructions of the language which is the vehicle of that information. Languages differ widely in these respects. Objects and events which in one language are expressed by simple terms, are in another expressed by combinations of simple terms. It is affirmed that a perfectly general method of solution must be independent of, and superior to, differences like these.

I will endeavour to illustrate this principle by an example. Let the problem to be resolved be the following. The probability of the concurrence of rain and snow is $p$, of the concurrence of snow and wind $q$ and of the concurrence of wind and rain $r$; required the probability of the concurrence of wind, rain, and snow.

Now suppose that we had to interpret the problem into a language in which there were no simple terms corresponding to the simple terms, " wind ", " rain ", " snow ", but in which there were simple terms for the three first of the concurrences above described.

We may, for simplicity, suppose the language to be a dialect of English, and the concurrence of rain and snow to be represented in it by the term " sleet ", the concurrence of snow and wind by the term " drift ", and the concurrence of wind and rain by the term " storm ".

The event whose probability is sought, viz., the concurrence of rain, snow, and wind, would, in such a language, be represented by the combination either of two of the terms above defined (as of sleet with drift), or of all the terms together, since the presence of any two of the phaenomena

" sleet ", " drift ", " storm ", implies that of the third, and involves the conjunction of the phaenomena of rain, snow, and wind.

The data of the problem we are considering might then, in the imagined dialect, assume the following form :

The probability of sleet is $p$, of drift $q$, and of storm $r$; required the probability of the concurrence of the phaenomena of sleet, drift, and storm.

But in this form the problem would not, in its data, express all the knowledge which the person using such language must possess of the connexion of the events to which it related.  He must know that it was impossible that any two of the events sleet, drift, and storm, should occur without the third, so that the problem, if so stated as to embody the same amount of actual knowledge as is conveyed in the previous statement of it, would assume the following form :

The probability of sleet is $p$, of drift $q$, of storm $r$, and these events are so connected, that no two of them can occur without the third occurring, What is the probability of their concurrence ?

Now the principle affirmed declares that the solution of the problem must be the same whichsoever of these forms of statement we adopt.

As languages increase in affluence, the number of their simple terms becomes augmented, partly through the necessity of giving expression to new ideas, partly through the wish to give more convenient expression to definite and oft-recurring combinations of the old ones.  With every term invented in subserviency to the latter purpose, a definition must be introduced.  A dictionary, setting aside its philological portion (and even this not wholly), is a record of such definitions.  As a consequence of such definitions of terms, spring up also propositions innumerable connecting these terms—propositions which in no degree add to the amount of our absolute knowledge, which are quite distinct from the discovered facts and laws of nature and of human history, but are merely logical deductions from the definitions. We might conceive of a language in which all possible combinations of ideas should be expressed by simple terms, with connecting definitions and propositions *ad infinitum*. The realization of such a conception is neither practicable nor desirable; but it is, nevertheless, the *limit* toward which all languages, which are not dead or decaying, do actually tend. The progressive action of this tendency does not affect the laws of expectation, neither, therefore, can it affect any consistent and scientific theory which is founded upon those laws.

We are not, therefore, permitted to assume that any events which, in the language of the problem, may be presented as simple events, must therefore be adopted as such into the hypothesis which is to form the basis of our method of solution. Nor, on the other hand, are we forbidden to employ transformations (sanctioned by the rules of Logic) which will have the effect of introducing an entirely new scheme of simple events as the elements of the hypothesis in question.

12. To what conditions then, must the hypothesis be subject? This question I now proceed to answer.

The hypothesis must be such that it may be consistently applied, without imposing upon the data any other conditions than those of possibility, i.e. of accordance with a possible experience.

This principle is so obviously true, that it will only be needful to show how the conditions of possible experience are discovered. I shall subsequently show how their discovery limits and determines the hypothesis upon which the solution of questions in the theory of probabilities, whose elements are logical, depends.

The data of such problems are the probabilities of events. The object sought is also the probability of an event. The numerical values of these probabilities must be expressible by positive proper fractions. At any rate, they must not transcend the limits 0 and 1. This is one condition to which they are subject. Generally, however, there will exist other conditions dependent upon the mutual relations of the events whose probabilities are given.

Thus, if $p$ were the probability that an event $x$ will happen,

$q$ the probability that $x$ and $y$ will both happen, we have, as a necessary condition,

$$p \gtrless q,$$

Again, if $p$ were the probability that $x$ and $y$ will both happen, $q$ the probability that they will both fail, we must have the condition,

$$p + q \lessgtr 1,$$

a condition which does not hold in the previous case.

I have, in the *Laws of Thought*, treated of these conditions, and of the principles by which they may be determined, in a special chapter (Chap. XIX., *On Statistical Conditions*). A more simple, and at the same time perfectly general method, was afterwards discovered by me, and published in the *Philosophical Magazine*, Aug. 1854. As the method is of fundamental importance, I shall here illustrate it by an example, at the same time introducing a slight change in the mode of treatment, which leaves nothing to be desired in point of simplicity. The conditions to the discovery of which the method is applicable will be termed in accordance with the language employed in the *Philosophical Magazine*, —the " Conditions of Possible Experience "; inasmuch as, whenever the numerical data of a problem are derived from actual experience these conditions will be satisfied, and whenever in data professing to be thus derived they are not satisfied, the presence of mistake or fraud may with certainty be affirmed.

### Determination of the Conditions of Possible Experience

13. To explain the method of effecting this object, by an example, I will first symbolically express the problem of Art. 11.

Let us then represent rain by $x$, snow by $y$, and wind by $z$. The problem in question then takes the following form :—

Given    Prob. $xy = p$, Prob. $yz = q$, Prob. $xz = r$    (1)
Required          Prob. $xyz$ . . . . . . (2)

The value required we shall represent by $u$. It is our present object, not to solve this problem, but to ascertain the conditions which must connect $p$, $q$, and $r$, in order that

the data may be possible, with the corresponding limitations
of $u$.    For if $u$ were itself determined by experience, it would
be subject to conditions of possibility similar to those which
govern $p$, $q$, and $r$.

Now let us write, resolving the events in the problem into
the possible alternations out of which they are formed,

Prob. $xyz = u$, Prob. $xy\bar{z} = \lambda$, Prob. $xz\bar{y} = \mu$, Prob. $yz\bar{x} = \nu$

We have then

$$u + \lambda = p,\ u + \nu = q,\ u + \mu = r\ .\quad.\quad(3)$$

The first of these equations only expresses that the probability of the concurrence of $x$ and $y$ is equal to the probability
of the concurrence of $x$, $y$, and $z$, and the probability of the
concurrence of $x$ and $y$ without $z$.    To the equations (3)
we must now add the inequations

$$u \gtrless 0,\ \lambda \gtrless 0,\ \mu \gtrless 0,\ \nu \gtrless 0,\Big\}\quad.\quad.\quad(4)$$
$$u + \lambda + \mu + \nu \lessgtr 1$$

expressing the conditions to which $u$, $\lambda$, $\mu$, $\nu$, 1st, as probabilities, and 2ndly, as probabilities which do not altogether
make up certainty, are subject.

First, we will eliminate $\lambda$, $\mu$, and $\nu$.    Their values found
from (3) are

$$\lambda = p - u,\ \mu = r - u,\ \nu = q - u.$$

Substituting these in (4) we have

$$u \gtrless 0,\ p - u \gtrless 0,\ q - u \gtrless 0,\ r - u \gtrless 0,$$
$$p + q + r - 2u \lessgtr 1.$$

Whence,

$$u \lessgtr p,\ u \lessgtr q,\ u \lessgtr r,\Big\}\quad.\quad.\quad.\quad(5)$$
$$u \gtrless 0,\ u \gtrless \frac{p + q + r - 1}{2}$$

Such are the conditions to which the quantity $u$ is subject,
conditions which the value of Prob. $xyz$ must à priori satisfy.

To determine the conditions connecting $p$, $q$, and $r$, we
must from (5) eliminate $u$.    Now, if we have any two inequations of the form

$$u \lessgtr a,\ u \gtrless b.$$

X

the only condition connecting $a$ and $b$ which they establish is,

$$a \gtrless b.$$

Applying this principle to (5), we have

$$p \gtrless 0 . p \gtrless \frac{p + q + r - 1}{2},$$

$$q \gtrless 0 . q \gtrless \frac{p + q + r - 1}{2},$$

$$r \gtrless 0 . r \gtrless \frac{p + q + r - 1}{2}.$$

These may be reduced to the somewhat simpler form

$$\left. \begin{array}{l} p \gtrless 0, q \gtrless 0, r \gtrless 0 \\ p \gtrless q + r - 1 \\ q \gtrless r + p - 1 \\ r \gtrless p + q - 1 \end{array} \right\} \quad . \quad . \quad . \quad (6)$$

Such are the conditions of possible experience in the data.

Suppose for instance, it was affirmed as a result of medical statistics, that in two-fifths of a number of cases of disease of a certain character, two symptoms, $x$ and $y$, were observed; in two-thirds of all the cases, the symptoms $y$ and $z$ were observed; and in four-fifths of all the cases, the symptoms $x$ and $z$ were observed; so that the number of cases observed being large, we might, on a future outbreak of the disease, consider the fractions two-fifths, two-thirds, and four-fifths, as the probabilities of recurrence of the particular combinations of the symptoms, $x$, $y$, and $z$, observed. The above formulae would show that the evidence was contradictory. For representing the respective fractions by $p$, $q$, and $r$, the condition

$$p \gtrless q + r - 1$$

is not satisfied.

It is an evident consequence of the principle enunciated in Art. 11, that in determining the conditions of possible experience and of limitation, we may employ any *translated* form of the problem, just as well as the form in which it is originally expressed. Thus, if we take the translated form of the problem of that article, and represent sleet by $s$, drift by $t$, storm by $u$, we shall have as the data

Prob. $s = p$, Prob. $t = q$, Prob. $u = r$

with the conditions

$$s t \bar{u} = 0, \; u t \bar{s} = 0, \; u s \bar{t} = 0 \quad . \quad . \quad . \quad (7)$$

the quæsitum being Prob. $stu$, which, as before, we shall represent by $u$.

Now if we write

Prob. $stu = u$, Prob. $st\bar{u} = 0$, Prob. $su\bar{t} = 0$, Prob. $s\bar{u}\bar{t} = \lambda$,

Prob. $tu\bar{s} = 0$, Prob. $t\bar{u}\bar{s} = \mu$, Prob. $u\bar{s}\bar{t} = v$ . (8)

we have the following equations :—

$$\left. \begin{array}{l} u + \lambda = p \\ u + \mu = q \\ u + v = r \end{array} \right\} \quad . \quad . \quad . \quad . \quad (9)$$

with the inequations

$$u \gtrless 0, \lambda \gtrless 0, \mu \gtrless 0, v \gtrless 0, u + \mu + v + \lambda \gtrless 1 \quad (10)$$

Determining from the equations $\lambda, \mu, v$, and substituting in the inequations, we get

$$u \gtrless 0, p - u \gtrless 0, q - u \gtrless 0, r - u \gtrless 0,$$
$$p + q + r - 2u \gtrless 1 \quad . \quad (11)$$

a system which agrees with that obtained by the previous investigation (5) Art. 13.

14. The general rule for the determination of the conditions of possible experience and of limitation in a question of probability may be thus stated.

Resolve the events whose probabilities are either given or sought, into the mutually exclusive alternatives which they involve. If the calculus of Logic is employed, this is done by development.

Represent the probabilities of these alternations by $\lambda$, $\mu$, $v$, &c., and express the probabilities given and sought by the corresponding sums of these quantities. This will furnish a series of *equations*, which we will suppose to be $n$ in number.

Determine from these equations any $n$ of the quantities $\lambda, \mu, v$, in terms of the others.

Substitute the values thus obtained in the *inequations*

$$\lambda \gtrless 0, \mu \gtrless 0, \nu \gtrless 0 \quad . \quad . \quad . \quad . \quad (1)$$

$$\lambda + \mu + \nu . . \gtrless 1 . \quad . \quad . \quad . \quad (2)$$

Eliminate in succession such of the quantities $\lambda, \mu, \nu, . .$ as are left in the above inequations after the substitution.

The elimination of any quantity as $\tau$ from the inequations, is effected by reducing each inequation to the form $\tau \gtrless a$, or to the form $\tau \lessgtr b$, and observing that two such forms as the above give $a \lessgtr b$.

If the " alternations " into which the events whose probabilities are given or sought are resolved extend to all possible combinations of the simple events out of which they are formed, the inequations (2) must be replaced by the equation

$$\lambda + \mu + \nu . . = 1 \quad . \quad . \quad . \quad . \quad (3)$$

The rest of the process will be the same as before.

In the form of the above method developed in the *Philosophical Magazine* the quantities $\lambda, \mu, \nu, . .$ represent the probabilities, not of those alternations alone, which are contained in the events whose probabilities are given or sought, but of all possible alternations which can be formed, by combining the simple events $x, y, z . .$ In this form, therefore, we have always an equation of the form (3) in the place of an inequation of the form (2). But though the result is the same, the form given to the method in this section is to be preferred, as it requires the eliminations of a smaller number of symbols, except when the condition referred to in (3) is fulfilled, in which case, the methods are identical.

15. It remains to show how the conditions of possible experience as above determined, restrict us in the choice of the hypothesis, by the aid of which the final solution is to be obtained.

Taking for example the above problem of Art. 13, let us enquire whether it would be lawful to assume $x$, $y$, and $z$ as the primary simple events of the problem.

If we make this assumption and then write

Prob. $x = \alpha$, Prob. $y = \beta$, Prob. $z = \gamma$,

we find

Prob. $xy = \alpha\beta$, Prob. $yz = \beta\gamma$, Prob. $zx = \gamma\alpha$,

whence comparing with (1) Art. 13—

$$\alpha\beta = p, \ \beta\gamma = q, \ \gamma\alpha = r,$$

solving which equations we have

$$\alpha = \sqrt{\frac{qr}{p}}, \beta = \sqrt{\frac{rp}{q}}, \gamma = \sqrt{\frac{pq}{r}},$$

$$\therefore \qquad \text{Prob. } xyz = \alpha\beta\gamma = \sqrt{pqr} \ . \ \ . \ \ . \ \ . \ \ (4)$$

Now, $\alpha$, $\beta$, $\gamma$, being by assumption probabilities, and there-fore, lying numerically between the limits 0 and 1, we must have

$$qr \lessgtr p, \ rp \lessgtr q, \ pq \lessgtr r \ . \ \ . \ \ . \ \ . \ \ (5)$$

as the conditions to which $p$, $q$, and $r$ (beside being fractional) must be subject. These conditions do not, however, agree with, and are not involved in, the conditions of possible experience, determined in (6) Art. 13. We may conclude, therefore, that the hypothesis upon which our solution is founded, involves elements, the introduction of which is unwarranted, and that the value of Prob. $xyz$ determined is erroneous.

We may show, in fact, that the conditions (5) imply the conditions of possible experience, and something more. If $qr \lessgtr p$ then, *à fortiori*, $qr \lessgtr p + (1 - q)(1 - r)$ since $(1 - q)(1 - r)$ is essentially positive. Therefore,

$$qr \lessgtr p + 1 - q - r + qr,$$

whence $\qquad\qquad p \gtrless q + r - 1,$

which is one of the conditions (6) Art. 13. In the same way the other conditions in that article may be deduced from (5). The reverse reduction is, however, impossible.

16. The hypothesis upon which the method developed in the *Laws of Thought*, cap. xvii., for the solution of questions in the theory of probabilities whose elements are logical, is founded, seems to be the only one which satisfied the require-ment referred to in Art. 12. It was not, however, upon such considerations as this that the method was founded. As presented in the *Laws of Thought*, it rests upon principles

which, to my own mind, have something of an axiomatic character. Viewed in this light, its perfect accordance with the requirement above explained may be considered as a verification of it *à posteriori*. In itself, however, this accordance affords a sufficient ground of confidence in the legitimacy of the hypothesis. On the proof of this accordance, I shall say something hereafter. At present I will only state the hypothesis, and show in what the accordance consists.

The hypothesis is the following :—Translating our problem by the aid of the calculus of Logic into a language in which the events whose probabilities are given, appear as simple events subject to conditions founded on their definitions, Art. 11, we ascend above these simple events to another scheme of simple events, which are free, and which, when actually subjected to the conditions to which the before-mentioned simple events are necessarily subject, shall have the same probabilities, and shall in every respect take their place. The unknown probabilities of the free simple events, which form the elements of this hypothesis, must be so determined as to render the substitution possible, and to permit a formal construction of the problem, both in its data and by its quæsitum, out of those new elements.

The unknown probabilities being thus determined, the problem assumes a form in which its elementary data are the probabilities of simple events unrestricted by any condition. In this form, the solution of the problem is possible by mere consequence of the fundamental definition of probability. The ground upon which this hypothesis was presented in the *Laws of Thought* was its intrinsic reasonableness. On this point I will only refer to my observations in the original work. The ground upon which, in the present essay, I wish to rest the hypothesis is, that it is the only one which does not impose upon the data other conditions than those of conformity with a possible experience. The conditions which must be fulfilled in order that $p'$, $q'$, &c., in the substituted and hypothetical data, may be measures of probability at all,—i.e. may be positive proper fractions, —are precisely the conditions of possible experience in the original data. (See Appendix.)

17. The application of this hypothesis is so fully explained in the *Laws of Thought*, cap. xvii., that I shall here only describe the general method for the solution of questions in probabilities to which it leads, and show the connexion which exists between the several parts of that method and the foregoing doctrine.

### General Method

Representing the problem to be solved under the form—

Given  Prob. $\phi_1(x, y, z, \ldots) = p$, Prob. $\phi_2(x, y, z \ldots) = q$, &c.

Required  Prob. $\psi(x, y, z \ldots)$,

and expressing the unknown value of Prob. $\psi(x, y, z, \ldots)$ by $u$, we form the logical equations :—

$$\phi_1(x, y, z \ldots) = s, \ \phi_2(x, y, z \ldots) = t, \ \text{&c.}, \ \psi(x, y, z \ldots) = w,$$

and hence, determining $w$ as a developed logical function of $s, t \ldots$ we have a result of the form

$$w = A + 0B + \frac{0}{0}C + \frac{1}{0}D \quad . \quad . \quad . \quad (1)$$

Here A, B, C, D, are logical combinations of the simple events, $s$, $t$, &c., and the connexion in which they stand to the event $w$ and to each other is the following : A expresses those combinations of $s$, $t$, &c., which are entirely included in $w$,—*i.e.* which cannot happen without our being permitted to say that $w$ happens.  B represents combinations which may happen, but are not included under $w$; so that when they happen, we may say that $w$ does not happen.  C represents those combinations, the happening of which leaves us in doubt whether $w$ happens or not.  D, those combinations, the happening of which is wholly interdicted.

Thus far we have only translated our problem into a language in which its data are the probabilities of simple events, viz. :—

$$\text{Prob. } s = p, \ \text{Prob. } t = q, \ \text{&c.} \quad . \quad . \quad (2)$$

The condition, founded on definition, to which these simple events are subject is,

$$D = 0,$$

or, which amounts to the same thing,

$$A + B + C = 1,$$

indicating that the combinations expressed by A, B, and C can alone happen. If we represent $A + B + C$ by V, we have

$$w = A + \frac{0}{0}C \quad . \quad . \quad . \quad . \quad . \quad (3)$$

with the condition

$$V = 1 \quad . \quad . \quad . \quad . \quad . \quad . \quad (4)$$

Of these equations, the latter expresses the conditions to which the simple events, $s$, $t$, &c., are subject; the former expresses $w$ as a logical combination of those events.

We now, in accordance with the hypothesis, ascend to a new scheme of simple events, $s'$, $t'$, &c., unrestricted by any condition, and possessed of unknown probabilities, $p'$, $q'$, which are to be so determined that when $s'$, $t'$.. are subjected to the same condition (4) to which $s$, $t$.. are subject, they will have the same probabilities as $s$, $t$.. The system of equations to which we are thus led, and which contains the implicit solution of the problem, is the following (*Laws of Thought*, cap. xvii., p. 267) :—

$$\frac{V_s}{p} = \frac{V_t}{q} .. = \frac{A + C}{u} = V \quad . \quad . \quad . \quad (5)$$

$V_s$ being formed by selecting those terms from V, which contain $s$ as a factor; $V_t$ those which contain $t$ as a factor, &c., and then regarding $s$, $t$, &c., as algebraic quantities. From the system thus formed, we must determine $u$ as a function of $p$, $q$.. and the arbitrary constant $c$, should it be present. This will be the solution of the problem.

The quantities $s$, $t$.. are the same as $p'$, $q'$.. and represent the probabilities of the hypothetical simple events, represented by $s'$, $t'$.. Accordingly, as probabilities, they must admit of being determined as positive proper fractions, and that the solution may not be ambiguous, they must admit of only one such determination. These conditions will be fulfilled whensoever the problem represents a possible experience, and it will be then only fulfilled. And in this way, or by directly investigating the conditions of possibility by the rule of Art. 14, a solution is made determinate.

The arbitrary constant $c$ does not, as has been intimated, always present itself. When it does, it represents the unknown probability, that if the event C occur, $w$ will occur. It indicates, therefore, the new experience which would be necessary in order to make the solution definite.

18. I will, for the sake of illustration, apply the method to the problem of Art. 11, and in so doing I will limit the solution by the conditions relative to $s$, $t$, &c.

The problem, as symbolically expressed in Art. 13, is as follows :—

Given        Prob. $xy = p$, Prob. $yz = q$, Prob. $zx = r$ $\Big\}$ (1)
Required                Prob. $xyz$

Translating the problem as directed in the first part of the rule, we write

$$xy = s, \; yz = t, \; zx = v, \; xyz = w \quad . \quad . \quad (2)$$

whence, by the calculus of Logic,

$$w = stv + 0(s\bar{t}\bar{v} + t\bar{s}\bar{v} + v\bar{s}\bar{t} + \bar{s}\bar{v}\bar{t}) + \frac{1}{0}(st\bar{v} + sv\bar{t} + tv\bar{s}) \; (3)$$

Hence we find

$$V = stv + s\bar{t}\bar{v} + t\bar{s}\bar{v} + v\bar{s}\bar{t} + \bar{s}\bar{t}\bar{v} \; . \quad . \quad (4)$$

and are led to the algebraic system of equations

$$\frac{stv + s\bar{t}\bar{v}}{p} = \frac{stv + t\bar{s}\bar{v}}{q} = \frac{stv + v\bar{s}\bar{t}}{r}$$

$$= \frac{stv}{u} = stv + s\bar{t}\bar{v} + t\bar{s}\bar{v} + v\bar{s}\bar{t} + \bar{s}\bar{t}\bar{v}. \quad (5)$$

These equations may be simplified by dividing every term by $stv$, and then assuming

$$\frac{s}{\underline{s}} = s', \frac{t}{\underline{t}} = t', \frac{v}{\underline{v}} = v' \quad . \quad . \quad . \quad . \quad (6)$$

They thus give

$$\frac{s't'v' + s'}{p} = \frac{s't'v' + t'}{q} = \frac{s't'v' + v'}{r} = \frac{s't'v'}{u}$$

$$= s't'v' + s' + t' + v' + 1 \; . \quad (7)$$

The condition to which $s't'v'$ are subject obviously is, that they shall be positive quantities, for this is equivalent to the condition that $s, t, v$ shall be positive fractions.

From (7) we readily find

$$\frac{s'}{p-u} = \frac{t'}{q-u} = \frac{v'}{r-u} = \frac{s't'v'}{u}$$
$$= s't'v' + s' + t' + v' + 1 \quad . \quad (8)$$

Whence

$$\left.\begin{aligned} s' &= \frac{p-u}{2u-p-q-r+1} \\[1mm] t' &= \frac{q-u}{2u-p-q-r+1} \\[1mm] v' &= \frac{r-u}{2u-p-q-r+1} \end{aligned}\right\} \quad . \quad . \quad . \quad (9)$$

Substitute these values in the equation

$$\frac{s'}{p-u} = \frac{s't'v'}{u},$$

and reducing we get

$$(p-u)(q-u)(r-u) = u(2u-p-q-r+1)^2 \quad (10)$$

an equation for determining $u$.

And now let us inquire into the consequences which flow from the condition that $s't'v'$ are positive quantities.

In the first place, the last member of (8), and therefore each other member of that system will be positive. This requires that the denominators, $p-u$, $q-u$, $r-u$, and $u$, should be positive, whence we have

$$\left.\begin{aligned} u &\gtrless 0 \\ u &\gtrless p, \; u \gtrless q, \; u \gtrless r \end{aligned}\right\} \quad . \quad . \quad . \quad (11)$$

Again, $p-u$, $q-u$, and $r-u$ being positive, the common denominators, $2u-p-q-r+1$ in (9), must be positive, whence

$$u \gtrless \frac{p+q+r-1}{2} \quad . \quad . \quad . \quad (12)$$

Such are the conditions relative to $u$. They agree in all respects with those assigned in the previous investigation, in (5), Art. 13; and, as in that article, the elimination of $u$

leads to the conditions of possible experience,

$$\left.\begin{array}{c} p \gtrless 0, q \gtrless 0, r \gtrless 0 \\ p \gtrless q + r - 1 \\ q \gtrless p + r - 1 \\ r \gtrless p + q - 1 \end{array}\right\} \quad \cdot \quad \cdot \quad \cdot \quad (13)$$

It may be well to notice, that these conditions involve the necessity of $p$, $q$, and $r$ being fractional, though of course, this does not exhaust their significance.

19. It remains to show that when the above conditions are satisfied, the system (7) will admit of but one solution in positive values of $s'$, $t'$, $v'$, and that (10) will furnish but one value of $u$ satisfying the conditions (11) and (12).

Let us write (10) in the form

$$u(2u - p - q - r + 1)^2 - (p - u)(q - u)(r - u) = 0 \quad (14)$$

or, for simplicity, in the form

$$U = 0.$$

The lower limit of $u$ is, by (11) and (12), either 0 or $\dfrac{p + q + r - 1}{2}$ according as the latter quantity is positive or negative; the upper limit of $u$ is the least of the quantities $p$, $q$, $r$. Suppose it $p$. First, let $\dfrac{p + q + r - 1}{2}$ be positive, then, making $u$ equal to this quantity, the value of U, as given in the first member of (14), becomes negative. Again, let $u = p$, then U becomes positive. Thus, as $u$ varies from $\dfrac{p + q + r - 1}{2}$ up to $p$, U changes from negative to positive. Now

$$\frac{dU}{du} = (2u - p - q - r + 1)^2 + 4u(2u - p - q - r + 1)$$
$$+ (p - u)(q - u) + (q - u)(r - u) + (r - u)(p - u) \quad (15)$$

which within the supposed limits is always positive. Hence U varies by continuous increase, and once only in its variation becomes equal to 0.

Secondly, let $\dfrac{p + q + r - 1}{2}$ be negative, then $u$, varying from 0 up to $p$, U as before will vary by continuous increase from a negative to a positive value. See the first member of (14). Whence U, changing by continuous increase from a negative to a positive value, will still only once become equal to 0.

Wherefore, in either case, one root of (10) will lie within the limits assigned to $u$ in (11) and (12). And this one value substituted in (9) will give one set of values for $s'$, $t'$, $v'$.

20. The solutions which we have now obtained of the same problem on different hypotheses with respect to the selection of the simple events, set in clear light the principles upon which the due selection of such hypotheses depends. The hypothesis which seems most readily to present itself utterly fails, while the other, based quite as much upon an apparently remote speculation on language, as upon the study of the laws of expectation as usually conceived, finds a support and confirmation within the realm of pure mathematics which is of the most remarkable kind.

21. A practical simplification of the general method is suggested by that step of the preceding solution, which reduces (5) to the form (7). If we remove the traces (') from the letters in the latter system (and they do not at all affect the solution), we obtain what (5) would become if we replaced each of the symbols $\bar{s}$, $\bar{t}$, $\bar{v}$, by unity. Practically, therefore, we may modify the general rule in the following manner :— Having obtained V, replace each of the symbols, $\bar{s}$, $\bar{t}$, &c., by unity, and proceed with the reduced value of V just as before, $i.e.$ let $V_s$ represent that portion of V of which $s$ is a factor, &c., then form the system of equations

$$\frac{V_s}{p} = \frac{V_t}{q} \dots = \frac{A + cC}{u} = V \quad . \quad . \quad . \quad (1)$$

and hence determine $u$ as a function of $p$, $q$ .. and $c$. The conditions of possible experience and of limitation will be found by supposing $s$, $t$, to admit of a single determination in positive values. Or as before, they may be found independently, and then applied to limit the solution.

22. We now proceed to the consideration of the problems referred to in Art. (1). We shall first examine the problem which has for its object the determination of the most

probable measure of a physical magnitude, two conflicting measures of which have been assigned by observation. The problem is not, as has been said, Art. 2, in its immediate presentation, one whose elements are logical, but it admits, as we shall see, of being so represented as to give it this character.

## Problem I

*Two simultaneous observations of a physical magnitude, as the elevation of a star, assign to it the respective values, $p_1$ and $p_2$. The probability, when the first observation has been made that it is correct, is $c_1$, the corresponding probability for the second observation is $c_2$. Required the most probable value of the physical magnitude hence resulting.*

## First Solution

23. The numerical elements which are not, in their immediate presentation, probabilities, are $p_1$ and $p_2$. But these become such if we contemplate the problem under another aspect. Let a quadrant be taken as the unit of magnitude, then $p_1$ and $p_2$ are proper fractions; $p_1$ actually expressing the probability afforded by the first observation, $p_2$ that afforded by the second observation, that a pointer, directed at random to that quadrant of elevation in which the star, regarded as a physical point, is situated, will point below the star. The problem thus regarded contains the following logical elements, which we shall express by appropriate symbols, viz.

The event which consists in the first observation, such as it is, being made $= x$.

The event which consists in the second observation, such as it is, being made $= y$.

The event which consists in the first observation being correct, $= w$.

The event which consists in the second observation being correct, $= v$.

The event which consists in a pointer, directed at random to the quadrant in which the star is situated, pointing below that star, $= z$.

We must now express symbolically the data, including therein whatever logical connexions we can establish among the events, $x$, $y$, $w$, $v$, and $z$.

The probability that the first observation, when made, is correct, is $c_1$. This is a conditional probability; or, to adopt a well-known form of expression, it is a probability *à posteriori*. Viewed from a point of time anterior to the observation, it is the probability that if the observation be made under its actual circumstances of care, personal fitness, instrumental accuracy, &c., it will be absolutely correct. Symbolically, it is the probability that if the event $x$ take place, the event $w$ will take place. The only mode of expressing this is by writing for the probability of $x$ an arbitrary constant $a_1$ we have then

$$\text{Prob. } x = a_1, \text{ Prob. } xw = a_1 c_1 . \quad . \quad (1)$$

The events $x$ and $w$ are not, however, independent. If we can affirm that a given observation is correct, we can affirm that that observation has been made. Symbolically, the occurrence of the event $w$ implies the occurrence of the event $x$. Expressing this proposition in the language of the calculus of Logic we have the equation

$$w\bar{x} = 0 \quad . \quad . \quad . \quad . \quad . \quad (2)$$

This forms a part of our data. It permits us to change also the form of one of the previous data, and instead of (1) to substitute

$$\text{Prob. } x = a_1, \text{ Prob. } w = a_1 c_1 . \quad . \quad (3)$$

In like manner, representing the arbitrary probability of the event $y$ by $a_2$ we have

$$\text{Prob. } y = a_2, \text{ Prob. } yv = a_2 c_2 . \quad . \quad (4)$$

With the connecting condition

$$v\bar{y} = 0 \quad . \quad . \quad . \quad . \quad . \quad (5)$$

which would permit us to substitute for (4) the system

$$\text{Prob. } y = a_2, \text{ Prob. } v = a_2 c_2 . \quad . \quad (6)$$

Again, when it is known that the first observation is a correct one, the probability that an indicator directed at random to the quadrant in which the star is situated will point below the star is $p_1$.   This, too, is a conditional probability.   Symbolically, it is the probability that if the event $w$ occur, the event $z$ will occur.   Hence, as the probability of the occurrence of $w$ is $a_1c_1$, we have

$$\text{Prob. } wz = a_1c_1p_1 \quad . \quad . \quad . \quad . \quad (7)$$

In like manner we find

$$\text{Prob. } vz = a_2c_2p_2 \quad . \quad . \quad . \quad (8)$$

Lastly, it is supposed that the values $p$ and $q$ are different. This involves the condition that the observations cannot both be correct.   Whence we have the logical equation.

$$wv = 0 \quad . \quad . \quad . \quad . \quad . \quad (9)$$

This completes the analysis of the logical elements involved in the data of the problem.   We now proceed to analyse those involved in its quæsitum or object proposed.

That object is to determine the probability of the event $z$, when the occurrence of the events $x$ and $y$ is known.   Symbolically expressed, it is the value of the fraction

$$\frac{\text{Prob. } xyz}{\text{Prob. } xy}$$

or, as it may, by resolving the denominator, be written,

$$\frac{\text{Prob. } xyz}{\text{Prob. } xyz + \text{Prob. } xy\bar{z}} \quad . \quad . \quad . \quad (10)$$

To effect this object, we shall determine the value of Prob. $xyz$ and Prob. $xy\bar{z}$ separately.

Collecting the elements furnished by the preceding analysis, the first of the partial problems herein involved may be thus stated :—

$$\text{Given} \quad \left. \begin{array}{ll} \text{Prob. } x = a_1 & \text{Prob. } y = a_2 \\ \text{Prob. } w = a_1c_1 & \text{Prob. } v = a_2c_2 \\ \text{Prob. } wz = a_1c_1p_1 & \text{Prob. } vz = a_2c_2p_2 \end{array} \right\} \quad . \quad (11)$$

with the conditions, $w\bar{x} = 0, v\bar{y} = 0, wv = 0$ . . (12)

Required $u$, the value of Prob. $xyz$.

In selecting the above, I have chosen to employ (3) in place of (1), and (6) in place of (4).   It makes no difference to the final result.

$$wz = s, \quad vz = t, \quad xyz = \phi \quad . \quad . \quad . \quad (13)$$

we must then from (12) and (13) determine $\phi$ as a developed function of $x$, $y$, $w$, $v$, $s$, and $t$.

This problem admits of perfectly definite solution on the principles of the calculus of Logic. I shall here merely give the result, and point out a method by which it may be independently verified. We find

$$\phi = xyws\bar{v}\bar{t} + xyvt\bar{w}\bar{s} + 0(xws\bar{y}\bar{v}\bar{t} + yvt\bar{x}\bar{w}\bar{s} + x\bar{y}\bar{w}\bar{v}\bar{s}\bar{t}$$
$$+ y\bar{x}\bar{w}\bar{v}\bar{s}\bar{t} + \bar{x}\bar{y}\bar{w}\bar{v}\bar{s}\bar{t} + xyw\bar{v}\bar{s}\bar{t} + xw\bar{y}\bar{v}\bar{s}\bar{t} + xyvw\bar{w}\bar{s}\bar{t}$$
$$+ yv\bar{x}\bar{w}\bar{s}\bar{t}) + \frac{0}{0}xy\bar{w}\bar{v}\bar{s}\bar{t} + \text{terms whose coefficient is} \frac{1}{0} \quad (14)$$

We may verify this expansion by substituting for $s$ and $t$ their values $wz$ and $vz$, paying attention to the conditions (12), and then comparing the result with the value of $\phi$, viz., $xyz$.

Thus the term $xyws\bar{v}\bar{t}$ becomes, on substitution

$$xyw\bar{v} \times wz \times (1 - vz) = xyzw\bar{v}$$

by the calculus of Logic. Now this represents a class entirely included in the class $xyz$, whence the coefficient of the term is unity.

The term $xws\bar{y}\bar{v}\bar{t}$ reduces to $xwz\bar{y}\bar{v}$, and represents a class no part of which is included in $xyz$, whence the coefficient is 0.

The term $xy\bar{w}\bar{v}\bar{s}\bar{t}$ reduces to $xy\bar{w}\bar{v}$, and represents a class some part of which is included, and some part not included under the class $xyz$, whence the coefficient $\frac{0}{0}$; for an event included under the former class may or may not be included under the latter.

Lastly, any term whose coefficient in the expansion is $\frac{1}{0}$ would, on effecting the above-named substitutions, become 0, indicating the absolute non-existence of the class which it represents.

Resuming the value of $\phi$, and adopting the simplification of Art. 21, we find for V the value

$$V = xyws + xyvt + xws + yvt + x + y + 1 + xy\ w$$
$$+ xw + xyv + yv + xy = (x + 1)(y + 1)$$
$$+ yv(x + 1)(t + 1) + xw(y + 1)(s + 1) \quad . \quad (15)$$

and hence we have the following system of algebraic equations :

$$\frac{x(y+1) + xyv(t+1) + xw(y+1)(s+1)}{a_1}$$

$$= \frac{y(x+1) + yv(x+1)(t+1) + xwy(s+1)}{a_2}$$

$$= \frac{xw(y+1)(s+1)}{a_1c_1} = \frac{yv(x+1)(t+1)}{a_2c_2}$$

$$= \frac{xw(y+1)s}{a_1c_1p_1} = \frac{yv(x+1)t}{a_2c_2p_2} = \frac{xyws + xyvt + cxy}{u}$$

$$= (x+1)(y+1) + yv(x+1)(t+1)$$
$$+ xw(y+1)(s+1) \quad . \quad . \quad (16)$$

From these equations, if we assume

$$(x+1)(y+1) + yv(x+1)(t+1)$$
$$+ xw(y+1)(s+1) = \lambda,$$

$\lambda$ being a subsidiary quantity introduced for convenience, we readily deduce

$$u = \frac{xyws + wyvt + cxy}{\lambda} \quad . \quad . \quad . \quad (17)$$

$$a_1c_1p_1 = \frac{xws(y+1)}{\lambda}$$

$$a_2(1-c_2) = \frac{y(x+1) + xwy(s+1)}{\lambda}$$

$$1 - a_2c_2 = \frac{(x+1)(y+1) + xw(y+1)(s+1)}{\lambda}.$$

Hence

$$\frac{a_1c_1p_1 \times a_2(1-c_2)}{1 - a_2c_2} = \frac{xyws}{\lambda} \quad . \quad . \quad . \quad (18)$$

In like manner

$$\frac{a_2c_2p_2 \times a_1(1-c_1)}{1 - a_1c_1} = \frac{xyvt}{\lambda} \quad . \quad . \quad (19)$$

Again we have

$$a_1(1-c_1) = \frac{x(y+1) + xyv(t+1)}{\lambda}$$

$$a_2(1-c_2) = \frac{y(x+1) + xwy(s+1)}{\lambda}$$

Y

$$1 - a_1 c_1 - a_2 c_2 = \frac{(x+1)(y+1)}{\lambda}$$

$$1 - a_1 c_1 = \frac{(x+1)(y+1) + yv(x+1)(t+1)}{\lambda}$$

$$1 - a_2 c_2 = \frac{(x+1)(y+1) + xw(y+1)(s+1)}{\lambda}$$

Whence we find

$$\frac{a_1(1-c_1)a_2(1-c_2)(1-a_1c_1-a_2c_2)}{(1-a_1c_1)(1-a_2c_2)} = \frac{xy}{\lambda} \quad . \quad (20)$$

By means of (18), (19), and (20), we reduce (17) to the form

$$u = \frac{a(1-c_2)}{1-a_2c_2}a_1c_1p_1 + \frac{a_1(1-c_1)}{1-a_1c_1}a_2c_2p_2$$
$$+ c\frac{a_1(1-c_1)a_2(1-c_2)(1-a_1c_1-a_2c_2)}{(1-a_1c_1)(1-a_2c_2)}$$

therefore effecting a slight reduction

$$\text{Prob. } xyz = \frac{a_1(1-c_1)a_2(1-c_2)}{(1-a_1c_1)(1-a_2c_2)} \left\{ \frac{1-a_1c_1}{1-c_1}c_1p_1 \right.$$
$$+ \left. \frac{1-a_2c_2}{1-c_2}c_2p_2 + c(1-a_1c_1-a_2c_2) \right\} \quad . \quad (21)$$

The arbitrary constant $c$, interpreted according to the rule, is the probability that if the event $xy\bar{w}\bar{v}\bar{s}\bar{t}$ take place, $xyz$ will take place. Putting for $\bar{s}$ and $\bar{t}$ their values, and reducing as before, we find that $c$ is the probability that if $xy\bar{w}\bar{v}$ take place, $xyz$ will take place. In the end this amounts to the following statement.

$c =$ probability that if both observations are incorrect, a pointer directed at random to the quadrant in which the star is situated will point below the star.

The value of Prob. $xy\bar{z}$ will be obtained from that of Prob. $xyz$ by changing $p_1 p_2$ and $c$ into $1 - p_1$, $1 - p_2$, and $1 - c$. If we effect this change, and then substitute the expressions above found, in the formula,

$$\frac{\text{Prob. } xyz}{\text{Prob. } xyz + \text{Prob. } xy\bar{z}}$$

we shall find

$$\frac{\text{Prob. } xyz}{\text{Prob. } xy}$$

$$
= \frac{\dfrac{1-a_1c_1}{1-c_1}c_1p_1 + \dfrac{1-a_2c_2}{1-c_2}c_2p_2 + c(1-a_1c_1-a_2c_2)}{\dfrac{1-a_1c_1}{1-c_1}c_1 + \dfrac{1+a_2c_2}{1-c_2}c_2 + 1 - a_1c_1 - a_2c_2}
$$

$$
= \frac{\dfrac{1-a_1c_1}{1-c_1}c_1p_1 + \dfrac{1-a_2c_2}{1-c_2}c_2p_2 + c(1-a_1c_1-a_2c_2)}{1 + \dfrac{1-a_1}{1-c_1}c_1 + \dfrac{1-a_2}{1-c_2}c_2} \qquad (22)
$$

This expression involves an arbitrary constant $c$ which we have no means of determining.   This circumstance indicates that those principles of probability which relate to the combination of *events* do not *alone* suffice to enable us to combine into a definite result the conflicting measures of an astronomical observation.

The arbitrary character of the final solution might have been inferred from the appearance of the symbol $\dfrac{0}{0}$ in (14). I have thought it better to complete the investigation, especially as it will serve as a model for the one which follows.

24.  Before proceeding to the second solution of the problem, I will endeavour to explain the principle on which it will be founded.   It is involved in the following definition.

*Definition.*   The mean strength of any probabilities of an event which are founded upon different judgments or observations is to be measured by that supposed probability of the event *à priori* which those judgments or observations following thereupon would not tend to alter.

Thus, suppose we were considering the question of the suitableness of a newly discovered island for the growth of a particular plant, and that the probability of its suitableness, as dependent upon general impressions of the climate were $r$;  but that added special observations,—such as analysis of the soil, determination of allied species growing in the locality, &c., had some of them the effect of raising, others that of depressing, the general expectation before entertained. Now we might suppose that expectation to have had such a measure, that the added observations should, when united, leave the mind in the same state as before. I call that measure the *mean value* of the testimonies—the value about which, to adopt (for illustration, not for argument) a mechanical analogy, they balance each other. I conceive that in thus doing, I am only giving a scientific meaning to a term which has been hitherto used in a vague sense. I shall show that the formula of the arithmetical mean is a special determination applicable only to particular problems, of the more general mean of which I here speak, and that other determinations of it exist, applicable to other problems, but possessing, in common, certain definite characteristics.

To apply this principle to the problem under consideration, we must add to the data a new element, viz., the *à priori* value of Prob. $z$, i.e. the value which the mind is supposed to attach to it before the evidence furnished by the observations. We will suppose this value $r$. We must then seek, as before, the *à posteriori* value of Prob. $z$, i.e. its value after the observations, and, equating the two expressions, determine thence the value of $r$.

I shall, in referring to the above principle, speak of it as the " principle of the mean ".

### Special solution of Problem I. founded upon the principle of the mean

Assigning to $z$ the *à priori* probability $r$, our data are the following :—

Prob. $x = a_1$, Prob. $y = a_2$, Prob. $z = r$, Prob. $w = a_1 c_1$, Prob. $v = a_2 c_2$, Prob. $wz = a_1 c_1 p_1$, Prob. $vz = a_2 c_2 p_2$

with the conditions

$$w\bar{x} = 0, \; v\bar{y} = 0, \; wv = 0$$

and hence we are to seek, as before, the value of

$$\frac{\text{Prob. } xyz}{\text{Prob. } xyz + \text{Prob. } xy\bar{z}} \quad . \quad . \quad . \quad (1)$$

Assuming then as before,

$$wz = s, \ vz = t, \ xyz = \phi$$

we find, by the calculus of Logic, the following expression for $\phi$ as a developed logical function of $x$, $y$, $w$, $v$, $s$, $t$, and $z$, viz. :

$$\phi = xywsz\bar{v}\bar{t} + xyvtz\bar{w}\bar{s} + xy\bar{w}\bar{v}s\bar{t} + 0(xyv\bar{w}\bar{s}\bar{t}z$$
$$+ yvzt\bar{x}\bar{w}\bar{s} + yv\bar{x}\bar{w}\bar{s}z\bar{t} + xyws\bar{z}\bar{v}\bar{t} + xwzs\bar{y}\bar{v}\bar{t}$$
$$+ xw\bar{y}\bar{z}\bar{v}s\bar{t} + xy\bar{z}\bar{v}\bar{w}s\bar{t} + xz\bar{y}\bar{v}\bar{w}s\bar{t} + yz\bar{x}\bar{s}\bar{v}\bar{w}\bar{t}$$
$$+ x\bar{y}\bar{z}\bar{v}\bar{w}s\bar{t} + y\bar{x}\bar{z}\bar{v}\bar{w}s\bar{t} + z\bar{x}\bar{y}\bar{v}\bar{w}s\bar{t} + \bar{x}\bar{y}\bar{z}\bar{v}\bar{w}s\bar{t})$$

$$+ \text{terms with coefficient } \frac{1}{0} \quad . \quad . \quad (2)$$

Hence, adopting the simplification of Art. 21, we have

$$V = xywsz + xyvtz + xyz + xyv + yvzt + yv + xyw$$
$$+ xwzs + xw + xy + xz + yz + x + y + z + 1$$
$$= xw(y + 1)(zs + 1) + yv(x + 1)(zt + 1)$$
$$+ (x + 1)(y + 1)(z + 1) \quad . \quad . \quad (3)$$

whence we form the algebraic system

$$\frac{xw(y + 1)(zs + 1) + xyv(zt + 1) + x(y + 1)(z + 1)}{a_1}$$

$$= \frac{xwy(zs + 1) + yv(x + 1)(zt + 1) + (x + 1)y(z + 1)}{a_2}$$

$$= \frac{xw(y + 1)(zs + 1)}{a_1 c_1} = \frac{yv(x + 1)(zt + 1)}{a_2 c_2}$$

$$= \frac{xw(y + 1)zs}{a_1 c_1 p_1} = \frac{yv(x + 1)zt}{a_2 c_2 p_2}$$

$$= \frac{xw(y + 1)zs + yv(x + 1)zt + (x + 1)(y + 1)z}{r}$$

$$= \frac{xyzws + xyzvt + xyz}{u}$$

$$= \frac{xw(y + 1)(zs + 1) + yv(x + 1)(zt + 1) + (x + 1)(y + 1)(z + 1)}{1} = \lambda . \quad (4)$$

$\lambda$ being a subsidiary quantity introduced for convenience.

From the above we find

$$a_2 - a_2 c_2 = \frac{xyw(zs + 1) + y(x + 1)(z + 1)}{\lambda}$$

$$a_1 c_1 p_1 = \frac{xwzs(y + 1)}{\lambda}$$

$$1 - a_2 c_2 = \frac{xw(y + 1)(zs + 1) + (x + 1)(y + 1)(z + 1)}{\lambda}$$

whence

$$\frac{a_2(1 - c_2)}{1 - a_2 c_2} a_1 c_1 p_1 = \frac{xyzws}{\lambda} \quad . \quad . \quad . \quad (5)$$

In like manner we find

$$\frac{a_1(1 - c_1)}{1 - a_1 c_1} a_2 c_2 p_2 = \frac{xyzvt}{\lambda} \quad . \quad . \quad . \quad (6)$$

Again, since we have from the above

$$\frac{a_2 - a_2 c_2}{1 - a_2 c_2} = \frac{y}{y + 1} \quad \text{and} \quad \frac{a_1 - a_1 c_1}{1 - a_1 c_1} = \frac{x}{x + 1}$$

we have

$$\frac{a_1(1 - c_1)a_2(1 - c_2)}{(1 - a_1 c_1)(1 - a_2 c_2)} = \frac{xy}{(x + 1)(y + 1)}$$

moreover,

$$r - a_1 c_1 p_1 - a_2 c_2 p_2 = \frac{(x + 1)(y + 1)z}{\lambda}.$$

Multiplying the two last equations together we find

$$\frac{a_1(1 - c_1)a_2(1 - c_2)}{(1 - a_1 c_1)(1 - a_2 c_2)}(r - a_1 c_1 p_1 - a_2 c_2 p_2) = \frac{xyz}{\lambda} \quad (7)$$

Now,

$$u = \frac{xyzws + xyzvt + xyz}{\lambda}.$$

Substituting in this expression the values found for its several terms in (5), (6) and (7), we have

$$u = \frac{a_2(1 - c_2)}{1 - a_2 c_2} a_1 c_1 p_1 + \frac{a_1(1 - c_1)}{1 - a_1 c_1} a_2 c_2 p_2$$
$$+ \frac{a_1(1 - c_1)a_2(1 - c_2)}{(1 - a_1 c_1)(1 - a_2 c_2)}(r - a_1 c_1 p_1 - a_2 c_2 p_2).$$

This is the value of Prob. $xyz$. That of Prob. $xy\bar{z}$ will be found by simply changing in the above expression $p_1$, $p_2$, and $r$, into $1 - p_1$, $1 - p_2$, and $1 - r$ respectively.   These expressions admit of some reductions, and give

Prob. $xyz$

$$= \frac{a_1(1 - c_1)a_2(1 - c_2)}{(1 - a_1c_1)(1 - a_2c_2)} \left\{ \frac{1 - a_1}{1 - c_1} c_1 p_1 + \frac{1 - a_2}{1 - c_2} c_2 p_2 + r \right\} \quad (8)$$

Prob. $xy\bar{z}$

$$= \frac{a_1(1 - c_1)a_2(1 - c_2)}{(1 - a_1c_1)(1 - a_2c_2)} \left\{ \frac{1 - a_1}{1 - c_1} c_1(1 - p_1) \right.$$
$$\left. + \frac{1 - a_2}{1 - c_2} c_2(1 - p_2) + 1 - r \right\} \quad . \quad (9)$$

whence we find for the *à posteriori* value of Prob. $z$,

$$\frac{\text{Prob. } xyz}{\text{Prob. } xy} = \frac{\dfrac{1 - a_1}{1 - c_1} c_1 p_1 + \dfrac{1 - a_2}{1 - c_2} c_2 p_2 + r}{\dfrac{1 - a_1}{1 - c_1} c_1 + \dfrac{1 - a_2}{1 - c_2} c_2 + 1}.$$

Equating this to $r$ we have

$$\frac{1 - a_1}{1 - c_1} c_1 p_1 + \frac{1 - a_2}{1 - c_2} c_2 p_2 + r = \left( \frac{1 - a_1}{1 - c_1} c_1 + \frac{1 - a_2}{1 - c_2} + 1 \right) r.$$

Whence

$$r = \frac{\dfrac{1 - a_1}{1 - c_1} c_1 p_1 + \dfrac{1 - a_2}{1 - c_2} c_2 p_2}{\dfrac{1 - a_1}{1 - c_1} c_1 + \dfrac{1 - a_2}{1 - c_2} c_2} \quad . \quad (10)$$

26. Such is the final general expression for the probable altitude of the star.   The following observations may throw light upon its real nature :—

1*st*.  In the analysis by which this expression was obtained, $p_1$ and $p_2$ are the observed altitudes of the star, a quadrant of the celestial are being taken as unity.   Considered, however, as the expression, not of a *probability*, but of the most probable measure of a physical magnitude, the truth of the formula will of course be independent of the unit of magnitude.

2*ndly*.  The formula is independent of mechanical analogy. We may place it in the well-known form

$$r = W_1 p_1 + W_2 p_2 \quad . \quad . \quad . \quad . \quad (1)$$

in which, as the subject is usually treated, $W_1$ and $W_2$ are called the *weights* of the observations. Here, however, these quantities are determined as functions of the initial data—these data being probabilities. We have

$$W_1 = \frac{\dfrac{1-a_1}{1-c_1}c_1}{\dfrac{1-a_1}{1-c_1}c_1 + \dfrac{1-a_2}{1-c_2}c_2} \qquad W_2 = \frac{\dfrac{1-a_2}{1-c_2}c_2}{\dfrac{1-a_1}{1-c_1}c_1 + \dfrac{1-a_2}{1-c_2}c_2} \ . \quad (2)$$

3*dly.* The initial probabilities, of which $W_1$ and $W_2$ are functions are neither foreign nor imaginary elements. They may be difficult to determine, but theoretically their determination rests upon considerations which are entirely proper to the subject. When an observation has been made, the question whether it is correct or not is a question of probability. We can never predicate absolute correctness. We can seldom affirm absolutely that an observation is incorrect. Our knowledge of the circumstances of the observation Art. 22, leads us to regard the probability in question as sometimes greater, sometimes less. To suppose it capable of a numerical value, as we have done, by the introduction of the constants $c_1 c_2$, is then perfectly legitimate. It has been said that an estimate of the correctness of the observation rests upon the circumstances by which it was accompanied. These circumstances, taken in the aggregate, are themselves a subject of probability. This we express by the introduction of the constants $a_1 a_2$. The probability after an observation is made that it is correct, and the probability before it is made that the state of things shall be such as to give to the result that particular probability of correctness, are quite different things.

4*thly.* In the same course of observations made by the same individual with consciously uniform regard to personal and instrumental accuracy the values of $a_1$ and $a_2$ would be sensibly equal. The formula (10) would thus reduce to the following, viz. :—

$$r = \frac{\dfrac{c_1}{1-c_1}p_1 + \dfrac{c_2}{1-c_2}p_2}{\dfrac{c_1}{1-c_1} + \dfrac{c_2}{1-c_1}} \ .$$

Here

$$W_1 = \frac{\dfrac{c_1}{1-c_1}}{\dfrac{c_1}{1-c_1} + \dfrac{c_2}{1-c_2}}. \qquad W_2 = \frac{\dfrac{c_2}{1-c_2}}{\dfrac{c_1}{1-c_1} + \dfrac{c_2}{1-c_2}}.$$

If $c_1 = 1$, we have

$$W_1 = 1, \; W_2 = 0$$

and

$$r = p_1.$$

This accords with the condition that if either of the observations is believed to be correct, the value which it furnishes for the altitude of the star must be taken as the true one.

$5thly$. If $c_1 = c_2$, i.e. if we have no right to give preference to one observation over the other, we have

$$r = \frac{p_1 + p_2}{2},$$

the formula of the arithmetical mean.

$6thly$. From the form of $W_1$, $W_2$ in (4), it is evident that the weights, so to speak, of the observations vary in a higher ratio than that of the simple probabilities of correctness of the observations. The practical lesson to be drawn from this is, that we ought to attach a greater weight to good observations, and a smaller to bad ones, than, according to usual modes of consideration, we should be disposed to do.

The above are the most important observations suggested by the formula to which the last investigation has led. One or two remarks remain to be offered upon the analysis by which it was obtained.

Although the two forms of investigation which we have exhibited differ, there is nothing inconsistent in the results to which they lead. If we compare corresponding formulae in the two, e.g. the values of Prob. $xyz$, or those of Prob. $xy\bar{z}$, we shall find that the one investigation assigns a definite but consistent value to what the other left arbitrary. Either comparison gives

$$c = \frac{r - a_1 c_1 p_1 - a_2 c_2 p_2}{1 - a_1 c_1 - a_2 c_2}.$$

We may prove, either by the " conditions of possible experience," or independently that this value is necessarily a proper positive fraction, and this accords with the interpretation of $c$ as a probability.    Art. 23.

27. But a much more important consideration is the following.    It is a plain consequence of the logical theory of probabilities, that the state of expectation which accompanies entire ignorance of an event is properly represented, not by the fraction $\frac{1}{2}$, but by the indefinite form $\frac{0}{0}$.    And this agrees with a conclusion at which Bishop Terrot, on independent, but as I think just grounds, has arrived.*    Now this shows, why, if the consideration of the *à priori* probability of $z$ is, from the insufficiency of the remaining data, necessary in order to give to the *à posteriori* probability of $z$ a definite value, the solution obtained when that *à priori* value is neglected should involve the symbol $\frac{0}{0}$.    The presence of this symbol in a solution always indicates insufficiency in the data.    And herein, as it seems to me, consists the reason why the mind, impatient of incertitude even while dealing with the very science of uncertain knowledge, is led to seek escape from its doubts, by calling in the aid, in some form or another, of that adventitious principle which I have denominated the principle of the mean.    I say in some form or another; for I can conceive of another form of the same principle connected more directly with the idea of a *limit* than with that of a mean.    Thus as testimonies which are insufficient of themselves to produce a definite expectation may definitely modify a definite expectation previously formed, we have suggested to us the idea of that limiting state to which perpetual and independent repetition of the same series of testimonies would cause the mind, whatever its starting point of expectation might be, to tend.    And as this limiting state would be one which a further repetition would not alter, we should thus arrive in effect at the same solution as is indicated by the principle of the mean, in its direct expression.

28. I have extended the preceding analysis to the case in which three observations are to be combined, a case which,

* Transactions of the Royal Society of Edinburgh, vol. xxi, p. 375.

in connection with the previous one, is sufficient to determine the general law.   The result is what the preceding analysis suggests, and may be expressed in the following theorem :—

If $n$ conflicting observations assign to the altitude of a star the respective values, $p_1 p_2 . . p_n$; if, moreover, $a_1 a_2 . . a_n$ are the antecedent probabilities that the observations will be such as they prove to be with respect to those circumstances which determine their relative accuracy, and $c_1 c_2 . . c_n$ their respective probabilities of correctness to a mind acquainted with these circumstances, i.e. to the mind of the observer after the observations have been made, then the most probable altitude of the star will be

$$\frac{\dfrac{1-a_1}{1-c_1}c_1 p_1 + \dfrac{1-a_2}{1-c_2}c_2 p_2 \cdots + \dfrac{1-a_n}{1-c_n}c_n p_n}{\dfrac{1-a_1}{1-c_1}c_1 + \dfrac{1-a_2}{1-c_2}c_2 \cdots + \dfrac{1-a_n}{1-c_n}c_n}.$$

This expression admits of the same deductions as the one before obtained for the case in which the observations are two in number, and in particular it leads, when the circumstances of the observations are judged to be in all respects the same, to the principle of the arithmetical mean expressed by the formula

$$\frac{p_1 + p_2 . . + p_n}{n}.$$

29.   I have remarked that the principle of the arithmetical mean has some claim to be regarded as axiomatic.   In the preceding sections it presents itself as a special result of a very complex analysis founded upon the logical theory of probabilities.   Now I wish to observe that there is nothing in these circumstances which we have a right to regard as denoting inconsistency.   Of the theory of probabilities it is eminently true that modes of investigation, which to our present conceptions must appear fundamentally different, habitually lead us to the same result.   A profounder acquaintance with the laws of the human mind, and a deeper insight into the relations of things, might perhaps show us that principles which appear to us to have nothing in common may yet have a necessary connexion with each other,—may

possibly spring up from a common origin.  I will endeavour to make my meaning clear by two illustrations, which will present this question in somewhat different lights.

30. An idea which seems naturally to suggest itself in connection with the theory of probabilities is that of mechanical analogy.  Evidence of this we see in the language, already referred to, which attributes *weight* to observation. The complete and scientific development of the idea will be found in a memoir by Professor Donkin,* who, establishing a kind of metaphysical statics on proofs of the same nature as those which are employed in deducing *à priori* the laws of ordinary statics, has arrived, by legitimate deduction, at the remotest consequences of Gauss's theory of the combination of observations.  The mind, in the developed analogy, is compared to a lever acted upon by different weights, or to a mechanical system subject to given forces, and seeking, under this action, a position of equilibrium. Now it is at least a very remarkable circumstance, that an analogy of this kind should not only admit of exact scientific expression, but should, through a long train of analytical consequences, present the same laws and results, and suggest the same methods, as the principle of the arithmetical mean already referred to.   All the abstract terms by which mental states and emotions are expressed derive, if philology be of any value, their origin from outward and material things. And hence, though it might be impossible to ascend historically to the first employment of those expressions which describe the mind under the action of *forces,* and speak of the *balancing* of opinions, we cannot doubt that a perceived analogy was their source.  But it could hardly have been anticipated that this analogy should remain complete and unimpaired through so lengthened a range of scientific deductions.

To what I have said above I will only add that it is as instruments of expression and communication, rather than of thought, that material symbols, and the analogies which they furnish, seem to me to possess importance.  Even the

* Sur la Theorie de la Combinaison des Observations. *Liouville's* Journal des Mathematiques, tom xv., 1850.

analogy which we have been considering cannot of itself occupy the place of a first principle, but seems to be a particular manifestation of that deeper truth of which Leibnitz had a glimpse when he spoke of the principle of fitness and congruity—"*principe de la convenance*," *—the ground of rational mechanics. Of course, I do not contemplate this or any subjective principle whatever, as affording us the slightest ground for affirming that the constitution of nature must, *à priori*, possess such and such a character. But it does seem to be a fact that the material system has been constituted in a certain degree of accordance with our rational faculties. The study of this accordance, *à posteriori*, is a perfectly legitimate object; and I think it the more interesting, when it brings before our view the scientific form of any of those analogies which commended themselves to the minds of the fathers of our race, which are embodied in our common speech, and without which we could apparently never hold converse with our fellows, except upon material objects.

31. The second illustration which I have to offer is the following. Many of the most important applications of the theory of probabilities, the method of least squares, for example, rest upon what has been termed the law of facility of error. This consists in the position, that in seeking to determine by observation a physical magnitude, as the elevation of a star, the probability that any measure will deviate by a quantity $x$ from the true value, will vary directly as the function $\epsilon^{-k^2 x^2}$ where $k$ is a constant quantity, the probability that our measure will fall between the limits $x$ and $x + dx$ being expressed by the function

$$\frac{k}{\sqrt{\pi}} \epsilon^{-k^2 x^2} dx \quad \ldots \ldots \ldots (1)$$

Gauss has shown that this is the only "law of facility" consistent with the assumption that, in a series of observations of the same magnitude, the arithmetical mean of the several measures obtained is the most probable value. It may even be shown, that whatever the actual "law of

* *Erdmann's* Edit., p. 716.

facility ", under given circumstances may be, and it is plain
that it must vary with circumstances, such as the constitution of the instrument and the character of the observer, &c.,
the probability that the arithmetical mean of a very large
number of values determined by observation will deviate
from some fixed value by a quantity $x$, will vary directly as
$\epsilon^{-k^2x^2}$, $k$ being a constant dependent upon the nature of
the observations.*   Such at least, is the limiting form of the
function to which the law of deviation approaches as the
number of observations is increased.   Now it is remarkable
that considerations of a totally different kind, and founded
mainly upon our conceptions of space, lead to a similar
result.   The probability of linear deviation (measured in a
given direction) of a ball from a mark at which it is aimed,
seems to obey the same law; the principle upon which that
law is determined being, not that of the arithmetical mean,
but rather a principle of geometrical consistency, intimately
connected with our ideas of the composition of motion.

The principle was first stated in a popular and somewhat
inexact form by Sir John Herschel, I believe, in the
Edinburgh Review.†   It was afterwards made the subject
of an adverse criticism in the Philosophical Magazine, by
Mr. Leslie Ellis.‡   There is no living mathematician for
whose intellectual character I entertain a more sincere
respect than I do for that of Mr. Ellis; and even while
stating the grounds upon which I differ from him, with
respect to the value of Sir John Herschel's principle, I
avail myself of his labours in giving to that principle a more
scientific form and expression and in developing its consequences.   The language adopted in the following statement
will be, as far as possible, that of the author of the principle,—
the analysis will be that of Mr. Ellis.

Suppose a ball dropped from a given height, with the
intention that it shall fall on a given mark.   Now, taking

* For some very interesting illustrations of this doctrine, see the letters
of M. Bravais, published in the notes to Quetelet's Letters on the Theory of
Probabilities.
† Vol. xcii, p. 17, Art. Quetelet on Probabilities.
‡ Vol. xxxvii. p. 321, "Letter addressed to J. D. Forbes, Esq., Professor
of Natural Philosophy in the University of Edinburgh, on an alleged proof
of the Method of Least Squares."

the mark as the origin of two rectangular axes, let it be assumed that the actual deviation observed is a compound event, of which the two components are the corresponding deviations measured along the rectangular axes. Grant also, that the latter deviations are independent events. Further, let us represent by $f(x^2), f(y^2)$, the probabilities of the respective component deviations measured along the axes $x$ and $y$,—we give to them this form because, positive and negative deviations being equally probable, the function expressing probability must be an *even* one, i.e. must not change sign with the error. Hence the probability of the actual deviations observed will be $f(x^2) f(y^2)$. Let it be observed that this is not the probability of a deviation to the extent $\sqrt{x^2 + y^2}$ from the mark, but of a deviation to that extent *in a particular line of direction*. Now, let the principle be assumed, that this expression is independent of the position of the axes, i.e. that we may regard component deviations along any two rectangular axes as independent events, by the composition of which the actual deviation is produced. We have then $x'$ and $y'$ representing two new component deviations,

$$f(x^2)f(y^2) = f(x'^2)f(y'^2) \quad . \quad . \quad . \quad (2)$$

if $y' = \sqrt{x^2 + y^2}$ then $x' = 0$ and we have

$$f(x^2)f(y^2) = f(0)f(x^2 + y^2) \quad . \quad . \quad . \quad (3)$$

An equation of which the complete solution is,

$$f(x^2) = A\epsilon^{hx^2}$$

A and $h$ being constants. The condition that the probability of the error must diminish as the amount of the error increases, requires that $h$ should be negative. We may therefore write, $-k^2$, for $h$. Whence

$$f(x^2) = A\epsilon^{-k^2x^2} \quad . \quad . \quad . \quad . \quad (4)$$

To apply this result to the case in which the ball is supposed at some point on the plane which, projected on the axis of $x$, will fall between $x$ and $x + \delta x$, we must give to A the form $C\,\delta x$. Thus we get the expression,

$$C\epsilon^{-k^2x^2}\delta x.$$

Lastly, the *certainty* that the ball must fall at some point for which the value of $x$ lies between $-\infty$ and $\infty$ gives us the equation,

$$\int_{-\infty}^{\infty} C\epsilon^{-k^2x^2}\delta x = 1,$$

whence $C\dfrac{\sqrt{\pi}}{k} = 1$ and $C = \dfrac{k}{\sqrt{\pi}}$. Thus, the probability of a deviation from the axis $y$ to a distance lying between $x$ and $x + \delta x$ will be given by the formula

$$\frac{k}{\sqrt{\pi}}\epsilon^{-k^2x^2}\delta x \quad . \quad . \quad . \quad . \quad . \quad (5)$$

an expression which agrees with (1).

In like manner, the probability that the ball will deviate to a distance greater than $y$ and less than $y + \delta y$ from the axis $x$ will be

$$\frac{k}{\sqrt{\pi}}\epsilon^{-k^2y^2},$$

whence the probability that it will actually fall upon the elementary area $\delta x\delta y$ will be

$$\frac{k^2}{\pi}\epsilon^{-k^2(x^2+y^2)}\delta x\delta y.$$

Now, this result admits of a remarkable confirmation. For it is manifest that the probability that the ball will fall *somewhere* between the distances $x$ and $x + \delta x$ from the axis $y$, ought to be equal to the above expression integrated with respect to $y$ between the limits $-\infty$ and $\infty$. But that probability has been already determined to be $\dfrac{k}{\sqrt{\pi}}\epsilon^{-k^2x^2}\delta x$; we ought, therefore, to have

$$\int_{-\infty}^{\infty} \left(\frac{k^2}{\pi}\epsilon^{-k^2(x^2+y^2)}\delta x\right)\delta y = \frac{k}{\sqrt{\pi}}\epsilon^{-k^2x^2}\delta x \quad . \quad . \quad (6)$$

an equation which is actually true

Mr. Ellis considers this as showing that the principle from which the demonstration sets out, viz., that the actual deviation of the ball from the mark may be regarded as a compound event, of which the two independent components are the deviations from the axes, involves either a mistake or a *petitio principii*. But consistency of results can never be a proof of mistake in the principles from which they are deduced; and *alone*, it offers no adequate ground for the suspicion of a *petitio principii*. It is to be observed, that it is only the probability of deviation from a fixed axis which follows, according to the above investigation, the law expressed by Gauss's function. The probability of deviation in *any* direction to a distance between $r$ and $r + \delta r$ from the mark, is expressed by a different function. This would be fatal to any hypothesis which should represent Gauss's function as determining, *à priori*, the actual law of deviation. There are indeed, few cases in which it can be determined what the law is, and writers on probability have been far too anxious to interpret nature in accordance with their formulae. No one has shown this more clearly than Mr. Ellis. The precise value of Sir John Herschel's principle, as corrected by him, I conceive to be this, —that it establishes an identity between the law of facility of error expressed by Gauss's function and the law which in a special problem involving the consideration of space and motion, seems to accord with our most elementary conceptions of these things; and this identity I apprehend to be, not an accidental thing, but a very distinct expression of that harmonious relation which binds together the different spheres of thought and existence.

33. We proceed next to the consideration of the second general problem—that in which it is proposed to determine the combined force of two testimonies or judgments in support of a fact, the strength of each separate testimony being given.

The problem has a material as well as a formal aspect. Thus, oral testimonies differ from the judgments which are furnished by the immediate personal observation of facts. And although no definite general laws have, so far as I am aware, been assigned concerning the mode in which the material character of the evidence affects expectation, it is not to be doubted that an influence does proceed from this source. As respects testimony alone, there are cases in which we feel that it is cumulative,—there are cases in which we feel that it is not so; and this difference we also feel

z

depends upon the nature of the testimony itself.  But in the majority of cases, we should probably feel that the elements upon which this difference of character depends are blended together, some decided preponderance being due to the one or the other.   Testimony will be chiefly or entirely cumulative which is given quite independently by different persons, and is at the same time, based upon different grounds. In proportion as these conditions fail of being satisfied, the testimony partakes less and less of the cumulative character. Still, this possession of cumulative character may be regarded as the standard by which the distinctive qualities of testimonies, as affecting belief or expectation, may be estimated. In judgments founded upon the personal observation of facts, though this character may be observed, the standard seems to be different.   When different modes of considering a subject—different courses of experiment or enquiry—lead to different probabilities of a fact, some making it more probable, some less, we generally feel that a kind of mean ought to be taken among them.   Perhaps the most succinct general statement would be, that it belongs to testimony, in its normal character, to be cumulative,—to judgment, to require the application, in some form or other, of the principle of means or averages; but that all departures from these normal states involve the blending of the two elements together, in proportions determined by the degree of the deflection.

Now, although it does not belong to the theory of probabilities, in its formal and scientific character, to pronounce upon the material character of a problem, and to say whether its data are in their own nature cumulative or not, yet the results to which the theory leads are, in a very remarkable degree, accordant with the distinctions which have just been pointed out.  I shall show that the solution of the problem of the combination of testimonies, when the data are presented in a purely formal character, and without any adventitious principle, involves arbitrary constants, and is therefore indefinite,—being capable, however, under certain circumstances, of assuming a definite form.  I shall show that such a form is assumed when the circumstances are such as to give to the testimonies the highest degree of cumulative character. I shall then solve the problem a second time, introducing that adventitious principle which I have already exemplified in the problem of the reduction of astronomical observations, and which appears to me to contain the true theory of means or averages. The form of the solution thus obtained, which is also perfectly definite, will apply to the case in which it is our object, not to combine testimonies in the ordinary sense of the term, but to determine the mean of expectations founded upon the issues of conflicting judgments. To one point of importance I must again, before entering upon the analytical investigation, ask the attention of the reader. It is, that in the present subject, the question of the right application of a formula is quite distinct from that of the validity of the processes by which that formula is derived from its data. The latter is a question of formal science, the former involves considerations which belong rather to the philosophy of the human mind.

I will first express the problem which we have to consider in a general form, equally applicable to the combination of testimonies or judgments. I shall consider the fact of a testimony having been borne, or an observation made, as a circumstance or event affecting our expectation of the event to which it has reference.

## Problem II

34. *Required the probability of an event* z, *when two circumstances* x *and* y *are known to be present—the probability of the event* z, *when we only know of the existence of the circumstance* x *being* p,—*and its probability when we only know of the existence of* y *being* q.

Here we are concerned with three events, $x$, $y$, and $z$. For convenience and uniformity I shall, in the solution of the problem, speak of $x$ and $y$ as *events*, as well as of $z$. A circumstance is an event—a state of things which comes to pass, or has come forth—*evenit*.

The data leave wholly arbitrary the probabilities of the

event $x$ and $y$. Thus $p$ and $q$ are *conditional* probabilities; $p$ is the probability that if the event $x$ occur, the event $z$ will occur; $q$ is the probability that if the event $y$ occur, the event $z$ will occur. Hence

$$p = \frac{\text{Prob. } xy}{\text{Prob. } x}, \quad q = \frac{\text{Prob. } yz}{\text{Prob. } y} \qquad . \quad . \quad . \quad (1)$$

Our object is to determine the probability that if the events $x$ and $y$ both occur, the event $z$ will occur. We have, therefore, to seek the value of the fraction

$$\frac{\text{Prob. } xyz}{\text{Prob. } xy},$$

or, as for our present purpose it is more convenient to say, of

$$\frac{\text{Prob. } xyz}{\text{Prob. } xyz + \text{Prob. } xy\bar{z}} \qquad . \quad . \quad . \quad (2)$$

In seeking the value of Prob. $xyz$, which we shall represent by $u$, the formal statement of our *data* and *quæsitum* will therefore be

Given $\quad \begin{cases} \text{Prob. } x = c, & \text{Prob. } y = c' \\ \text{Prob. } xz = cp, & \text{Prob. } yz = c'q \end{cases} \quad . \quad . \quad (3)$

Required $\qquad$ Prob. $xyz$.

$c$ and $c'$ being arbitrary constants expressing the unknown probabilities of the events $x$ and $y$.

A misconception may here arise respecting the meaning of Prob. $x$, Prob. $y$, which it is worth while to anticipate. In the case of testimony, Prob. $x$ would not mean the probability that a testimony would be borne, but the probability that the particular kind of testimony actually recorded considered with reference to its object, credibility, &c. would be borne. Testimonies differ not merely as to their degree of credibility, but as to their *unexpectedness*—as to the *surprise* which they occasion. And it is, I think, matter of personal experience that this unexpectedness is in itself an element affecting the strength of that expectation which combined testimonies produce. So too, if $x$ and $y$ are facts of observation, e.g. observed symptoms of a disease $z$, the probability of that disease, when both symptoms present themselves is not determined by the strength of the separate

XVI] STUDIES IN LOGIC AND PROBABILITY 357

presumptions merely, but is consciously increased by our knowledge of the rarity of the symptoms themselves. And thus the elements Prob. $x$ Prob. $y$ which have been introduced by a formal necessity of the statement of the problem are seen to belong to the very matter of its solution.

Making
$$xz = s,\ yz = t,\ xyz = \phi,$$
we find, by the calculus of Logic,

$$\phi = xyst + 0(xs\bar{y}\bar{t} + yt\bar{x}\bar{s} + xy^s\bar{t} + x\bar{y}\bar{s}\bar{t} + y\bar{x}\bar{s}\bar{t} + \bar{x}\bar{y}\bar{s}\bar{t})$$
$$+ \text{terms whose coefficients are } \frac{1}{0} \quad . \quad . \quad (4)$$

a result which may be verified by the method applied to (14) in Art. 23.

Hence we find, adopting the simplification of Art. 21.

$$V = xyst + xs + yt + xy + x + y + 1,$$
and since we have

Prob. $x = c$, Prob. $y = c'$, Prob. $s = cp$,
$$\text{Prob. } t = c'q, \text{ Prob. } xyz = u \quad . \quad (5)$$

we find, as an algebraic system of equations,

$$\left.\frac{xyst + xs + xy + x}{c} = \frac{xyst + yt + xy + y}{c'}\right.$$
$$= \frac{xyst + xs}{cp} = \frac{xyst + yt}{c'q}$$
$$\left.= \frac{xyst}{u} = xyst + xs + yt + xy + x + y + 1\right\} \quad (6)$$

This system is easily reduced to the form

$$\frac{xs}{cp - u} = \frac{yt}{c'q - u} = \frac{xy + x + y + 1}{1 + u - cp - c'q}$$
$$\left.= \frac{x + 1}{1 + u - cp - c'} = \frac{y + 1}{1 + u - c - c'q} = \frac{xyst}{u}\right\} \quad (7)$$

And if we equate the respective products of the first three and of the last three members of the above, we find

$$(cp - u)(c'q - u)(1 + u - cp - c'q)$$
$$= (1 + u - c' - cp)(1 + u - c - c'q)u \quad . \quad (8)$$

a quadratic equation by which the value of $u$ must be determined.

If, in like manner, we assume

$$\text{Prob. } xy\bar{z} = t$$

we shall find

$$\overline{(c\overline{1 - p}} - t)(c'\overline{1 - q} - t)(1 + t - c\overline{1 - p} - c'\overline{1 - q})$$
$$= (1 + t - c' - c\overline{1 - p})(1 + t - c - c'\overline{1 - q})t \quad . \quad (9)$$

From these equations the values of $u$ and $t$ being determined, we have finally

$$\frac{\text{Prob. } xyz}{\text{Prob. } xy} = \frac{u}{u + t} \quad . \quad . \quad . \quad (10)$$

Before we can apply this solution, we must determine the conditions of possible experience, and the conditions limiting the values of $u$ and $t$. For this purpose writing

$$\text{Prob. } xyz = u, \text{ Prob. } xy\bar{z} = t, \text{ Prob. } xz\bar{y} = \mu,$$

$$\text{Prob. } x\bar{y}\bar{z} = v, \text{ Prob. } yz\bar{x} = \rho, \text{ Prob. } y\bar{x}\bar{z} = \sigma,$$

we have, from the data, the equations,

$$u + t + \mu + v = c$$
$$u + t + \rho + \sigma = c'$$
$$u + \mu = cp$$
$$u + \rho = c'q,$$

to which must be added the inequations

$$u \gtrless 0, t \gtrless 0, \mu \gtrless 0, v \gtrless 0, \rho \gtrless 0, \sigma \gtrless 0$$

$$u + t + \mu + v + \rho + \sigma \lessgtr 1.$$

Proceeding as in Art. 14, we find ultimately as the conditions of possible experience

$$cp \lessgtr 1 - c'(1 - q), c'q \lessgtr 1 - c(1 - p) \quad . \quad (11)$$

together with the usual condition that $c$, $c'$, $p$ and $q$ must be positive proper fractions, or at any rate, must not transcend the values 0 and 1. We find, too, as the conditions limiting $u$ and $t$,

$$\left.\begin{array}{lll}
u \lessgtr cp & u \lessgtr c'q & \\
u \gtrless c + c'q - 1 & u \gtrless c' + cp - 1 & u \gtrless 0 \\
t \lessgtr c\overline{1 - p} & t \lessgtr c'\overline{1 - q} & \\
t \gtrless c + c'\overline{1 - q} - 1 & t \gtrless c' + \overline{c - p} - 1 & t \gtrless 0
\end{array}\right\} \quad (12)$$

The solution of the problem assumes therefore, the following form and character :—

1st. It involves two constants $c$ and $c'$, which are arbitrary, except in that they are subject to the conditions (11).

2ndly. The values of $u$ and $t$, determined from (8) and (9), in subjection to the conditions (12) are to be substituted in the formula (10).

3dly. In the absence of any means of determining $c$ and $c'$, the value obtained will be indeterminate, except for particular values of $p$ and $q$. Some general conclusions may, nevertheless, be deduced from its expression indicating the manner in which expectation is influenced by circumstances insufficient of themselves to give it a definite amount of strength. This will appear from the following analysis.

## Analysis of the Solution

35. The solution is contained in the numbered results, from (8) to (12) inclusive, of the preceding Article. Of these, (11) expresses the conditions of possible experience, (12) the conditions of limiting $u$ and $t$. From (8) and (9), these quantities are to be determined in accordance with (12), and the resulting values substituted in (10).

By a proper reduction of (8) and (9), the solution may also be put in the following form :—

$$a'u^2 + (cc'm - aa')u - acc'pq = 0 \quad . \quad (1)$$
$$at^2 - (cc'm + aa')t - a'cc'(1 - p)(1 - q) = 0 \quad (2)$$

where

$$a = cp + c'q - 1, \quad a' = c(1 - p) + c'(1 - q) - 1,$$
$$m = p + q - 1.$$

The values of $u$ and $t$ hence found, in accordance with the limitations expressed by (12), are to be substituted in the equation

$$\frac{\text{Prob. } xyz}{\text{Prob. } xy} = \frac{u}{u + t} \quad . \quad . \quad . \quad (3)$$

The following special deductions may now be noted.

1st. If either of the quantities $p$ and $q$ is equal to 1, the probability sought is equal to 1, whatever the values of $c$ and $c'$ may be.

Thus let $p = 1$. Then (2) gives $t = 0$; the only value which satisfies the conditions (12), in connexion with (11). The equation (1) is not satisfied by $u = 0$, whence

$$\frac{u}{u+t} = \frac{u}{u} = 1 \quad . \quad . \quad . \quad . \quad (4)$$

This result is obviously correct. If, for example, of two symptoms which are present, and which furnish ground of inference respecting a particular disease, one be of such a nature as to make the existence of the disease a matter of certainty, the fact of that existence is established, however adverse to such a conclusion the presumption furnished by the other symptom, supposing it our only ground of inference, would be.

So, too, the verdict of an authority deemed infallible is consistently held to annul and make void all opposing testimony or argument, however powerful such testimony or argument, considered in itself, may be.

*2ndly.* If either of the quantities $p$ and $q$ is equal to 0, the probability sought reduces to 0, as it evidently ought to do.

*3dly.* If $p = \frac{1}{2}$ and $q = \frac{1}{2}$, the equations for determining $u$ and $t$ become identical. Hence $u = t$, and

$$\text{Probability sought} = \frac{u}{u+u} = \frac{1}{2} \quad . \quad . \quad (5)$$

This result is quite independent of the values of $c$ and $c'$. And it is obviously a correct result. If the causes in operation, or the testimonies borne are, separately, such as to leave the mind in a state of equipoise as respects the event whose probability is sought, united they will but produce the same effect, whatever the *à priori* probability may be that such causes will come into operation, or that such testimonies will be borne.

*4thly.* If $c = 1$, and at the same time $c'$ is not equal to 0, we find, for the equations determining $u$ and $t$,

$$(p - u)(c'q - u)(u - p - c'q + 1)$$
$$= u(u - c' - p + 1)(u - c'q)$$
$$(1 - p - t)(c'\overline{1-q} - t)(t - c'\overline{1-q} + p)$$
$$= t(t - c' + p)(t - c'\overline{1-q}).$$

These give

$$u = c'q, \; t = c'(1 - q)$$

as the only values which satisfy (12).    Hence

$$\text{Probability sought} = \frac{c'q}{c'q + c'\overline{1 - q}} = q \quad . \quad (6)$$

The result is evidently correct.    The probability that such an event will take place when two other events, $x$ and $y$, are present, is the same as the probability that it will take place when the event $y$ is present, if it is known that the other event $x$ is never absent.

*5thly.* If $c = c'$ and $q = 1 - p$, we find in like manner $u = t$, whence

$$\text{Probability sought} = \frac{1}{2} \quad . \quad . \quad . \quad (7)$$

This result is evidently correct.    If the events or testimonies $x$ and $y$ are equally likely to happen, and if the first yields the same presumption *in favour* of that event whose probability is sought as the other yields *against* it, the chances are equally balanced, and the probability required is $\frac{1}{2}$.

*6thly.* But if $q = 1 - p$, while $c$ and $c'$ are *not* equal, then the value of the probability sought is no longer $\frac{1}{2}$.    It may be shown, by a proper discussion of the formulae, that the presumption afforded by the event $x$, whether favourable or unfavourable, is stronger than the *opposite* presumption afforded by the event $y$, whenever $c$ is less than $c'$, and vice versa.    And hence it follows, that if there be two events which, by themselves, afford equal presumptions, the one for and the other against some third event, of whose probability nothing more is known, then, if the said two events present themselves *in combination*, that one will yield the stronger presumption, which is itself of the more rare occurrence.    This too, is agreeable to reason.    For in those statistical observations by which probability is determined, we can only take account of co-existences and successions. We do not attempt to pronounce whether the presence of the event $z$ in conjunction with the event $x$ is due to the efficient action of the event $x$, or whether it is a product of some other cause or causes.   The more frequent the occurrence of $x$, the less entitled are we to assert that those things which accompany or follow it derive their being from it, or are dependent upon it.   If, for instance, $x$ were a standing event, or a state of things *always* present, the probability that any event $z$ would occur when $x$ and $y$ were jointly present, would be the same as the simple probability of that event $z$ when $y$ was present, and it would be wholly un-influenced by the presence of $x$.   This is the limiting case of the general principle.

*7thly*.  The case in which $c = c'$ and $p = q$, is a very interesting one.   A careful analysis leads to the following results.

If there be two events $z$ and $y$, which are in themselves equally probable, the probability of each being $c$, and if when the event $x$ is known to be present, while it is not known whether $y$ is present or not, the probability of $z$ is $p$, the same probability being assigned to $z$, when it is known that $y$ is present, but not known whether $x$ is present or not ; then, considering $p$ as a presumption for or against $z$, according as $p$ is greater or less than $\frac{1}{2}$:

1.  That presumption is strengthened if the events $x$ and $y$ are known to be jointly present, *i.e.*, the probability of $z$ is greater than $p$, if $p$ is greater than $\frac{1}{2}$, but less than $p$ in the contrary case.

2.  The strengthening of the presumption is greatest when $c$ is least.   In other words, the less likely the events $x$ and $y$ are to happen, the more does their actual concurrence strengthen the presumption, favourable or unfavourable, which either of them alone must afford.

*8thly*.  If we suppose $c$ and $c'$ both to approximate to 0, the values of $u$ and $t$ also approximate to 0, and the ratio $\frac{u}{u+t}$ assumes at the limit the form $\frac{0}{0}$.   It may however, be shown that its actual value at the limit is

$$\frac{pq}{pq + (1 - p)(1 - q)} \qquad \cdots \qquad (8)$$

This is most readily obtained from (1) and (2), by rejecting the terms $a'u^2$ and $at^2$, which we may do when $u$ and $t$ are infinitesimal. We thus find that $u$ and $t$ tend to assume the values $cc'pq$ and $cc'(1 - p)(1 - q)$, whence

$$\frac{u}{u + t} = \frac{pq}{pq + (1 - p)(1 - q)}.$$

It is interesting here to enquire whether the appearance of the limiting value $\dfrac{pq}{pq + \overline{1 - p}\ \overline{1 - q}}$ is due merely to the *smallness* of $c$ and $c'$. In studying this question, it occurred to me that it is generally not the mere improbability of events, or the mere unexpectedness of testimonies considered in themselves, but the improbability of the *concurrence* of such events or testimonies which gives to their *union* the highest degree of force. I therefore anticipated that, if I should introduce among the primary data of the problem, the probability of the concurrence of the events $x$ and $y$, assigning to it a value $m$, it would appear that whenever $m$ approached to 0, the presumptions with reference to the event $z$, founded upon $x$ and $y$, would receive strength, whatever the values of $c$ and $c'$ might be. And this expectation was verified. On taking for the data

Prob. $x = c$, Prob. $y = c'$, Prob. $xy = m$,
Prob. $xz = cp$, Prob. $yz = c'q$.

and representing the sought value of $\dfrac{\text{Prob. } xyz}{\text{Prob. } xy}$ by $w$, I found, for the determination of $w$, the equation

$$(cp - mw)(c'q - mw)(1 - w)$$
$$= w(c\overline{1 - p} - m\overline{1 - w})(c'\overline{1 - q} - m\overline{1 - w}) \qquad . \qquad (9)$$

the conditions of possible experience being that $c$, $c'$, $p$, $q$, and $m$, should be positive proper fractions, subject to the relation

$$c + c' \lesseqgtr 1 + m \qquad \cdots \qquad (10)$$

that root of (9) being taken, which satisfies the conditions

$$w \gtrless \frac{cp}{m}, \; w \gtrless \frac{c'q}{m}, \; w \gtrless 1,$$

$$1 - w \gtrless \frac{c\overline{1 - p}}{m}, \; 1 - w \gtrless \frac{c'\overline{1 - q}}{m}.$$

Now if in (9) we suppose $m$ to vanish, we find

$$cpc'q(1 - w) = wc\overline{1 - p}c'\overline{1 - q},$$
$$pq\overline{1 - w} = w\overline{1 - p}\;\overline{1 - q},$$

whence

$$w = \frac{pq}{pq + (1 - p)(1 - q)} \quad \cdot \quad \cdot \quad (11)$$

The condition (10) becomes simply $c + c' \gtrless 1$. The remaining conditions are all satisfied by the value of $w$.

The formula (11), which in the present investigation appears as a kind of limiting value, applicable only to cases in which the presumption for or against the event $z$ increases most by the combination of the testimonies given, is usually regarded as expressing the *general* solution. The reasoning by which it is supposed to be established is the following.

Let $p$ be the general probability that A speaks truth, $q$ the general probability that B speaks truth; it is required to find the probability, that if they agree in a statement they both speak truth. Now, agreement in the same statement implies that they either both speak truth, the probability of which beforehand is $pq$, or that they both speak falsehood, the probability of which beforehand is $(1 - p)(1 - q)$. Hence the probability beforehand that they will agree is $pq + (1 - p)(1 - q)$, and the probability that if they agree, they will agree in speaking the truth is accordingly expressed by the formula (11).* In the case of $n$ testimonies whose separate probabilities are $p_1 p_2 \ldots p_n$, the corresponding formula is

$$\frac{p_1 p_2 \ldots p_n}{p_1 p_2 \ldots p_n + (1 - p_1)(1 - p_2) \ldots (1 - p_n)} \quad \cdot \quad (12)$$

In applying which, it is usual to regard one of the testimonies

* *Cournot* Exposition de la Theorie des Chances, p. 411. *De Morgan*, Formal Logic, p. 191.

as the initial testimony of the mind itself.* Substantially
the same reasoning is applied to determine the probability
of correctness of a decision pronounced unanimously by a
jury, the probabilities of a correct decision by each member
of the jury being given.

In this reasoning there is no recognition that it is to the
*same fact* that the several testimonies are borne. Take the
case of two testimonies, and the problem which is substituted
for the true one is the following. The probability that A
speaks truth is $p$, that B speaks truth is $q$; what is the
probability that, if they both make assertions, and these
assertions are both true or both false, they are both true?
Whether A and B make the same assertion or not is assumed
to be a matter of indifference. But this assumption is, in
point of fact, as erroneous as it is unwarranted. The
problem which we have solved in the preceding sections,
interpreted in relation to testimony, is the following. Two
witnesses, A and B, assert a fact. The probability of that
fact, if we only knew of A's statement, would be $p$, if we only
knew of B's, would be $q$; what is its probability when we
know of both? The formal expression of this problem will
be seen in Art. 34. The most complete formal expression
of the problem which has been substituted for it, taking
into account all its elements, is as follows. Let $x$ and $y$
represent the testimonies of A and B, $w$ and $z$ the facts to
which these testimonies respectively relate. Observe that
no hypothesis is here made as to the connexion, by sameness
or difference, of $w$ and $z$. And the simple absence of any
such hypothesis is properly signified by expressing the events
by different symbols, unaccompanied by any logical equation
connecting these symbols.

If we wish to indicate that the events $w$ and $z$ are identical,
we must write as a connecting logical equation,

$$w = z,$$

though it must be simpler to express the identity by the
employment of a single symbol as before. Any other
definite relation may be expressed in a similar way.

* Formal Logic, p. 195.

The Problem now stands thus :—

Given    $$\text{Prob. } x = c, \text{ Prob. } xw = cp \atop \text{Prob. } y = c', \text{ Prob. } yz = c'q \Big\}$$    . . . (13)

Required    $$\frac{\text{Prob. } xywz}{\text{Prob. } xywz + \text{Prob. } xy\bar{w}\bar{z}}$$    . . . (14)

First, we will seek the value of Prob. $xywz$.

Let    $$xw = s, \; yz = t, \; xywz = v.$$

From these logical equations we must now determine $v$ as a developed logical function of $x, y, s,$ and $t$. The result is

$$v = xyst + 0(xys\bar{t} + xyt\bar{s} + xy\bar{s}\bar{t} + xs\bar{y}\bar{t} + x\bar{y}\bar{s}\bar{t} \\ + yt\bar{x}\bar{s} + y\bar{x}\bar{s}\bar{t} + \bar{x}\bar{y}\bar{s}\bar{t})$$

$$+ \text{ terms whose coefficients are } \frac{1}{0}.$$

Let $u$ be the value of Prob. $v$. Then, by the simplification of Art. 21, we have

$$\frac{xyst + xys + xyt + xy + xs + x}{c}$$

$$= \frac{xyst + xys + xyt + xy + yt + y}{c'}$$

$$= \frac{xyst + xys + xs}{cp} = \frac{xyst + xyt + yt}{c'q}$$

$$= \frac{xyst}{u} = xyst + xys + xyt + xy + xs + x + yt + y + 1.$$

Equating the product of the third and fourth to that of the fifth and sixth members of the above system, we have

$$u = cc'pq = \text{Prob. } xywz$$

whence

$$c'c(1 - p)(1 - q) = \text{Prob. } xy\bar{w}\bar{z}.$$

And hence

$$\frac{\text{Prob. } xywz}{\text{Prob. } xywz + \text{Prob. } xy\bar{w}\bar{z}} = \frac{pq}{pq + (1 - p)(1 - q)}.$$    (15)

Here it will be noted, that although the arbitrary constants $c$ and $c'$ were necessarily introduced into the expression of the data of the problem, they have no place in its solution.

The result, it will also be seen, agrees with (8); and it thus shows that that formula would express the true solution of the problem originally proposed, if it were permitted to neglect the circumstance that it is to the *same* fact that the testimonies have reference, and so to regard their agreement as merely an agreement in being true or in being false, but not in being true or in being false about the same thing.

*Special Solution of Problem II, founded upon the principle of the limit*

36. In the present investigation we employ the principle stated in Art. 24, our object being to determine the mean between $p$ and $q$, when they represent probabilities founded upon different judgments, just as in Art. 25, we have determined the mean between $p$ and $q$, when they represent different observed values of a physical magnitude.

To the previous data, viz.,

$$\text{Prob. } x = c, \text{ Prob. } y = c', \text{ Prob. } xz = cp,$$
$$\text{Prob. } yz = c'q \quad . \quad (1)$$

we now add, as the supposed *à priori* value of Prob. $z$,

$$\text{Prob. } z = r \quad . \quad . \quad . \quad . \quad (2)$$

From these collective data we determine the fraction

$$\frac{\text{Prob. } xyz}{\text{Prob. } xy} \text{ or } \frac{\text{Prob. } xyz}{\text{Prob. } xyz + \text{Prob. } xy\bar{z}} . \quad (3)$$

representing the *à posteriori* value of Prob. $z$, and, equating the *à priori* and *à posteriori* values, determine $x$. The principle upon which the investigation proceeds is, that we attribute to the mean strength of the probabilities $p$ and $q$ such a value, that if the mind had previously to the evidence been in the state of expectation which that value is supposed to measure, the evidence would not have tended to alter that state. By the evidence I mean, of course, that which forms the basis of the judgments.

Making, as before,

$$xz = s, zy = t, xyz = u,$$

and determining $v$ as a developed logical function of $x$, $u$, $z$, $s$, and $t$, we find

$$v = xyzst + 0(xy\overline{z}\overline{s}\overline{t} + xzs\overline{y}\overline{t} + yzt\overline{x}\overline{s} + x\overline{y}\overline{z}\overline{s}\overline{t}$$
$$+ y\overline{x}\overline{z}\overline{s}\overline{t} + z\overline{x}\overline{y}\overline{s}\overline{t} + \overline{x}\overline{y}\overline{z}\overline{s}\overline{t})$$
$$+ \text{ terms whose coefficients are } \frac{1}{0}.$$

Hence, availing ourselves of the simplification of Art. 21. we have

$$\frac{xyst + xy + xzs + x}{c} = \frac{xystz + xy + ytz + y}{c'}$$
$$= \frac{xystz + xsz}{cp} = \frac{xystz + ytz}{c'q}$$
$$= \frac{xystz + xsz + ytz + z}{r} = \frac{xystz}{u}$$
$$= xystz + xy + xsz + ytz + x + y + z + 1.$$

If we equate the product of the third and fourth to that of the fifth and sixth members of the above system, we find

$$\text{Prob. } xyz = \frac{cc'pq}{r},$$

whence by symmetry,

$$\text{Prob. } xy\overline{z} = \frac{cc'(1-p)(1-q)}{1-r} \quad . \quad . \quad (4)$$

Substituting these values in (3), we have

$$\frac{\text{Prob. } xyz}{\text{Prob. } xy} = \frac{pq(1-r)}{pq(1-r) + (1-p)(1-q)r} . \quad (5)$$

Before proceeding further, it will be well to note that in this formula $p$ and $q$ represent, not the general probabilities which the testimonies or evidences upon which our judgments are founded would give to the event $z$, but the probabilities which they would separately produce in a mind embued with a previous expectation of the event $z$, the strength of which is measured by $r$. And there are some curious confirmations of the truth of the theorem, two of which I shall notice.

If we represent the *à posteriori* value of Prob. $z$ by R, and accordingly make

$$\frac{pq(1-r)}{pq(1-r) + (1-p)(1-q)r} = \text{R} \quad . \quad . \quad (6)$$

we find, on solving the equation relatively to $r$,

$$\frac{pq(1 - R)}{pq(1 - R) + (1 - p)(1 - q)R} = r \quad . \quad . \quad (7)$$

from which it appears, that if $r$ is the *à priori* expectation of an event $z$, and if evidences are presented which severally would change $r$ to $p$ and $q$, and unitedly would change it to R; then, reciprocally, if R measured the *à priori* expectation of the event, and evidences were received which would severally change it to $p$ and $q$, unitedly they would reduce it to $r$. Now this is evidently what ought to be the case, since testimonies simply countervailing those by which $r$ was changed to R, would simply undo what was done, and again reduce R to $r$.

We see that $p$ and $q$ being the same, R is greater when $r$ is less, and less when $r$ is greater; and this, though it is contrary to what we might at first expect, is agreeable to reason. For the effect of evidence is to be measured, not by the state of expectation which exists after it has been offered, but by the degree in which the previous state of expectation has been changed by it. Suppose $p$ and $q$ much greater than $r$, which we will conceive to be a small quantity, then the separate evidences greatly increase the probability of an event which was before very improbable; and unitedly they do this in a much higher degree than if the separate evidences had merely been such as to raise to the measures $p$ and $q$, an expectation which was before not much below these measures.

Now, introducing the principle of the mean already explained, Art. 24, let us in (6) make R = $r$, we have

$$\frac{pq(1 - r)}{pq(1 - r) + (1 - p)(1 - q)r} = r,$$

and solving this equation relatively to r, we find

$$r = \frac{\sqrt{pq}}{\sqrt{pq} + \sqrt{(1 - p)(1 - q)}} \quad . \quad . \quad (8)$$

the formula required.

37. Upon this result, the following observations may be made :—

In the first place it may be shewn, from the formula

A A

itself, that it always expresses a value intermediate between the values $p$ and $q$.   Thus we have

$$r - p = \frac{\sqrt{pq}}{\sqrt{pq} + \sqrt{(1-p)(1-q)}}$$

$$= \frac{\sqrt{q(1-p)} - \sqrt{p(1-q)}}{\sqrt{pq} + \sqrt{(1-p)(1-q)}} \times \sqrt{p(1-p)} \quad . \quad (9)$$

on reduction.   In like manner we have

$$r - q = \frac{\sqrt{p(1-q)} - \sqrt{q(1-p)}}{\sqrt{pq} + \sqrt{(1-p)(1-q)}} \times \sqrt{q(1-q)}$$

$$= - \frac{\sqrt{q(1-p)} - \sqrt{p(1-q)}}{\sqrt{pq} + \sqrt{1-p}\,\sqrt{1-q}} \times \sqrt{q(1-q)} \quad (10)$$

As $p$ and $q$ are positive fractions, the values of $r - p$ and $r - q$, given in (9) and (10), are clearly of opposite signs, whence $r$ must lie between $p$ and $q$.

In the second place, it may be shewn, that $r$ approaches more nearly to that one of the two values $p$ and $q$, which most nearly approaches either of the limits 0 and 1.   To show this, let us suppose $q$ greater than $p$, and let us first inquire, under what circumstances $r$ approaches more nearly to $q$ than to $p$.

We must then assume

$$q - r < r - p.$$

Substituting the values of these members from (9) and (10) we have

$$\frac{\sqrt{q(1-p)} - \sqrt{p(1-q)}}{\sqrt{pq} + \sqrt{(1-p)(1-q)}} \times \sqrt{q(1-q)}$$

$$< \frac{\sqrt{q(1-p)} - \sqrt{p(1-q)}}{\sqrt{pq} + \sqrt{(1-p)(1-q)}} \times \sqrt{p(1-p)}.$$

Now, $q$ being by hypothesis greater than $p$, it is evident that $\sqrt{q(1-p)} - \sqrt{p(1-q)}$ will be positive.   Rejecting then, the common positive factor on both sides of the inequation we have

$$\sqrt{q(1-q)} < \sqrt{p(1-p)}$$
$$q - q^2 < p - p^2$$
$$q - p < q^2 - p^2,$$

and dividing both sides by the positive factor $q - p$

$$1 < p + q$$
$$1 - q < p$$

a condition which shows that $q$ must be nearer to 1 than $p$ is to 0.

On the other hand, as would appear from the very same analysis, changing only the signs $<$ into $>$, the condition that $r$ may approach more nearly to $p$ than to $q$, is that $p$ may be nearer to 0 than $q$ is to 1.

Now, 1 and 0, as limiting the measures of probability of the event $z$, indicate, the one that it certainly will, the other that it certainly will not occur.   And the approach of any measure of probability to these limits indicates the approach of the probability to certainty.   We see then, that when $p$ and $q$ are measures of the probability of an event founded on different judgments, the *mean* between these measures, as determined by (8) will not be the usual arithmetical mean, but will always fall nearer to that one of the two values $p$ and $q$ which expresses a probability the most nearly approaching to certainty.

Now, this seems to be in accordance with reason.   Evidence of any kind which enables us to pronounce judgment with certainty, entirely preponderates over that which only enables us to affirm a probable judgment, Art. 35.   And the more of the character of certainty that is possessed, the greater is the weight which is due to the evidence to which it belongs.

38. By an analysis similar to that which is applied in the previous sections, I have determined the general value of $r$, when the number of judgments is $n$, and the values which they respectively give to the probability of the event $z$ are $p_1 p_2 \cdot \cdot p_n$.   The result is

$$r = \frac{(p_1 p_2 \cdot \cdot p_n)^{\frac{1}{n}}}{(p_1 p_2 \cdot \cdot p_n)^{\frac{1}{n}} + \{(1 - p_1)(1 - p_2) \cdot \cdot (1 - p_n)\}^{\frac{1}{n}}} \cdot \quad (1)$$

This is the general formula of the mean in reference to judgments, and much as it differs from the formula of the mean, in reference to the observations of a physical

magnitude, some remarkable points of analogy exist. I will
notice but one. The arithmetical mean is not altered if to
the quantities among which it is taken we add another equal
to the previous mean. Thus we have

$$\frac{p_1 + p_2 \cdots + p_{n+1}}{n+1} = \frac{p_1 + p_2 \cdots p_n}{n},$$

provided that

$$p_{n+1} = \frac{p_1 + p_2 : \cdots + p_n}{n}.$$

Or representing

$$\frac{p_1 + p_2 \cdot + p_n}{n} \text{ by } P_n,$$

we have

$$P_{n+1} = P_n$$

provided that

$$p_{n+1} = P_n \quad . \quad . \quad . \quad . \quad . \quad (2)$$

The same relation may readily be shown to hold also, if $P_n$
represent the mean of judgment, as expressed in (1).

39. The following is a brief summary of the conclusions
established in this paper.

1*st*. The solution of the problem of astronomical observations by the logical theory of probabilities is, in its general
form, indefinite.

2*ndly*. It becomes definite, if we introduce the general
principle of means. The result is in accordance with the
usual formulae, but expresses the so-called *weights* of the
observations as determinate functions of certain probabilities relating to the correctness of the observations, and
the character of the observers.

3*dly*. When, as respects the two last elements, the observations are considered equal, the formula is reduced to the
expression of the arithmetical mean.

4*thly*. The complete solution of the problem of the combination of two probabilities of an event founded upon different testimonies or judgments is indefinite, but admits, in
various cases, of being reduced to a definite form.

5*thly*. This indefiniteness is due to the circumstance
indicated by the formula, that the strength of the probabilities in combination is due, not to the strength of the

separate probabilities alone, but also to the degree of un-expectedness of the testimonies or judgments themselves.

*6thly.* Combined presumptions, whether for or against an event, are generally strengthened by the unexpectedness of the combination.

*7thly.* When probabilities as $p_1$, $p_2$, $..p_n$ are in a high degree cumulative, owing to the exceeding improbability *à priori* of their combination, the expression for their united force tends to assume the form

$$\frac{p_1 p_2 \cdot \cdot p_n}{p_1 p_2 \cdot \cdot p_n + (1 - p_1)(1 - p_2) \cdot \cdot (1 - p_n)}$$

commonly assumed to express the *general* solution.

*8thly.* When the probabilities are so far from being cumulative that we feel that we ought to take a mean between them, the above formula is replaced by the following, viz. :—

$$\frac{\{p_1 p_2 \cdot \cdot p_n\}^{\frac{1}{n}}}{\{p_1 p_2 \cdot \cdot p_n\}^{\frac{1}{n}} + \{(1 - p_1)(1 - p_2) \cdot \cdot (1 - p_n)\}^{\frac{1}{n}}}.$$

*9thly.* This formula takes, in reference to ordinary judg-ments, the place of the arithmetical mean, with relation to the problem of astronomical observations, both being expressions of a more general principle.

40. It will probably appear to some of the readers of this paper, that I have dwelt more upon questions of philosophy and of language than it is usual to do in mathematical treatises, and that I have also, in various parts, assumed the office of a critic, rather than that of an expositor of original views. Respecting the first of these points, I will only express a hope, that I have nowhere in this paper entered into discussions that are not strictly relevant to the subject. Upon the second, I have to observe, that the theory of probabilities is one in which as it seems to me, the critical office is especially needed. I do not think that it is likely to gain much advance from mere analysis. As respects the original portions of this paper, it is my strongest wish, that they should be regarded chiefly as materials for future judgment. Thus it is possible that the theory which I have developed with reference to problems of which the elements

are logical, may be found to involve inconsistencies as a scientific theory, though I do not think this likely to be the case. But whether that theory shall finally be accepted or not, it is, I conceive, of some present importance to establish the necessary dependence of *any* theory, professing to deal with the same class of problems, upon what I have termed the conditions of possible experience,—to show how those conditions may be determined, and how they are to be applied. As respects the so-called principle of the mean, applied in certain portions of this paper, it is open to inquiry, whether it in all cases leads to results possessing the characteristic property, noted in Art. 38, and the decision of this question would materially affect our estimate of its value. Lastly, it is I think, highly probable that conditions which we do not yet know of may be discovered, affecting not the *possibility* of the data of a problem as discussed in this paper, but their *adequacy*, and the principles which, in statistical research especially, ought to guide us in their selection. I am so conscious how limited, imperfect, and in some cases fluctuating my own views upon important questions connected with this subject are, that I should regret having engaged in inquiries so lengthened and laborious as those of which I now take leave, if I did not think that as materials for future judgment, they may possess value and importance. And although the interest attaching at present to these inquiries is chiefly speculative, it may be that they will yet be found to possess a practical utility. The vast collections of modern statistics seem to demand some kind of reduction. I am sure that all who read this paper will feel that even towards this end I regard the labours of the mathematician as contributing only in a secondary degree.

## APPENDIX A

The following proposition in Algebra is of extreme importance in connexion with the theory of probabilities. It was originally published by me in the *Philosophical Magazine* for March 1855; but the present paper would be incomplete without some notice of it.

## Proposition

If V be a rational and integral function of $n$ variables $x, y, z..$, involving no power of these variables higher than the first, and having all its coefficients positive, and being complete in all its terms, then if $V_x$ represent that part of V which contains $x$, $V_y$ that part which contains $y$, and so on; the system of equations

$$\frac{V_x}{p} = \frac{V_y}{q}.. = V . \qquad . \quad . \quad . \quad . \quad (1)$$

$p$, $q$, &c., being positive fractions, admits of one solution, and of only one solution in positive values of $x, y, z..$

To exemplify this proposition, let us suppose

$$V = axy + bx + cy + d$$

$a, b, c,$ and $d$ being all greater than 0; then it is affirmed that the system of equations

$$\frac{axy + bx}{p} = \frac{axy + cy}{q} = axy + bx + cy + d . \quad (2)$$

$p$ and $q$ being positive, admits of one, and only one solution, in positive values of $x$ and $y$.

The proposition is true when $n = 1$. For then $V = ax + b$ and the system (1) is reduced to the single equation

$$\frac{ax}{p} = ax + b.$$

Whence we have

$$x = \frac{bp}{a(1 - p)},$$

and this value is positive if $a$ and $b$ are positive, and $p$ a positive fraction.

The general proof consists in showing that if the proposition is true for a particular value of $n$, it is true for the next greater. Whence, being true for the case of $n = 1$, it is true universally. I will exemplify the method by showing how the truth of the proposition when $n = 2$, is dependent upon its truth when $n = 1$.

Let $n = 2$, then we have to consider the system (2), which may be reduced to the form

$$\frac{axy + bx}{axy + bx + cy + d} = p \quad . \quad . \quad (3)$$

$$\frac{axy + cy}{axy + bx + cy + d} = q \quad . \quad . \quad (4)$$

Let us represent by Y the variable value of the first member of (4), when $x$ and $y$ are supposed to vary in subjection to the single condition (3).   We have then

$$Y = \frac{axy + cy}{axy + bx + cy + d} \quad . \quad . \quad (5)$$

Now differentiating (3) and (5) relatively to $x$ and $y$ we find, after slight reductions,

$$(ay + b)(cy + d)dx + (ad - bc)xdy = 0 \quad . \quad (6)$$

$$dY = \frac{(ad - bc)y}{V^2}dx + \frac{(ax + c)(bx + d)}{V^2}dy \quad . \quad (7)$$

where, as before, $V = axy + bx + cy + d$.   Substituting in (7) the value of $dx$ found from (6), we have

$$dY = \frac{(ax + c)(bx + d)(ay + b)(cy + d) - (ad - bc)^2xy}{(ay + b)(cy + d)V^2}dy.$$

The numerator of this expression may be reduced to the form

$$V(abcxy + abdx + acdy + bcd)$$

whence

$$\frac{dY}{dy} = \frac{abcxy + abdx + acdy + bcd}{(ay + b)(cy + d)V} \quad . \quad . \quad (8)$$

This represents the differential coefficient of Y taken with respect to $y$ as independent variable, $x$ being regarded as a function of $y$ determined by (3).   The expression is always positive, if $x$ and $y$ are positive.

Now let $y$ vary from 0 to $\infty$ through the whole range of positive magnitude.   Writing (3) in the form

$$\frac{Ax}{Ax + B} = p \quad . \quad . \quad . \quad . \quad (9)$$

where $A = ay + b$, $B = cy + d$, the quantity $x$ must, by reference to the case of $n = 1$, have a positive value, since A and B are positive and $p$ fractional. Whence, as $y$ varies from 0 to $\infty$, the value of $\dfrac{dY}{dy}$ is always positive.

Now when $y = 0$, $Y = 0$, and when $y = \infty$, $Y = 1$, as is evident from (5). Therefore, as $y$ increases from 0 to $\infty$, Y continuously increases from 0 to 1. In this variation it must once, and only once, become equal to $q$. Wherefore the system (3) (4) admits of one, and only one, solution in positive values of $x$ and $y$.

The reasoning might also be presented in the following form. The condition of Y having a maximum or minimum value is expressed by the equation

$$abcxy + abdx + acdy + bcd = 0 \quad . \quad . \quad (10)$$

It is obvious that this, as all the terms in the first member are positive, can never be satisfied by positive values of $x$ and $y$. Hence Y has no maximum or minimum, consistently with (3) being satisfied, and thus it never resumes a former value, and is only once, in the course of its variation, equal to $q$.

In the case of $n = 3$, we have

$$V = axyz + byz + cxz + dxy + ex + fy + gz + h$$

and the system to be considered is

$$\frac{axyz + cxz + dxy + ex}{V} = p \quad . \quad . \quad . \quad (11)$$

$$\frac{axyz + byz + dxy + fy}{V} = q \quad . \quad . \quad (12)$$

$$\frac{axyz + byz + cxz + gz}{V} = r \quad . \quad . \quad (13)$$

Let the first number of the last equation, considered as a variable function of $x$, $y$, $z$ be represented by Z, and suppose $x$, $y$ and $z$ to vary in subjection to the conditions (11) (12). Just as before, it may be shown that Z increases continuously with $z$. The condition of Z having a maximum or minimum value, will be expressed by the following equation :

$$
\begin{aligned}
(D + H + E + F)&(ABC + ACG + ABG + BCG) \\
+ (A + B + C + G)&(DHE + DHF + DEF + HEF) \\
+ (AC + BG)&(DF + DH + EF + EH) \\
+ (AG + BC)&(DF + EH + DE + FH) \\
+ (AB + CG)&(DE + DH + FE + FH) \\
+ 4AGFE + 4BCDH &= 0 \quad . \quad . \quad . \quad . \quad . \quad . \quad (14)
\end{aligned}
$$

Wherein

$$
\begin{aligned}
A &= axyz, \ B = byz, \ C = czx, \ D = dxy, \\
E &= ex, \ F = fy, \ G = gz, \ H = h.
\end{aligned}
$$

And as this equation has positive values only in its first member, it cannot be satisfied by positive values of $x$, $y$, $z$; whence, by the same reasoning as before, the system (11), (12), (13) cannot have more than one solution in positive values of $x$, $y$, $z$.

To show that it will have one such solution, let $z$ vary from 0 to $\infty$, then Z continuously increases from 0 to 1, and once becomes equal to $r$. At every stage of its variation we may give to (11) and (12) the form

$$
\frac{Axy + Bx}{V} = p
$$

$$
\frac{Axy + Cy}{V} = q
$$

which corresponds with the form of the general system (3) (4) in the case of $n = 2$. Whence, for each positive value of $z$, one positive set of values of $x$ and $y$ will be found. The system (11), (12), (13) admits, therefore, of one solution in positive values of $x$, $y$, $z$, and of only one.

To prove the proposition generally, it ought to be shown that the function exemplified in the first members of (10) and (14), for the cases of $n = 2$ and $n = 3$ possesses universally the same property of consisting only of positive terms. I have proved that it does for the case of $n = 4$, and the analysis was such as to leave no doubt whatever of its general truth.

I will now offer a few remarks on the application of the above proposition.

The system of equations for determining $s$ and $t$.., Art. 21, is of the form

$$\frac{V_s}{p} = \frac{V_t}{q} .. = V \quad . \quad . \quad . \quad . \quad (15)$$

V being a function of the same general character as the one discussed in the foregoing proposition, but with this difference, that its coefficients, if we regard it as a complete function, are all equal either to 1 or to 0.

Thus in Art. 18, we have

$$V = stv + s + t + v + 1.$$

Here the terms $st$, $tv$, and $vs$, must be considered as present, but with the coefficient 0.

This limitation does not affect the essentially positive character of the determining function exemplified in (10) and (14). Whence the system (15) cannot have more than one solution in positive values of $s$, $t$, &c. *This shows that the solution of the system of equations furnished by the general method can never be ambiguous.*

The vanishing of some of the coefficients of V does, however, affect the reasoning by which it has been shown, that for the general form of V discussed in the last proposition, one solution of the algebraic system in positive values will exist. Thus Y in (5) does not vanish with $y$, if both $b$ and $d$ vanish. And generally this vanishing of coefficients in V entails conditions among the quantities $p, q, r$.., in addition to that of their being fractional, in order that the derived algebraic system may admit of a solution in positive values.

Thus if we take, as in (7) Art. 18,

$$V = stv + s + t + v + 1,$$

with the derived algebraic system

$$\frac{stv + s}{V} = p, \frac{stv + t}{V} = q, \frac{stv + v}{V} = r,$$

it is evident that if $s$, $t$, and $v$ are positive quantities, and if we write

$$\frac{stv}{V} = u, \frac{s}{V} = \lambda, \frac{t}{V} = \mu, \frac{v}{V} = \nu,$$

$u$, $\lambda$, $\mu$, and $v$ must be positive fractions, whence, in addition to the equations

$$u + \lambda = p$$
$$u + \mu = q$$
$$u + v = r$$

we shall have the inequations

$$u \gtrless 0, \lambda \gtrless 0, \mu \gtrless 0, v \gtrless 0$$
$$u + \lambda + \mu + v \lessgtr 1.$$

This system is identical with the one obtained in (10), Art. 13, for the determination of the conditions of possible experience in the particular question of Probabilities, in which the above function V presents itself. And a very little attention will show, that if in any case we express as above the relations which must obviously be fulfilled in order that $s$, $t$, &c., may be positive quantities, we shall form a system of equations and inequations precisely agreeing with those which we should have to form in order to obtain the conditions of possible experience, if we sought those conditions, not from the data in their original expression but from the translated data, as employed in Art. 13.

*Hence, in order that* s, t.. *in the system of Art.* 21 *may be positive, or in the prior system, positive fractions, the problem of which these systems of equations involve the solution must represent a possible experience.*

*Conversely if that problem represent a possible experience, the quantities* s, t.. *will admit of being determined in the system of Art.* 21, *in positive values, or in the prior system in positive fractional values.*

I have not succeeded in obtaining a perfectly rigorous proof of the latter, or converse proposition in its general form,* but I have not met with any individual cases in which it was not true. I will here only exemplify it in Problem II., Art. 34.

Here the value of V is

$$V = xyst + xs + yt + xy + x + y + 1$$

* [See next paper.]

and the algebraic system employed in the determination of Prob. $xyz$ is

$$\frac{xyst + xs + xy + x}{c} = \frac{xyst + yt + xy + y}{c'}$$

$$= \frac{xyst + xs}{cp} = \frac{xyst + yt}{c'q} = \frac{xyst}{u}$$

$$= xyst + xs + yt + xy + x + y + 1 \quad . \quad (16)$$

For the determination of $u$ we hence find the following equation :—

$$u(u - \overline{c' + cp - 1})(u - \overline{c + c'q - 1})$$
$$- (cp - u)(c'q - u)(u - \overline{cp + c'q - 1}) = 0 \quad . \quad (17)$$

the conditions of limitation being

$$u > 0, \; u > c' + cp - 1, \; u > c + c'q - 1,$$
$$u < cp, \; u < c'q \quad . \quad . \quad . \quad (18)$$

Now, since $u$ is greater than $c + c'q - 1$ it is *à fortiori* greater than $cp + c'q - 1$. Thus within the limits assigned to $u$ all the factors of each term of (17) will be positive.

If then we give to $u$ the value which belongs to the highest of its inferior limits, the first member of (17) will be reduced to its second term, and will be negative. If we give to $u$ the value which belongs to the lowest of its superior limits, the first member of (17) will be reduced to its first term, and will be positive. Moreover, that member is a quadratic function of $u$. Hence there is one root, and only one, within the limits specified.

We must now express $x$, $y$, $x$, and $t$, in terms of $u$. Their values determined from the system (16) are as follows, viz. :—

$$x = \frac{c(1 - p)}{u - (c + c'q - 1)}, \; y = \frac{c'(1 - q)}{u - (c' + cp - 1)},$$

$$s = \frac{u - (c + c'q - 1)}{c(1 - p)} \times \frac{u}{c'q - u},$$

$$t = \frac{u - (c' + cp - 1)}{c'(1 - q)} \times \frac{u}{cp - u}.$$

All these expressions become positive when $u$ is determined in accordance with the conditions (18).

It would seem from the above, as well as from reasonings

analogous to those of Proposition I., that when the algebraic system belonging to a problem in the theory of probabilities is placed in the form

$$\frac{V_x}{V} = p, \frac{V_y}{V} = q \cdot \cdot,$$

the limits of variation of the first member of any equation subject to the condition, that the variables shall all be positive, and shall vary in subjection to all the other equations of the system, will not in general be 0 and 1, as in the case contemplated in Prop. I., but will correspond with the limits of value of the second member of the same equation as determined by the conditions of possible experience.

This conclusion I have in various cases independently verified. The analytical theory still, however, demands a more thorough investigation.

## APPENDIX B

A note to Archbishop Whately's Logic, Book III. sec. 14, contains a rule for computing the joint force of two probabilities in favour of a conclusion which, as actually applied, is at variance with the preceding results. For this reason, and also because the validity of the rule in question has been made the subject of recent controversy, I design to offer a few remarks upon the subject here. The rule is contained in the following extract. " As, in the case of two probable premises, the conclusion is not established except on the supposition of their being *both* true, so, in the case of two (and the like holds good with any number) distinct and independent indications of the truth of some proposition, unless *both* of them *fail*, the proposition must be true : we therefore multiply together the fractions indicating the probability of *failure* of each,—the chances *against* it ;—and the result being the total chances against the establishment of the conclusion by these arguments, this fraction being deducted from unity, the remainder gives the probability *for* it. E.g. A certain book is conjectured to be by such and such an author, partly, 1*st*, from its resemblance in style to his known works, partly (2*ndly*) from its being attributed to him by someone likely to be pretty well informed; let the probability of the Conclusion, as deduced from one of these arguments by itself, be supposed $\frac{2}{5}$, and in the other case $\frac{3}{7}$; then the *opposite* probabilities will be, respectively $\frac{3}{5}$ and $\frac{4}{7}$; which multiplied together give $\frac{12}{35}$, as the probability *against* the Conclusion; i.e. the chance that the work may *not* be his, notwithstanding those reasons for believing that it is; and consequently the probability in *favour* of that Conclusion will be $\frac{23}{35}$, or nearly $\frac{2}{3}$."

A confusion may here be noted between the probability that a conclusion is proved, and the probability in favour of a conclusion furnished by evidence which does not prove it. In the proof and statement of his rule, Archbishop Whately adopts the former view of the nature of the probabilities concerned in the data. In the exemplification of it, he adopts the latter. He thus applies the rule to a case for which it was not intended, and to which it is, in fact, inapplicable.

The rule is given, and the conditions of its just application are assigned in Professor De Morgan's *Formal Logic*, p. 201. Its origin may be thus explained. Let there be two independent causes, A and B, either of which, when present, necessarily produces an effect E. Let $a$ be the probability that A is present, $b$ the probability that B is present; then $1 - a$ is the probability that A is absent, $1 - b$ the probability that B is absent, $(1 - a)(1 - b)$ the probability that they are both absent; finally, $1 - (1 - a)(1 - b)$ the probability that they are not both absent. This then, is the probability that one at least of the causes is present; and therefore, it is the probability that the event E, so far as it is dependent upon these causes, will occur. In its special application to arguments viewed as causes of belief or expectation, it would lead to the following theorem. If there are two independent arguments in favour of a conclusion which the premises of either, if granted, are sufficient to establish, the doubt only existing as to the truth of the premises, and if the probability that the premises of the first argument are true is $a$, the probability that the premises of the second argument are true $b$, then the probability that the conclusion is established is $1 - (1 - a)(1 - b)$. Interpreted, this formula gives Archbishop Whately's rule, but the conditions of its valid application are evidently not fulfilled in the example which he has given. To satisfy these conditions, this problem ought to be changed into the following : " There exists a certain quality of style, the possession of which would *prove* the work to be by the author supposed. The probability that the work possesses that quality is $\frac{2}{5}$. There is a person so well informed that his attributing the work to the supposed author would be *conclusive*. The probability that he does attribute it to the author in question is $\frac{3}{7}$. Required the probability, on these grounds, that the supposed author is the real one." But this is evidently not the sense in which the problem was meant to be understood. Thus to take one point, it is not the quality of the style that is a matter of probability, but the mode in which a known and observed quality affects the question of authorship.

Taking the problem in its intended meaning, each of the fractions, $\frac{2}{5}$, $\frac{3}{7}$, measuring, not the probability of the truth of certain premises, but the probability drawn from these premises, as conditions, in favour of a certain supposition (I use this word in preference to conclusion), we are no longer permitted to apply the formula above determined. And we are not permitted to do so, because the probabilities with which we are concerned are conditional, and their possession of this character greatly increases the difficulty of the problem. Its rigorous formal solution is given in Art. 34, and shows that the probability sought is, generally speaking, indefinite,—a result which agrees with the conclusions of Bishop Terrot, by whom the error to which attention has been directed was first pointed out, Transactions of the Royal Society of Edinburgh, vol. xxi., p. 369.*

I trust that I have not in any way misrepresented Archbishop Whately's reasoning; and I am the more encouraged to believe that I have not, as a defence of it which appeared in the United Church Journal expressly proceeds upon the assumption that the probabilities with which we are con-

* [See pp. 487–496 of this volume.]

cerned are probabilities that the authorship is *proved*. To this view Bishop Terrot justly demurred. Nor was its inconsistency materially diminished by assigning to proof a meaning less absolute than belongs to demonstration. For whatever degree of cogency,—of power to produce conviction,—we suppose to characterize proof, the thing itself belongs to consciousness, and the question whether given evidence is sufficient to convey proof to our minds or not, is a matter of knowledge, not of probability.

B B

# XVII

## ON THE THEORY OF PROBABILITIES *

THIS paper has for its object the investigation of the general analytical conditions of a Method for the solution of Questions in the Theory of Probabilities, which was proposed by me in a work entitled " An Investigation of the Laws of Thought " (London, Walton and Maberly, 1854).†

The application of this method to particular problems has been illustrated in the work referred to, and yet more fully in a " Memoir on the Combination of Testimonies and of Judgments " published in the Transactions of the Royal Society of Edinburgh (vol. xxi., Part 4).‡ Some observations, too, on the general character of the solutions to which the method leads, founded upon induction from particular cases, were contained in the original treatise, and the outlines, still in some measure conjectural, of their general theory were given in an Appendix to the Memoir. But the complete development of that theory was attended with analytical difficulties which I have only lately succeeded in overcoming. It involves discussions relating to the properties of a certain functional determinant, and to the possible solutions of a system of algebraic equations of peculiar form—discussions which will, I trust, be thought to possess a value, as contributions to Mathematical Analysis, independent of their present application.

As concerns the nature of the problems to which the method is applicable, it may be stated that they are such that the numerical elements, both given and sought, are the probabilities of events or states of things the definitions of which, and the connexions of which, are capable of expression by logical propositions. There is ground for believing that all

---

\* [*Philosophical Transactions* of the Royal Society of London, vol. 152, 1862.]
† [Republished by The Open Court, Chicago and London, 1916.]
‡ [See above pp. 308–385.]

questions whatever involving probability are ultimately reducible to this general form. This point, however, I do not purpose to discuss here. It has been already in some degree considered in the Memoir referred to.

In order to explain more fully the necessity for the present investigation, it will be requisite to state the fundamental principles upon which the method in question rests. There are only two of them which can possibly afford matter for discussion.

1st. The expression in language of the data of a problem in the Theory of Probabilities is to a certain extent arbitrary, because it depends upon the extent of meaning of the primary simple terms employed to express the events the conceptions of which it involves. But the choice of simple terms is, if we consider it with respect to our absolute power of choice, arbitrary. Any complex combination of events can be contemplated as a single whole in thought, and expressed by a single term. The invention of new simple terms to express what was before expressed by a combination of terms is a normal phenomenon in the growth of language.

Now the first principle upon which the method rests is the following :—

*Principle I.*—The different forms which a problem may be made to assume by different elections with respect to the simple terms of its expression are mutually equivalent.

For instance, if the following data were given,

> The probability of rain is $p$,
> The probability of rain with snow is $q$,

the form which the problem would assume in a language in which there was no word for snow, but in which the combination of snow with rain was called sleet, would be

> The probability of rain is $p$,
> The probability of sleet is $q$,

with the added conditions, expressed as a logical proposition, that sleet always implies rain. And this as a statement of the data would, it is affirmed, be equivalent to the former statement. If these were the data of an actual problem, the event of which the probability is sought would require similar translation.

I desire to guard here against a possible misapprehension. I have said that the choice of simple terms, if considered with respect to our power of choice, is arbitrary. I do not mean by this to affirm that the actual growth of language is arbitrary. We know that it is far otherwise. Unity of sensuous impression in the early stages of its growth, unity of thought in the latter, seems to govern the invention and introduction of simple terms. It has indeed been said that there is a λόγος in the constitution of things of which language in its varied forms is the human reflexion, but never without the inseparable human element of choice and voluntary power.

It is then affirmed that whatever the grounds of fitness or propriety (and the existence of such grounds is fully conceded) may be, which have governed the actual choice of the simple terms of language, those grounds have nothing whatever to do with the calculation of probability. This depends upon the *information* contained in the data, information supposed to be derived from actual experience, or at least to be of such a nature that experience might have furnished it.

The different forms in which a problem is capable of being expressed, though differing in consequence of the different arbitrary elections which are possible with respect to its simple terms, are not independent of each other. They are connected together by the Laws of Thought, and pass one into the other by the processes of the calculus of Logic, which is an organized expression of those Laws.

Among these forms there is one which presents exclusive advantages. It is that in which those events, however originally expressed, the probabilities of which constitute the data, are assumed as the simple events of the problem, and expressed by logical symbols corresponding to the simple terms of ordinary language; the event of which the probability is sought being also expressed logically by means of the same symbols. The calculus of Logic enables us to do this, determining at the same time in an *explicit* form, i.e. in a form capable of expression in ordinary language by definite logical propositions, the connexion which exists among all the events in question—a connexion which in the original form of the data was only *implied*.

This leads us to the statement of the second Principle of the Method.

*Principle II.*—When the data have been translated into probabilities of events connected by conditions logical in form and explicitly known, the problem may be constructed from a scheme of corresponding ideal events which are free, and of which the probabilities are such that when they (the ideal events) are restricted by the same conditions as the events in the data, their calculated probabilities will become the same as the given probabilities of the events in the data.

To take a material illustration : the problem, in the form to which it is reduced by the calculus of Logic in accordance with Principle I., might be represented by the supposition of an urn containing balls distinguished by certain properties, e.g. by colour, as white or not white, by form, as round or not round, by material, as ivory or not ivory, and by the supposition that, while these properties enter into every conceivable combination, all the balls in which certain combinations are found are attached by strings to the sides of the urn, so that only the balls in which the remaining combinations are realised can be drawn.   Suppose, further, that the probabilities of drawing under the actual conditions a white ball, a round ball, an ivory ball, etc., are given and the probability of drawing a free ball fully defined with respect to the above elements of distinction is required. The principle affirmed is that we must proceed as if the balls were all free, and with probabilities such that the calculated probability of drawing any one of the balls which under the previous supposition are free, would be the same as under that supposition it is given to be.

Confining ourselves to the above material case, I remark, that the supposed mode of solution represents, 1st, a *possible* order of things; 2ndly, an order of things in which no preference is given to any one combination over any other which falls under the same category, or mode of thought.   All the procedure of the theory of probabilities is founded upon the mental construction of the problem from some hypothesis, either, 1st, of events known to be independent; or, 2ndly, of events of the connexion of which we are totally ignorant; so that, upon the ground of this ignorance, we can again construct a scheme of alternatives all equally probable, and distinguished merely as favouring or not favouring the event of which the probability is sought. In doing this we are not at liberty to proceed arbitrarily. We are subject, first, to the formal Laws of Thought, which determine the possible conceivable combinations; secondly, to that principle, more easily conceived than explained, which has been differently expressed as the " principle of non-sufficient reason ", the " principle of the equal distribution of knowledge or ignorance ",* and the " principle of order ". We do not know that the distribution of properties in the actual urn is the same as it is conceived to be in the ideal urn of free balls, but the hypothesis that it is so involves an equal distribution of our actual knowledge, and enables us to construct the problem from ultimate hypotheses which reduce it to a calculation of combinations.

I pass from the particular and material to the general problem. In the form to which this is brought by the calculus of Logic, the probabilities are those of events of which certain combinations are, as a logical consequence of the original definitions of those events, impossible. It might at first sight appear that this establishes a fundamental difference between this problem and that of the urn, in which certain combinations are prevented from issuing by a material hindrance. In the one case the restriction appears as logically necessary, in the other as only actual.

Upon this I remark, that the data of the problem in its

* Knowledge and ignorance being in the theory of probabilities supplementary to each other, the equal distribution of the one implies that of the other.

I take this opportunity of explaining a passage in the *Laws of Thought*, p. 370, relating to certain applications of the principle. Valid objection lies not against the principle itself, but against its application through arbitrary hypotheses, coupled with the assumption that any result thus obtained is necessarily the true one. The application of the principle employed in the text and founded upon the general theorem of development in Logic, I hold to be *not* arbitrary.

ultimate reduced form *might* result from the same kind of dependence as in the actual data; that they in fact *would* thus result if the mind of the observer were capable of contemplating, and were in a position to contemplate, each of the events in this ultimate translated form simply as a whole, and of recording, through an approximately infinite series of observations, what combinations of those wholes come into being, and what do not, in the actual universe. What appears as necessary in the translated data would now appear as actual—as a result of observation; what is impossible would be received as non-existent. The question is, then, whether the difference between the conception of what is impossible from involving a logical contradiction, and the conception of what in the actual constitution of things never exists, is of a kind to affect expectation. I do not hesitate to say that it is not. We are concerned with events in so far as they are capable of happening or not happening, of combining and not combining; but we are not concerned with the reasons in virtue of which they happen or do not happen, combine or do not combine. If we went beyond this, we should enter upon a metaphysical question to which I presume that no answer can, upon rational grounds, be given, viz., upon the question whether, when two things or events are in the actual constitution of things incapable of happening together, it would, if our knowledge were sufficiently extended, be found that the resulting conceptions of them were logically inconsistent.

I have but one further observation on Principle II. to make. It is that in the general problem we are not called upon to interpret the ideal events. The whole procedure is, like every other procedure of abstract thought, formal. We do not say that the ideal events exist, but that the events in the translated form of the actual problem are to be considered to have such relations with respect to happening or not happening as a certain system of ideal events would have if conceived first as free, and then subjected, without their freedom being otherwise affected, to relations formally agreeing with those to which the events in the translated problem are subject.

We are now able to explain more clearly the nature of the analytical investigation which will follow.  Let $p_1$, $p_2$, $\ldots p_n$ represent the probabilities given in the data.  As these will in general not be the probabilities of unconnected events, they will be subject to other conditions than that of being positive proper fractions, viz. to other conditions beside

$$\left. \begin{array}{l} p_1 \gtreqless 0, p_2 \gtreqless 0 \ldots p_n \gtreqless 0 \\ p_1 \lesseqgtr 1, p_2 \lesseqgtr 1 \ldots p_n \lesseqgtr 1 \end{array} \right\} \quad . \quad . \quad . \quad (1)$$

Those other conditions will, as will hereafter be shown, be capable of expression by equations or inequations reducible to the general form

$$a_1 p_1 + a_2 p_2 \ldots + a_n p_n + a \gtreqless 0,$$

$a_1$, $a_2$, $\ldots a_n$, being numerical constants which differ for the different conditions in question.  These, together with the former, may be termed the conditions of possible experience. When satisfied they indicate that the data *may* have, when not satisfied they indicate that the data *cannot* have resulted from actual observation.  On the other hand, the ideal events are regarded as independent, and their probabilities, which enter as auxiliary quantities into the process of solution, are subject to no other condition than that of being positive proper fractions.  It is the general object of the analytical investigation to establish the two following conclusions, viz.,—

1st. The probabilities of the ideal independent events, as involved in the method under consideration, will in the process be determinable, without ambiguity, as positive proper fractions, whenever the data satisfy the conditions of possible experience, and not otherwise.

And, as a consequence of the above,

2ndly. The probability determined by the method will have such a value as it consistently might have had if, instead of being calculated from the data, it had been determined by observation under the same experience as the data.

These conclusions rest upon the ground of certain analytical theorems relating to functional determinants, and to the possible solutions of simultaneous algebraic equations, which will be demonstrated in this paper. But, in order to explain the application of those theorems, it will be necessary to show first, how the " conditions of possible experience " in problems in the Theory of Probabilities may be determined; secondly, what the analytical method in question for the solution of such problems is.

### Determination of the Conditions of possible Experience

The method for determining the conditions of possible experience given in the *Laws of Thought*, Chap. XIX., may be advantageously replaced by the following one, which is taken from the Memoir " On the Combination of Testimonies and Judgments ", already referred to.

Let the events in the data be resolved into the ultimate possible alternatives which they involve, and let the unknown probabilities of these alternatives be represented by $\lambda$, $\mu$, $\nu$, &c., then, as the probability of each event in the data is equal to the sum of the probabilities of the alternatives which it involves, we shall have a system of equations connecting $\lambda$, $\mu$, $\nu$, &c. with $p_1$, $p_2$, $\ldots p_n$, the probabilities supposed given. Again, $\lambda$, $\mu$, $\nu \ldots$, as probabilities, are subject to the conditions

$$\lambda \gtrless 0, \mu \gtrless 0, \nu \gtrless 0, \ldots \&c.,$$

and, as alternatives mutually excluding each other, to the condition

$$\lambda + \mu + \nu + \ldots = 1,$$

or the condition

$$\lambda + \mu + \nu + \ldots \gtrless 1,$$

according as the alternatives in question together make up certainty or not.

Thus we have a system consisting of equations and inequations from which $\lambda$, $\mu$, $\nu$, &c., must be eliminated. To effect this elimination we must determine as many of the quantities $\lambda$, $\mu$, $\nu$, $\ldots$ as possible from the equations, substitute their values in the inequations, and then eliminate the remainder of the quantities $\lambda$, $\mu$, $\nu$ ... by means of the theorem that if we have simultaneously

$$\lambda \gtrless a_1, \lambda \gtrless a_2, \ldots \lambda \gtrless a_m,$$
$$\lambda \lessgtr b_1, \lambda \lessgtr b_2, \ldots \lambda \lessgtr b_n,$$

then we have the system of conditions of which the type is

$$a_i \lessgtr b_j,$$

$a_i$ representing any one of the set $a_1$, $a_2$, $\ldots a_m$, and $b_j$ any one of the set $b_1$, $b_2$, $\ldots b_n$. Thus there are $mn$ conditions in all.

This method is illustrated in the following problem, in the expression and solution of which it is to be noticed, that when in the calculus of Logic an event is represented by $x$, the event which consists in its not happening is denoted by $1 - x$, or for brevity by $\bar{x}$; that when two events are represented by $x$ and $y$, their concurrence is denoted by $xy$, the happening of the first without the second by $x\bar{y}$, and so on.

*Problem.* Given that the probability of the concurrence of the events $x$ and $y$ is $p$, of the events $y$ and $z$, $q$, and of the events $z$ and $x$, $r$. Required the conditions to which $p$, $q$, and $r$ must be subject in order that the above data may be consistent with a possible experience.

Resolving the events $xy$, $yz$, $xz$ into the possible alternations out of which they are formed, let us write,

Prob. $xyz = \lambda$, Prob. $xy\bar{z} = \mu$, Prob. $x\bar{y}z = \nu$, Prob. $\bar{x}yz = \rho$.

Then we have the equations

$$\lambda + \mu = p, \lambda + \rho = q, \lambda + \nu = r,$$

together with the inequations

$$\lambda \lessgtr 0, \mu \lessgtr 0, \nu \lessgtr 0, \rho \lessgtr 0,$$
$$\lambda + \mu + \nu + \rho \gtrless 1.$$

From the equations we find

$$\mu = p - \lambda, \rho = q - \lambda, \nu = r - \lambda,$$

which, substituted in the inequations, give

$$\lambda \lessgtr 0, p - \lambda \lessgtr 0, q - \lambda \lessgtr 0, r - \lambda \lessgtr 0,$$
$$p + q + r - 2\lambda \gtrless 1 :$$

and it only remains to eliminate $\lambda$.   Now from the above,

$$\lambda \lessgtr p, \lambda \lessgtr q, \lambda \lessgtr r, \lambda \gtrless 0, \lambda \gtrless \frac{p + q + r - 1}{2},$$

therefore,

$$p \gtrless 0, q \gtrless 0, r \gtrless 0,$$

$$p \gtrless \frac{p + q + r - 1}{2}, q \gtrless \frac{p + q + r - 1}{2}, r \gtrless \frac{p + q + r - 1}{2}.$$

The three last conditions are reducible to the simpler form,

$$p \gtrless q + r - 1, q \gtrless r + p - 1, r \gtrless p + q - 1.$$

Such are the conditions of possible experience in the data.

Suppose, for instance, it was affirmed as a result of medical statistics that, in two-fifths of a number of cases of disease of a certain character, two symptoms $x$ and $y$ were observed; in two-thirds of the cases the symptoms $y$ and $z$ were observed; and in four-fifths of the cases the symptoms $z$ and $x$ were observed; so that, the number of cases observed being large, we might on a future outbreak of the disease consider the fractions $\frac{2}{5}$, $\frac{2}{3}$, and $\frac{4}{5}$ as the probabilities of recurrence of the particular combinations of the symptoms, $x, y$, and $z$, observed.   The above formulæ would show that the evidence was contradictory.   For, representing the respective fractions by $p$, $q$, and $r$, the condition $p \gtrless q + r - 1$ is not satisfied.   (*Edinburgh Memoir.*)

In applying the above method to the *à priori* limitation of questions in the theory of probabilities, it will be necessary to represent the probability sought by a single letter $u$, and treat this as if it were one of the numerical data.   The resolution of the event of which the probability is sought into alternatives belonging to the same scheme as those of the events in the data gives us a new equation, which must be combined with the equations involving $p$, $q$, $r$, &c.   The elimination of $\lambda$, $\mu$, $\nu$, &c. then determines not only the conditions of possible experience limiting $p$, $q$, $r$, but also the conditions which $u$ must satisfy *à priori*, whatever method for its actual determination may be employed.   Thus, if from the foregoing data it were required to determine the *à priori* limits of Prob. $xyz$, i.e. of the probability of the conjunction of the events $x$, $y$, $z$, we should have as the additional equation

$$u = \lambda,$$

and therefore, after elimination of $\lambda$, $\mu$, $\nu$,

$$u \gtrless p,\ u \gtrless q,\ u \gtrless r,$$

$$u \gtrless 0,\ u \gtrless \frac{p + q + r - 1}{2},$$

the conditions required.

It will, however, in most of the following investigations suffice to consider the conditions of possible experience in the data alone, because it will be shown that when these are satisfied the corresponding conditions for the probability sought, when its value is determined by the method of the following section, will also be satisfied.

## Statement of the Method for the Solution of Questions in the Theory of Probabilities

For the general demonstration of this method the reader is referred to the *Laws of Thought*, Chap. XVII. For the purpose of the analytical investigation the statement of the method will suffice.

Let $s$, $t$, $v$, &c. represent the events of which the probabilities are given, $p$, $q$, $r$, &c. those probabilities, and $w$ the event of which the probability is sought; then, whatever the definitions of $s$, $t$... and $w$ may be, and whatever connecting relations may exist, it is always possible by the calculus of Logic to determine the logical dependence of $w$ upon $s$, $t$, &c. in the following most general form, viz.

$$w = A + 0B + \frac{0}{0}C + \frac{1}{0}D.$$

Here A, B, C, D are logical combinations of the events $s$, $t$, &c., and the connexion in which these stand to the event $w$ and to each other is the following : A expresses those combinations of $s$, $t$, &c. which are entirely included in $w$, i.e. which cannot happen without our being permitted to say that $w$ happens. B represents those combinations which may happen but are not included under $w$; so that when they happen we may say that $w$ does not happen.  C represents those combinations the happening of which leaves us in doubt whether $w$ happens or not;  D those combinations the happening of which would involve logical contradiction.

It follows from the above that the *translated* form of the problem is

Given Prob. $s = p$, Prob. $t = q$, Prob. $v = r$, &c., $s$, $t$, $v \ldots$ being regarded as events subject to the explicit logical condition

$$A + B + C = 1.$$

Required the probability $u$ of the event of which the logical expression is

$$w = A + \frac{0}{0}C;$$

and it is shown (*Laws of Thought*, p. 265), upon grounds essentially the same as those expressed in Principles I. and II. of this paper, that the solution of the problem is involved in the following *algebraic* equations, viz.

$$\frac{V_s}{p} = \frac{V_t}{q} \ldots = \frac{A + cC}{u} = V \quad . \quad . \quad . \quad \text{(I.)}$$

in which the functions V, $V_s$, $V_t \ldots$ are formed in the following manner, viz.,—

1st. V is derived from $A + B + C$ without change of form by interpreting $s$, $t$, &c. no longer as logical symbols, but as symbols of quantity.  They represent the probabilities of the ideal events of Principle II.

2ndly. $V_s$ is the sum of those terms in V which contain $s$ as a factor, $V_t$ the sum of those which contain $t$ as a factor, &c.

The quantity $c$ is an arbitrary constant, admitting of any value between 0 and 1.

To effect the solution, the quantities $s$, $t$, &c. are to be eliminated from the system (I.), and $u$ then determined as a function of $p$, $q$, $r \ldots$ and $c$.  The arbitrary constant $c$ may not appear in the final result, because the developed form of $w$ may not contain any terms affected with the symbol $\frac{0}{0}$.

When such terms do appear, the constant $c$ admits of an interpretation indicating what new data are required to make the solution definite.*

It is proper here to observe that the conditions of possible experience can be determined as well from the " translated " as from the original form of the problem. That the results will agree is evident à priori, but it may be desirable to point out the analytical connexion of the two processes. I will take the example just considered, and then offer some general remarks on the subject.

Representing the events $xy, yz, zx$ by $s, t, v$, the translated data would be found to be

$$\text{Prob. } s = p, \text{ Prob. } t = q, \text{ Prob. } v = r,$$

$s, t,$ and $v$ being connected by the explicit logical condition

$$stv + s\bar{t}\bar{v} + \bar{s}t\bar{v} + \bar{s}\bar{t}v + \bar{s}\bar{t}\bar{v} = 1.$$

It is easily shown that the first member of this equation represents the sum of those combinations of the events $s, t, v$, with respect to happening or failing, which involve no logical contradiction.

If then, we represent under the above condition

$$\text{Prob. } stv = \lambda', \text{ Prob. } s\bar{t}\bar{v} = \mu', \text{ Prob. } \bar{s}t\bar{v} = \nu', \text{ Prob. } \bar{s}\bar{t}v = \rho',$$

we shall have

$$\lambda' + \mu' = p, \lambda' + \nu' = q, \lambda' + \rho' = r,$$
$$\lambda' \gtrless 0, \mu' \gtrless 0, \nu' \gtrless 0, \rho' \gtrless 0, \lambda' + \mu' + \nu' + \rho' \gtrless 1.$$

This system of equations and inequations agrees with that employed in the previous solution, if we only make

$$\lambda' = \lambda, \mu' = \mu, \nu' = \rho, \rho' = \nu$$

so that the elimination of $\lambda', \mu', \nu', \rho'$, will lead to the same results as before.

In general it may be observed that each combination of $s, t, v$, which is possible without logical contradiction, gives, on substituting for $s, t, v \ldots$ their expressions in the simple terms of the original problem, either a single combination of those simple terms, or a sum of such combinations; but the same combination of those simple terms will not

* *Laws of Thought*, p. 267.

arise from two different combinations of $s, t \ldots$   It is clear from this that the systems of united equations and inequations arising in the two forms of the problem will be related in the following manner, viz.—

For each positive quantity $\lambda'$ in the one set, there will exist either a single positive quantity $\lambda$, or a sum of such quantities $\lambda_1 + \lambda_2 + $ &c. in the other; but each such sum is inseparable, and the elements it is composed of are distinct from those of any other sum arising from any other of the quantities $\lambda' \ldots$   It is evident, then, that the final results of elimination will be the same.   The same formal processes which eliminate single quantities in the one set will eliminate the corresponding single quantities, or sums of single quantities, in the other.

*Simplification of the General Equations for the Solution of Questions in the Theory of Probabilities*

Let us express the system (I.) in the form

$$\frac{V_s}{V} = p, \; \frac{V_t}{V} = q, \; \&c., \; u = \frac{A + cC}{V},$$

and let us suppose the quantities $p, q \ldots$ (and therefore $s, t \ldots$) to be $n$ in number.   Then all the terms in V will be composed of products of $s, t \ldots \bar{s}, \bar{t} \ldots$, each term involving either $s$ or $\bar{s}$, either $t$ or $\bar{t}$, &c., but not the combinations $s\bar{s}$, $t\bar{t}$, &c.   Each term is therefore homogeneous and of the $n$th degree.

It follows, therefore, that if we divide the numerator and denominator of each of the first members of the above system by $\bar{s}\bar{t}\bar{v} \ldots$, and then make

$$\frac{s}{s} = x_1, \; \frac{t}{t} = x_2, \; \frac{v}{v} = x_3, \; \&c.,$$

and if at the same time we, for symmetry, change $p, q, r \ldots$ into $p_1, p_2, \ldots p_n$, the system will assume the following form,—

$$\frac{V_1}{V} = p_1, \; \frac{V_2}{V} = p_2 \cdot\cdot, \; \frac{V_n}{V} = p_n,$$

$$u = \frac{A + cC}{V},$$

in which V, A, C, are formed from their former values by suppressing $\bar{s}$, $\bar{t}$, $\bar{v}$, &c., or, which is the same thing, changing each of them into unity, and then changing $s$, $t$, $v \ldots$ into $x_1$, $x_2$, $x_3 \ldots$, while $V_1$ consists of those terms of V which contain $x_1$, $V_2$ of those which contain $x_2$, and so on.

In its new form V is a rational and entire function of $x_1$, $x_2$, $\ldots x_n$ not involving powers of those quantities, and with all its coefficients equal to unity. Again, as $s$, $t$, &c. are from the theory of their origin required to be positive proper fractions, $x_1$, $x_2$, $\ldots x_n$ are, from the nature of their connexion with $s$, $t \ldots$, required to be positive quantities. And it is sufficient that $x_1$, $x_2$, $\ldots x_n$ be determinable as positive quantities in order that $s$, $t \ldots$ may be determinable as positive fractions.

Now we shall proceed to shew that $x_1$, $x_2$, $\ldots x_n$ are determinable as positive quantities precisely when $p_1$, $p_2$, $\ldots p_n$ satisfy the conditions of possible experience. We shall further shew, as a consequence of this, that the value of the probability sought, when determined by the General Rule will, under the same conditions, lie within such limits as if it were itself given by the same experience. In the order of this proof, we shall first demonstrate the theorems of pure Analysis upon which the conclusions depend, then in a distinct section make the particular application.

### Analytical Theorems relating to Functional Determinants and Systems of Algebraic Equations

A symmetrical determinant may be conveniently expressed in the form

$$
\begin{vmatrix}
A_1 & A_{12} & \ldots & A_{1n} \\
A_{21} & A_2 & \ldots & A_{2n} \\
\ldots & \ldots & \ldots & \ldots \\
A_{n1} & A_{n2} & \ldots & A_n
\end{vmatrix} \quad \ldots \quad \ldots \quad \text{(I.)}
$$

the conditions of symmetry being

$$ A_{ij} = A_{ji}, \ A_{ii} = A_i. $$

It is desirable to employ fixed language in referring to this.

We shall, therefore, call the quantities $A_1$, $A_2 \ldots A_n$ the " principal elements ", and the diagonal series of terms which they form the " principal diagonal ". The elements $A_{ij}$, when $i$ and $j$ differ, we shall call " subordinate elements ". The element $A_i$, together with all the subordinate elements which occur upon the same horizontal or vertical line of the determinant, we shall designate the " $i$-system of elements ". Lastly, in comparing two rows or two columns of elements together, those elements will be said to correspond which occupy the same numerical place in their respective rows or columns.

The following Lemma will next be established.

*Lemma.*—A symmetrical determinant expressed in the form (I.) will be unaltered in value, if from each subordinate element of its $i$-system we subtract the corresponding element of its $j$-system multiplied by a quantity $\lambda$, which is invariable for the same system,—and for the principal element $A_i$ substitute $A_i - 2\lambda A_{ij} + \lambda^2 A_j$.

It is known that a determinant vanishes if two of its lines or columns are identical, and it is known as a consequence of this that if from a particular line or column of a determinant the corresponding elements of another line or column, multiplied each by the same constant, are subtracted, the determinant is unaltered in value. From the $i$th line of the above symmetrical determinant subtract, term by term, $\lambda$ times the $j$th line, and then from the $i$th column of the resulting determinant subtract $\lambda$ times the $j$th column. As respects any subordinate element, the result will obviously accord with the statement in the Lemma. But the element $A_i$ will be successively converted into

$$A_i - \lambda A_{ji}$$

$$(A_i - \lambda A_{ji}) - \lambda(A_{ij}\lambda - A_j).$$

The last expression, since $A_{ii} = A_{ij}$, is reducible to

$$A_i - 2\lambda A_{ij} + \lambda^2 A_j.$$

Upon this property the demonstration of the following general proposition will be founded.

c c

## PROPOSITION I

*Let the symmetrical determinant* (I.) *possess the following properties, viz.:—*

1st. *That all its elements are linear homogeneous rational functions of certain quantities a, b, c, &c., unlimited in number.*

2ndly. *That if the coefficients of any one of these quantities a in the elements of any particular line or column taken in order are* $\alpha_1, \alpha_2, \ldots \alpha_n$ *and in any other line or column* $\beta_1, \beta_2, \ldots \beta_n$ *then these two series of quantities are respectively proportional.*

3rdly. *That the principal Terms* $A_1, A_2, \ldots A_n$ *are positive,* i.e. *that the coefficients of all the quantities a, b, c, &c. which appear in these terms are positive.*

*Then the developed determinant will be itself positive, and will consist of products of the quantities a, b, c, &c. without powers, each product affected by a positive sign.*

First, it may be observed that any letter $a$ of the set $a, b, c \ldots$ which appears in the subordinate term $A_{ij}$ will appear in both the principal terms $A_i, A_j$.

For let $m$ be the coefficient of $a$ in $A_{ij}$, and therefore also in $A_{ji}$; let $l$ be the coefficient of $a$ in $A_i$, and $n$ its coefficient in $A_j$. Thus to the elements $A_i, A_{ji}$ in the $i$-column correspond $A_{ij}, A_j$ in the $j$-column. Hence, by the definition of the determinant,

$$l : m :: m : n,$$
$$m^2 = ln,$$

which implies that neither $l$ nor $n$ vanishes, so that $a$ appears in $A_i$ and $A_j$.

Secondly, we shall shew that the determinant can, without alteration of its final developed value, be reduced to a form in which any letter $a$ of the system, $a, b, c \ldots$ shall appear in only one system of elements, and therefore only in the principal term of that system, since every subordinate term is common to *two* systems.

Let us suppose $a$ to be contained in two at least of the systems of elements, and for convenience of expression, let these be the 1-system and the $n$-system. Let then, $\alpha_1, \alpha_2, \ldots \alpha_n$ be the successive coefficients of $a$ in $A_1, A_{21}, \ldots A_{n1}$, and therefore, by definition, of the determinant, $\lambda a_1$, $\lambda a_2$, $\ldots \lambda a_n$, its coefficients in $A_{n1}$, $A_{n2}$, $\ldots A_n$.  Any of the quantities $\alpha_1$, $\alpha_2$, $\ldots \alpha_n$ may be 0.  But by the Lemma above demonstrated the determinant may, without alteration of value, be reduced to the following form, viz :—

$$\begin{vmatrix} A_1, A_{12}, \ldots A_{1n} - \lambda A_1 \\ A_{21}, A_2, \ldots A_{2n} - \lambda A_{21} \\ \cdots\cdots\cdots\cdots\cdots\cdots \\ A_{n1} - \lambda A_1, A_{n2} - \lambda A_{12} \ldots A_n - 2\lambda A_{n1} + \lambda^2 A_1 \end{vmatrix} \qquad \text{(B.)}$$

Now in the determinant thus transformed the quantity $a$ will no longer occur in the $n$-system.

This is obvious with respect to the subordinate elements of that system.  With respect to the principal element, we observe that the coefficient of $a$ is

in $A_1$, equal to $\alpha_1$,

in $A_{n1}$, equal to $\lambda \alpha_1$,

$\cdots\cdots\cdots\cdots\cdots\cdots\cdots\cdots\cdots$

in $A_n$, equal to $\lambda \times \lambda \alpha$, or $\lambda^2 \alpha_1$,

whence the coefficient of $a$ in $A_n - 2\lambda_{n1} + \lambda^2 A_1$ is equal to 0.

Thus $a$ has been eliminated from the $n$-system, and as the process has not affected any elements but those which belong to the $n$-system, it will not affect the relations under which $a$ enters into the other systems.

Consider then any other quantity $b$ in the set $a$, $b$, $c$, then by hypothesis the coefficients of $b$ in any line or column of elements

$$A_{i1}, A_{i2} .. A_{in}, \text{ or } A_{1i}, A_{2i}, .. A_{ni}$$

may be represented by

$$\mu_i \beta_1, \mu_i \beta_2, \ldots \mu_i \beta_n$$

$\beta_1$, $\beta_2$, $\ldots \beta_n$ being an arbitrary set of quantities which are the same for all lines or columns, while $\mu_i$ differs for different lines or columns, and vanishes for those in which $b$ does not enter.

It is to be noted that as $A_{ij} = A_{ji}$, we have in general

$$\mu_i \beta_j = \mu_j \beta_i,$$

while as the principal elements of the determinant (I.) are positive, we have always $\mu_i\beta_i =$ a positive quantity.

Now reverting the derived determinant (B.), we see that its $i$th line or column of elements will be

$$A_{i_1}, A_{i_2}, \ldots A_{in} - \lambda A_{i_1},$$

and its $j$th line or column

$$A_{j_1}, A_{j_2}, \ldots A_{jn} - \lambda A_{j_1},$$

supposing $i$ and $j$ to be both less than $n$.

In these lines or columns the successive coefficients of $b$ will therefore be

$$\mu_i\beta_1, \mu_i\beta_2 \ldots \mu_i\beta_n - \lambda\mu_i\beta_1,$$
$$\mu_j\beta_1, \mu_j\beta_2 \ldots \mu_j\beta_n - \lambda\mu_j\beta_1,$$

which stand to each other in the constant ratio $\mu_i : \mu_j$.

Next let $j = n$. The coefficients of $b$ in the $n$th line or column of (B.) are obviously

$$\mu_n\beta_1 - \lambda\mu_1\beta_1, \mu_n\beta_2 - \lambda\mu_1\beta_2, \ldots \mu_n\beta_n - 2\lambda\mu, \beta_n + \lambda^2\mu_1\beta_1,$$

of which the last term may be reduced as follows,

$$\mu_n\beta_n - 2\lambda\mu_1\beta_n + \lambda^2\mu_1\beta_1 = \mu_n\beta_n - \lambda\mu_1\beta_n - \lambda\mu_n\beta_1 + \lambda^2\mu_1\beta_1$$
$$= (\mu_n - \lambda\mu_1)(\beta_n - \lambda\beta_1) ;$$

so that the series of coefficients of $b$ becomes

$$(\mu_n - \lambda\mu_1)\beta_1, (\mu_n - \lambda\mu_1)\beta_2 \ldots (\mu_n - \lambda\mu_1)(\beta_n - \lambda\beta_1),$$

and they are now seen to stand to those of $b$ in the $i$-line and column in the constant ratio $\mu_n - \lambda\mu_1 : \mu_i$.

We have, lastly, to prove that the new principal element $A_n - 2\lambda A_{1n} + \lambda^2 A_1$ is positive.

Let N be the coefficient of any one of the quantities $a$, $b$, $c \ldots$ in the above element, L its coefficient in the principal element $A_i$, and M its coefficient in each of the subordinate elements common to the two systems of which the above are the respective principal elements, viz. in $A_{in} - \lambda A_{i_1}$ and $A_{ni} - \lambda A_{1i}$. Then, by what has already been proved,

$$L : M : : M : N,$$
$$\therefore \quad M^2 = LN ;$$

but L is positive ; therefore N is so, and the principal element in question consists wholly of positive terms.

The above demonstration shews that the elimination of $a$ from the $n$-system produces a new determinant equivalent to the original one, and in which the characters noted in the original one still remain.   Should $a$ occur in any other system or systems of elements of the new determinant beside the 1-system, it can, by repetitions of the same process, be eliminated thence.   Ultimately, then, it will only remain in the 1-system, and therefore only in the principal term of that system.   Again, as it enters that term in the first degree, it follows that the developed determinant will involve only the first power of $a$.   Hence, as $a$ may represent any of the quantities $a$, $b$, $c$, $\ldots$, it is seen that no powers, but only products of these quantities will appear in the developed determinant.

Let us represent the determinant, after the elimination of $a$ from all the elements but $A_1$, in the form

$$\begin{vmatrix} A_1 \, B_{12} \ldots B_{1n} \\ B_{21} \, C_2 \ldots C_{2n} \\ \ldots\ldots\ldots\ldots \\ B_{n1} \, C_{n2} \ldots C_n. \end{vmatrix}$$

Now let $ah_1$ represent that term in $A_1$ which involves $a$. Then the portion of the determinant which involves $a$ will be

$$ah_1 \begin{vmatrix} C_2 \ldots C_{2n} \\ \ldots\ldots\ldots \\ C_{n2} \ldots C_n. \end{vmatrix}$$

And here it is to be observed that $ah_1$ is positive, while the new determinant to which it is attached as a coefficient possesses all the characters of the old one.   This determinant we can, therefore, transform in the same way, so as to eliminate any other letter $b$ from all but a single principal element, which we shall suppose to contain it in a term $bh_2$. That portion of the original determinant which involves $ab$ will, therefore, assume the form

$$abh_1h_2 \begin{vmatrix} D_3 \ldots D_{3n} \\ \ldots\ldots\ldots \\ D_{n3} \ldots D_n. \end{vmatrix}$$

Ultimately then, as the result of such processes continued, the portion of the original determinant which involves any particular combination of $n$ letters selected from $a$, $b$, $c$ . . . will consist of the product of a series of positive terms, each of which has appeared in some residual principal element. Every such combination being positive, it follows that the determinant itself consists solely of positive terms.

## PROPOSITION II

*If* V *be any rational entire function of the* $n$ *variables* $x_1$, $x_2$, . . .$x_n$, *but involving no powers of those variables above the first, and if, further, all the different terms of* V *have positive signs, then the determinant*

$$\begin{vmatrix} V & V_1 & V_2 \ldots V_n \\ V_1 & V_1 & V_{12} \ldots V_{1n} \\ V_2 & V_{21} & V_2 \ldots V_{2n} \\ \cdots\cdots\cdots\cdots\cdots \\ V_n & V_{n1} & V_{n2} \ldots V_n \end{vmatrix}$$

*in which* $V_i$ *denotes the sum of the terms in* V *which contain* $x_i$, *and* $V_{ij}$ *the sum of the terms in* V *which contain* $x_i$, $x_j$, *will, when developed as a rational and entire function of* $x_1$, $x_2$, . . .$x_n$, *consist wholly of terms with positive coefficients.*

From the definition it is plain that in general

$$V_{ij} = V_{ji}, \quad V_{ii} = V_i,$$

whence the above determinant is symmetrical.

Again, all its elements are homogeneous linear functions of the terms in V.

Again, if $\alpha$, $\alpha_1$, $\alpha_2$, . . .$\alpha_n$ represent the successive coefficients of any one of the terms of V in any row or column of the determinant, and $\beta$, $\beta_1$, $\beta_2$, . . . $\beta_n$ the successive corresponding coefficients of the same term in any other row or column of the determinant, the one series of coefficients shall be proportional to the other.

Let us compare the first column and the $i$-column headed with the element $V_i$. Selecting any term in V, suppose it to contain $x_i$, then in whatever element of the first column that term is found, it will be found in a corresponding element of the $i$-column, and in each case with unity for its coefficient, since all the elements are mere collections of terms from V. But when it is not found in a particular element of the first column, it will not be found in the corresponding element of the $i$-column. The entire series of coefficients in the one being then the same as that in the other, the common ratio of the corresponding terms is unity.

Suppose, secondly, that the proposed term is found in V and not in $V_i$; then in all the elements of the $i$-column its coefficient is 0, so that the series of coefficients in the $i$-column might be formed from those in the first column by multiplying the latter successively by 0. This again represents a common ratio.

The same reasoning may be applied to the comparison of any two columns of the determinant. Thus in comparing the $i$-column and the $j$-column :—terms of V which contain both $x_i$, and $x_j$ will be wholly absent from the $j$-column. Thus in all cases if $\alpha$, $\alpha_1$, $\alpha_2$, $\ldots \alpha_n$ represent the coefficients of a term of V in one column, its coefficients in any other column, taken in the same order, will be of the form $\lambda\alpha$, $\lambda\alpha_1$, $\lambda\alpha_2$, $\ldots \lambda\alpha_n$, the coefficient $\lambda$ being either 1 or 0.

Lastly, the principal elements consist, as do all the elements, of positive terms.

Therefore by the last proposition the developed determinant will consist of products (without powers higher than the first) of different terms of V, and the coefficients of all such products will be positive.

Therefore, the determinant will be expressible as a rational entire function of $x_1$, $x_2$, $\ldots x_n$ with positive coefficients.

The rapidity with which the complexity of the determinant increases as the number of variables increases, is remarkable. For example, if $n = 2$ and $V = axy + bx + cy + d$, the determinant is

$$\begin{vmatrix} axy + bx + cy + d & axy + bx & axy + cy \\ axy + bx & axy + bx & axy \\ axy + cy & axy & axy + cy \end{vmatrix}$$

and its calculated value will be found to be

$$abcx^2y^2 + abdx^2y + acdxy^2 + bcdxy,$$

consisting of four positive terms.

But if $n = 3$ and

$$V = axyz + byz + cxz + dxy + ex + fy + gz + h,$$

the developed determinant will consist of fifty-eight positive terms. Its calculated value will be found in the Memoir on Testimonies and Judgments.

## PROPOSITION III

*The functions* V, $V_1$, $V_2$, $...V_n$ *being defined as above, if* V *be complete in form, i.e. if it consist of all the terms which according to definition it can contain, each with a positive coefficient, then the system of equations*

$$\frac{V_1}{V} = p_1, \frac{V_2}{V} = p_2, ...\frac{V_n}{V} = p_n. \quad . \quad . \quad (1)$$

*will, when* $p_1$, $p_2$, $...p_n$ *are proper fractions, admit of one solution, and only one, in positive values of* $x_1$, $x_2$, $...x_n$.

We shall shew, first, that the above proposition is true when $n = 1$, secondly, that on the hypothesis that it is true for $n - 1$ variables, it is true for $n$ variables. Hence it will follow that it is true generally.

Suppose $n = 1$. Then $V = ax_1 + b$, whence the system (1) reduces to the single equation

$$\frac{ax_1}{ax_1 + b} = p_1, \quad x_1 = \frac{bp}{a(1 - p_1)},$$

whence, since $a$ and $b$ are positive, and $p$ is a positive fraction, $x_1$ is positive.

Thus the proposition is true when $n = 1$.

Now, let $x_1 = 0$, and let $x_2$, $x_3$, $...x_n$ be determined to satisfy the last $n - 1$ equations of the system (1.). These $n - 1$ equations will, when $x_1 = 0$, form a system of the same nature with respect to the $n - 1$ variables $x_2$, $x_3$, $...x_n$, as (1) is with respect to the $n$ variables $x_1$, $x_2$, $...x_n$, will be determinable as positive quantities, and their values substituted in the first member of the first equation of (1.) will reduce it to the form

$$\frac{Ax_1}{Ax_1 + B},$$

A and B being finite and positive.   Hence the function $\dfrac{V_1}{V}$ will become 0.

Secondly, let any finite positive value be assigned to $x_1$. The last $n-1$ equations of the system (1) will again form a system of the same nature as before, and will by hypothesis determine a set of finite positive values for $x_2$, $x_3$, $\ldots x_n$. These values again substituted in $\dfrac{V_1}{V}$, will give to it again the form

$$\frac{Ax_1}{Ax_1 + B},$$

A and B being finite and positive.   Hence as $x_1$ is finite and positive, $\dfrac{V_1}{V}$ will be a positive fraction.

Lastly, let $x_1$ be infinite.   Still the last $n-1$ equations of the system (1) will assume the same form as before.   Determining thence $x_2$, $x_3$, $\ldots x_n$, and substituting in $\dfrac{V_1}{V}$, we have

$$\frac{V_1}{V} = \frac{Ax_1}{Ax_1 + B},$$

in which A and B are finite and positive and $x_1$ is infinite. Hence $\dfrac{V_1}{V} = 1$.   It is seen then that as $x_1$ varies from 0 to infinity $x_2$, $x_3$, $\ldots x_n$ being at the same time always by hypothesis determined to satisfy the last $n = 1$ equations of the system (1), the function $\dfrac{V_1}{V}$ will vary from 0 through positive fractional values to unity.   It is manifest too, that it varies continuously.   If then it vary by continuous *increase*, it will once, and only once in its change, become equal to $p_1$, and the whole system of equations thus be satisfied together. I shall shew that it does vary by continuous *increase*.

If it vary continuously from 0 to 1 and not by continuous increase, it must in the course of its variation, assume at least once, a maximum or minimum value.   Let us then seek the condition of possibility of

$$\frac{V_1}{V} = \text{a maximum or minimum},$$

the variables being subject to the relations

$$\frac{V_2}{V} = p_2, \ \frac{V_3}{V} = p_3, \ \ldots \frac{V_n}{V} = p_n.$$

Here, proceeding in the usual way by differentiation, we have

$$\frac{VdV_1 - V_1dV}{V^2} = 0, \ \frac{VdV_2 - V_2dV}{V^2} = 0, \ \ldots \frac{VdV_n - V_ndV}{V^2} = 0,$$

or

$$\frac{dV}{V} = \frac{dV_1}{V_1} = \frac{dV_2}{V_2} \ldots = \frac{dV_n}{V_n}.$$

Let the common value of these fractions be represented by $-dt$, then we have a system of $n + 1$ equations of which the first is

$$Vdt + dV = 0,$$

while the $n$ others are of the type

$$V_idt + dV_i = 0,$$

$$V_1dt + \frac{dV_1}{dx_1}dx_1 \ldots + \frac{dV_1}{dx_n}dx_n = 0,$$

$$\cdot \quad \cdot \quad \cdot \quad \cdot \quad \cdot \quad \cdot \quad \cdot$$

$$V_ndt + \frac{dV_n}{dx_1}dx_1 \ldots \frac{dV_n}{dx_n}dx_n = 0.$$

Now from the nature of the function V we have

$$\frac{dV}{dx_1} = \frac{V_i}{x_i}, \ \frac{dV_i}{dx_i} = \frac{V_i}{x_i}, \ \frac{dV_i}{dx_j} = \frac{V_{ij}}{x_j},$$

so that the above equations become

$$Vdt + V_1\frac{dx_1}{x_1} + V_2\frac{dx_2}{x_2} \ldots + V_n\frac{dx_n}{x_n} = 0,$$

$$V_1dt + V_1\frac{dx_1}{x_1} + V_{12}\frac{dx_2}{x_2} \ldots + V_{1n}\frac{dx_n}{x_n} = 0,$$

$$V_2dt + V_{21}\frac{dx_1}{x_1} + V_2\frac{dx_2}{x_2} \ldots + V_{2n}\frac{dx_n}{x_n} = 0,$$

$$\cdot \quad \cdot \quad \cdot \quad \cdot \quad \cdot \quad \cdot \quad \cdot$$

$$V_ndt + V_{n1}\frac{dx_1}{x_1} + V_{n2}\frac{dx_2}{x_2} \ldots + V_n\frac{dx_n}{x_n} = 0,$$

and the elimination of $dt, \dfrac{dx_1}{x_1}, \dfrac{dx_2}{x_2} \ldots \dfrac{dx_n}{x_n}$ from these equations gives the sought condition of possibility of a maximum value of $\dfrac{V_1}{V}$, consistently with the satisfaction of the last $n = 1$ equations of the system (1).

This condition is therefore expressed by the equation

$$\begin{vmatrix} V & V_1 & V_2 & \cdot\cdot V_n \\ V_1 & V_1 & V_{12} & \cdot\cdot V_{1n} \\ V_2 & V_{21} & V_2 & \cdot\cdot V_{2n} \\ \cdot\cdot & \cdot\cdot & \cdot\cdot\cdot & \cdot\cdot \\ V_n & V_{n1} & V_{n2} & \cdot\cdot V_n \end{vmatrix} = 0.$$

But we have already seen (Prop. II.) that the first member of this equation is essentially positive for positive values of $x_1$, $x_2$, $\ldots x_n$. Hence the function $\dfrac{V_1}{V}$ varies by continuous increase, and on the hypothesis that the proposition to be proved is true for $n - 1$ variables, it is true for $n$ variables.

Therefore, connecting this with the former result, the proposition is true universally.

## PROPOSITION IV

*If* V *be an incomplete function, some of the terms belonging to the complete form being wanting, but the terms present having their coefficients positive, it will in general be necessary not only that the quantities* $p_1$, $p_2$, $\ldots p_n$ *should be positive fractions, but also that they should satisfy certain inequations of the form*

$$a_1 p_1 + a_2 p_2 \cdots + a_n p_n + b \gtrless 0,$$

*in order that the system*

$$\frac{V_1}{V} = p_1, \; \frac{V_2}{V} = p_2, \; \ldots \frac{V_n}{V} = p_n \quad . \quad . \quad (1)$$

*may admit of a solution in positive values of* $x_1$, $x_2$, $\ldots x_n$.

For let $A x_r x_s x_t \ldots$ be any term in V, A being a constant which is positive in all the terms, but which may be different in the different terms. Suppose that in $V_i$ there exist $e$ terms like the above, and let the several ratios of these terms to V be denoted by $\lambda_1$, $\lambda_2$, $\ldots \lambda_e$. Then the $i$th equation of the system (1) will become

$$\lambda_1 + \lambda_2 \cdots + \lambda_e = p_i \quad . \quad . \quad . \quad (2)$$

and the system (1) will be converted into a system of $n$ equations of this nature. We will suppose that there exist $m$ distinct quantities of the nature of $\lambda_1, \lambda_2, \ldots \lambda_e$ in the first members of this transformed system, and we will represent these by $\lambda_1, \lambda_2, \ldots \lambda_m$. Then, if these constitute all the ratios of the separate terms of V to V itself, we have a new equation,

$$\lambda_1 + \lambda_2 \ldots + \lambda_m = 1 \quad \ldots \quad (3)$$

If they do not constitute all those separate ratios, we have, on the contrary, an inequation,

$$\lambda_1 + \lambda_2 \ldots + \lambda_m \lessgtr 1 \quad \ldots \quad (4)$$

Lastly, the condition that $\lambda_1, \lambda_2, \ldots \lambda_m$ are positive fractions, gives the inequations

$$\lambda_1 \gtrless 0, \lambda_2 \gtrless 0, \ldots \lambda_m \gtrless 0 \quad \ldots \quad (5)$$

The conditions $\lambda_1 \lessgtr 1$, &c. are already implied in (3) or (4).

The $\lambda$ quantities are thus subject to a system of united *equations* and *inequations*, from which they must be eliminated by the method already explained.

The result of such elimination will be a final system of inequations connecting $p_1, p_2, \ldots p_n$. Equations connecting these quantities can only present themselves when the equations of the original system are not independent, or, which really falls under the same hypothesis, when one or more of the variables, $x_1, x_2, \ldots x_n$ is wholly absent from that system. Thus if $x_1$ were a common factor of all the terms of V, it would divide out from the numerators and denominators of the system, which would thus become a system of $n$ simultaneous equations connecting the $n - 1$ variables $x_2, x_3, \ldots x_n$. Considered with reference to these variables, therefore, the equations of the system would not be independent.

All resulting equations will be capable of expression under the one general form,

$$a_1 p_1 + a_2 p_2 \ldots + a_n p_n + b \gtrless 0,$$

the coefficients $a_1, a_2, \ldots a_n$ and $b$ being positive, negative, or vanishing, numerical constants. For any inequation which presents itself in the form

$$a'_1 p_1 + a'_2 p_2 \ldots + a'_n p_n + b \lessgtr 1$$

may be transformed into

$$- a'_1 p_1 \ldots - a'_n p_n + 1 - b \gtrless 0.$$

Again, the general inequation

$$a_1 p_1 + a_2 p_2 \ldots + a_n p_n + b \gtrless 0$$

determines an inferior limit of $p_1$ when $a_1$ is positive, and a superior limit of $p_1$ when $a_1$ is negative.

For in the former case we have

$$p_1 \gtrless - \left( \frac{a_2}{a_1} p_1 \ldots \frac{a_n}{a_1} p_n + \frac{b}{a_1} \right),$$

the second member of which is an inferior limit of $p_1$; and it will be observed that the calculated value of this member may be positive, as there is no general restriction on the signs of $a_2, \ldots a_n, b$.

In the latter case, changing $a_1$ into $-a'_1$, and observing that $a_1$ is positive, we have

$$p_1 \gtrless \frac{a_2}{a'_1} p_2 + \frac{a_3}{a'_1} p_3 \ldots + \frac{a_n}{a'_1} p_n + \frac{b}{a'_1},$$

the second member of which is a superior limit of $p_1$.

Lastly, the final system of inequations is totally independent of the numerical value of the coefficients of V. The only restriction is that these coefficients are positive.

## PROPOSITION V

*Let* V *be incomplete in form; then, provided that the equations*

$$\frac{V_1}{V} = p_1, \frac{V_2}{V} = p_2, \ldots \frac{V_n}{V} = p_n \quad . \quad . \quad (1)$$

*are independent with respect to the quantities* $x_1, x_2, \ldots x_n$, *and that the inequations of condition deducible by the last proposition are satisfied, the equations will admit of one solution, and only one, in positive finite values of* $x_1, x_2, \ldots x_n$.

The proof of this proposition will, in its general character, resemble the proof of Proposition III. It will be shown that when we assign to $x$ any value *between* the limits 0 and infinity, the quantities $x_2, x_3, \ldots x_n$ will admit of determination from the last $n - 1$ equations of the system as positive

finite quantities, and the function $\frac{V_1}{V}$ will receive a value
falling within the limits assigned by Proposition IV to the
quantity $p_1$; that when $x_1$ is equal to 0 or infinity, $x_2$,
$x_3, \ldots x_n$ will admit of determination either as positive finite
quantities, or as limits (0 and $\infty$) of such quantities; and
that these values together will give to $\frac{V_1}{V}$ a value coinciding
with the highest of the inferior, or lowest of the superior
limits of $p_1$, as determined by Proposition IV; that when
$x_1$ varies from 0 to $\infty$, $x_2, x_3, \ldots x_n$ being determined as above,
$\frac{V_1}{V}$ will vary by continuous increase from the highest of
the inferior to the lowest of the superior limits of $p_1$, and
once in its variation become equal to $p_1$. Thus the truth
of the proposition for $n$ variables will flow necessarily from
its assumed truth for $n - 1$ variables. And on this ground
it will be shown that it may ultimately be reduced to a direct
dependence upon Proposition III.

In the system (1) let $x_1$ receive any finite positive value,
and let V by the substitution of this value become U; the
last $n - 1$ equations of (1) will thus assume the form

$$\frac{U_2}{U} = p_2, \frac{U_3}{U} = p_3, \ldots \frac{U_n}{U} = p_n \quad . \quad . \quad (2)$$

in which the quantities $p_2, p_3 \ldots p_n$ satisfy the conditions to
which the direct application of Proposition IV to this
reduced system of equations would lead.

For what is important to notice in the change from V to
U is, that any two terms in V which differ only in that one
contains $x_1$ and the other does not, reduce to a single term
in U. The effect of the change upon the primary system of
equations and inequations formed in the application of
Proposition IV to the system (1) is the following :—

1st. The equation between $\lambda_1, \lambda_2 \ldots$ derived from the first
equation of (1) will be annulled.

2ndly. In the remaining equations connecting $\lambda_1, \lambda_2 \ldots$
some *pairs* of those quantities may be replaced by single

quantities, with corresponding changes in the inequations. Thus if $\lambda_1 + \lambda_2$ be replaced by $\mu$, the inequations

$$\lambda_1 \gtrless 0, \lambda_2 \gtrless 0$$

will be replaced by what they before *implied*, viz.

$$\mu \gtrless 0.$$

But these changes do not affect the truth of the relations, or introduce any new relations. They cannot, therefore, lead to any new final conditions. The conditions connecting $p_2, p_3, \ldots p_n$, in accordance with Proposition IV in the system (2), must have been already involved in the equations connecting $p_1, p_2, \ldots p_n$ in the system (1).

Hence by hypothesis the system (2) gives one set of positive finite values of $x_2, x_3, \ldots x_n$ corresponding to the assumed positive finite value of $x_1$. And these values together make $\frac{V_1}{V}$ a positive proper fraction. We may notice that, representing $\frac{V_1}{V}$ under the form

$$\frac{Ax_1}{Ax_1 + B},$$

it cannot be that either A or B is wanting so as to reduce $\frac{V_1}{V}$ to the value 0 or 1. For if A were wanting, V would not contain $x_1$ at all, as by hypothesis it does; and if B were wanting, V would contain $x_1$ in every term. Thus $x_1$ would divide out from the system (1) which would thus become a system of $n$ equations between $n - 1$ variables, and would cease to be independent, as by hypothesis it is.

But when $x_1 = 0$, or $x_1 = $ infinity, the form of V, considered as a function of $x_2, x_3, \ldots x_n$ will not generally be the same as in the case last considered; and the connecting $p_2, p_3, \ldots p_n$ will no longer be such that we can affirm the possibility of deducing from the last $n - 1$ equations of the system (1) as transformed, positive finite values of $x_2, x_3, \ldots x_n$.

The theory of this case depends upon a remarkable transformation.

The most general form of the inequations of condition

connecting $p_1$, $p_2$, $\ldots p_n$, as determined by Proposition IV, is

$$a_1 p_1 + a_2 p_2 \ldots + a_n p_n + b \gtrless 0 \quad . \quad . \quad (3)$$

Hence, from the nature of the system (1) it follows that the function

$$a_1 V_1 + a_2 V_2 \ldots + a_n V_n + b V \quad . \quad . \quad . \quad (4)$$

must consist wholly of positive terms. Therefore, V must consist of terms which would either appear in the development of the above function with positive signs, or not appear in it at all. Let $A x_r x_s x_t \ldots$ be any term of V. Then, as the coefficient of this term in (4) would be

$$a_r A + a_s A + a_t A \ldots + b A,$$

and as A is positive, we have

$$a_r + a_s + a_t \ldots + b \gtrless 0,$$

a general condition which determines not what terms have actually entered, but what could alone possibly have entered into the constitution of V.

From the system (1) we have

$$\frac{a_1 V_1 + a_2 V_2 \ldots + a_n V_n + b V}{V} = a_1 p_1 + a_2 p_2 \ldots + a_n p_n + b.$$

Hence if we write

$$a_1 V_1 + a_2 V_2 \ldots + a_n V_n + b V = H,$$

we have

$$\frac{H}{V} = a_1 p_1 + a_2 p_2 \ldots + a_n p_n + b \quad . \quad . \quad (5)$$

an equation by which we may replace any one of the equations of the system (1), and which has the peculiarity that for every term $A x_r x_s x_t \ldots$ which appears in the numerator H the particular condition

$$a_r + a_s + a_t \ldots + b > 0$$

is satisfied.

Let K be the aggregate of those terms in V for which the remaining particular condition

$$a_r + a_s + a_t \ldots + b = 0$$

is satisfied.   The $V = H + K$.   If we now substitute (5) in place of the first equation of the system (1) and then write $H + K$ for $V$, $H_1 + K_1$ for $V_1$, &c., the system becomes converted into the following one, viz.

$$\frac{H}{H + K} = a_1 p_1 + a_2 p_2 \cdots + a_n p_n + b, \quad \frac{H_2 + K_2}{H + K} = p_2,$$

$$\frac{H_3 + K_3}{H + K} = p_3, \quad \cdots \frac{H_n + K^n}{H + K} = p_n \quad . \quad (6)$$

Now let us transform the above equations by assuming

$$x_2 = x_1^{\frac{a_2}{a_1}} y_2, \; x_3 = x_1^{\frac{a_3}{a_1}} y_3, \; \ldots x_n = x_1^{\frac{a_n}{a_1}} y_n,$$

The general type of these equations is

$$x_i = x_1^{\frac{a_i}{a_1}} y_i,$$

and it includes the particular case if $i = 1$, provided that we suppose, as we shall do, $y_1 = 1$.

Then representing, as before, any term of $V$ by $A x_r x_s x_t \ldots$, we have

$$A x_r x_s x_t \ldots = A x_1^{\frac{a_r + a_s + a_t}{a_1}} y_r y_s y_t \ldots$$

Let this substitution be made in the different terms both of the numerators and denominators of the fractions which form the first members of the above system, and then let each numerator and denominator be multiplied by $x_1^{\frac{b}{a_1}}$. The result will be the same as if for each term $A x_r x_s x_t \ldots$ in numerator or denominator we substituted the term

$$A x_1^{\frac{a_r + a_s + a_t}{a_1}} y_r y_s y_t \ldots$$

In considering the effect of this transformation we will first suppose $a_1$ positive, and afterwards suppose it negative.

*Case* 1 : the coefficient $a_1$ positive.   Here, since for all the terms in $H$ and in $H_2, H_3, \ldots H_n$ we have

$$\frac{a_r + a_s + a_t \ldots + b}{a_1} > 0,$$

all such terms in the transformed equations will be affected with positive powers of $x_1$.

D D

And since for all terms in K, $K_2$, ...$K_n$ we have

$$\frac{a_r + a_s + a_t \ldots + b}{a_1} = 0,$$

all such terms in the transformed equations will be free from $x_1$. Now let

$$a_1 p_1 + a_2 p_2 \ldots + a_n p_n + b = 0.$$

This, as $a_1$ is positive, is to suppose that $p_1$ coincides with one of its own inferior limits. We must suppose this to be the highest of those limits, as otherwise some of the other limiting conditions would be violated. Now, since all the terms in H are affected with positive powers of $y_1$, while those in K do not contain $x_1$, the first equation of the system (6) will be satisfied by $x_1 = 0$, provided that the remaining $n - 1$ equations give finite positive values for $y_2 \ldots y_n$. But the vanishing of $x_1$ reduces these equations to the form

$$\frac{K_2}{K} = p_2, \quad \frac{K_3}{K} = p_3, \quad \ldots \frac{K_n}{K} = p_n \qquad . \quad . \quad (7)$$

It is therefore necessary to show that $p_2$, $p_3$, ...$p_n$ in this system are actually subject to the conditions to which the application of the method of Proposition IV to the system itself would lead.

The $n$ quantities $p_1, p_2, \ldots p_n$ are by hypothesis subject to the conditions furnished by the application of the method of Proposition IV to the original system (1). In applying this method each of the original equations yields an equation of the form

$$\lambda_1 + \lambda_2 \ldots + \lambda_e = p_i \qquad . \quad . \quad . \quad . \quad (8)$$

and to the equations thus formed are added the inequations

$$\lambda_1 + \lambda_2 .. + \lambda_m \lessgtr 1,$$
$$\lambda_1 \gtrless 0, \lambda_2 \gtrless 0, \ldots \lambda_m \gtrless 0$$

$\lambda_1, \lambda_2, \ldots \lambda_m$ having reference to the whole system of original equations.

Now the satisfaction of the equation

$$\frac{H}{H + K} = 0$$

by the value $x_1 = 0$, involves the vanishing of all those

quantities of the system $\lambda_1, \lambda_2, \ldots \lambda_m$, which are derived from terms in V that are also found in H.   Hence the $\lambda$ quantities that do not vanish are those derived from terms in V which appear in K.

Again, the condition

$$a_1 p_1 + a_2 p_2 \ldots + a_n p_n + b = 0$$

shows that the system of equations of which (8) is the type are not independent.  They must, under the particular circumstances of the case, be such that the above equation shall be derivable from them.   Hence one of these equations may be rejected.  If we reject the first, viz. the one which contains $p_1$, and then reduce the others by making the $\lambda$ quantities which are not derived from K to vanish, the system typified by (8) evidently reduces to the system which we should have to employ if we applied the method of Proposition IV directly to the system of $n - 1$ equations (7).  Hence the quantities $p_2$, $p_3$, $\ldots p_n$ satisfy the final conditions to which that application would lead, and therefore, by hypothesis the equations (7) admit of solution by a single system of finite positive values of $y_2, y_3, \ldots y_n$.

Now in general

$$x_i = x_1^{\frac{a_i}{a_1}} y_i.$$

Hence, since $x_1 = 0$ and $y_1$ is infinite and positive for all values of $i$ from 2 to $n$, we see that $x_1$ will be 0 for all values of $i$ for which $a_i$ is positive, finite and positive for all values of $i$ for which $a_i$ is 0, and infinite for all values of $i$ for which $a_i$ is negative.

*Case* 2 : the coefficient $a_i$ negative.   Here the inequation of condition (3) must be supposed to determine the lowest of the superior limits of $p_1$, and therefore when $p_1$ coincides with that limit we have

$$a_1 p_1 + a_2 p_2 \ldots + a_n p_n + b = 0.$$

The transformations remaining formally the same as before, the following results will present themselves.

The terms in H and in $H_2, H_3, \ldots H_n$ will be affected with negative instead of positive powers of $x_1$.   Hence the same determination of $y_2, y_3, \ldots y_n$ from the last $n - 1$ equations of (6), which before followed from the assumption $x_1 = 0$, will now follow from the assumption $x_1 = \infty$, which at the same time satisfies the first equation of (6).

The equation

$$x_i = x_1^{\frac{a_i}{a_1}} y_i$$

shows, since $a_1$ is here negative and $x_1$ infinite, that $x_i$ will be infinite for those values of $i$ for which $a_i$ is negative, finite for those values of $i$ for which $a_i$ is 0, nothing for those values of $i$ for which $a_i$ is positive.

In all these cases the values 0 and $\infty$ appear as limits of finite positive values. This results from the connexion of the second member of the first equation of the system (6) with the condition (3).

Lastly, as the incompleteness of form of V only causes certain terms of the developed determinant of Proposition II to vanish, but leaves the signs of the terms which remain positive, it follows that as $x_1$ varies from 0 to infinity, $x_2, x_3, \ldots x_n$ being always determined by the last $n - 1$ equations of (1), the function $\frac{V_1}{V}$ will vary by continuous increase between the limits above investigated, viz. from the highest inferior to the lowest superior limit of $p_1$. Once, therefore, in its progress it becomes equal to $p_1$, and all the equations are satisfied together.

The above reasoning establishes rigorously that if the proposition is true for $n - 1$ variables, it is true for $n$ variables. It remains then to consider the limiting case of $n = 1$.

Here, however, only the complete form of V, viz. $V = ax + b$, leads to a definite value of $x$, and this, as has been seen, is finite and positive. If we give to V the particular form $ax$, the equation $\frac{V_x}{V} = p$ becomes

$$\frac{ax}{ax} = p, \text{ or } p = 1,$$

which determines $p$, but leaves $x$ indefinite. If we employ the other particular form $V = b$, we obtain no equation whatever, and here again $x$ is indefinite. But as the reducing transformations are all definite, the above indefinite forms cannot present themselves in the last stage of the problem when the original equations are independent and admit of definite solution.

The proposition is, therefore, established.

## APPLICATION

The general system of algebraic equations upon which the solution of questions in the theory of probabilities depends, is a particular case of that discussed in Proposition V. Its peculiarity is, that all the coefficients which appear in the function V are equal to unity.

The conditions of possible experience, as determined by the method, agree with the conditions shown in Proposition IV. to be necessary, and in Proposition V. to be sufficient, in order that $x_1$, $x_2$, $\ldots x_n$ may be determinable as positive finite quantities. For in both cases the equations among those quantities depend simply on the forms of the functions $V_1$, $V_2$, $\ldots V_n$, and therefore ultimately on the form of V, irrespectively of the values of the positive coefficients of V. In both cases, the systems of inequations are the same.

It follows, therefore, that precisely when the data represent a possible experience, the probabilities of the ideal events from which in the process of solution the problem is mentally constructed admit of determination as positive proper fractions.

Again, as the process for determining the à *priori* limits of the probability sought rests ultimately upon the assumption that the ratio of any term or partial aggregate of terms in V to V itself is a positive fraction, and as this assumption is satisfied when $x_1$, $x_2$, $\ldots x_n$ are positive quantities, it follows that the calculated value of the probability sought will always lie within the limits which it would have had if determined by observation from the same experience as the data.

But though the test last mentioned is one which must necessarily be satisfied by a true method, it is of infinitely less theoretical importance than that from which it is derived, viz. the test which consists in the absolute connexion between possibility in the data and formal consistency in the method.

As the conclusions of Propositions IV and V depend upon the form of the function V and the fact that its coefficients are positive, it follows that if in the application of the method to questions of probability we substituted any other positive values for unity in the coefficients of V, leaving the rest of the process as before, we should still be able to determine $x_1$, $x_2$, $\ldots x_n$ as positive quantities, or as limits of such, and the altered value of the probability sought would still be consistent with the experience from which the data are supposed to be derived. It would, however, properly speaking, be a value of interpolation, not a probability.

I will close with a few remarks upon the general nature of the method, and of the solutions to which it leads.

1st. The probability determined is not precisely of the same nature as the probabilities given.

For the data are supposed to be derived from experience; and therefore, on the supposition that the future will resemble the past, the events of which the probabilities are given will, in the long run, recur with a frequency proportioned to their probability.

But the probability determined is always an intellectual rather than a material probability. We cannot affirm that in the long run an event will occur with a frequency proportional to its calculated probability; but we can affirm that it is more likely to occur with this than with any other precise degree of frequency; that if it do not occur with this degree of frequency, the data are in some measure *one-sided*.

At the same time, the limits of possible deviation are determined.

2ndly. General solutions obtained by the method do sometimes, but not always, admit * of being verified by other methods. I believe that this is solely because it is not often possible to solve the problem by other methods without introducing hypotheses which are of the nature of additional

---

* Professor Donkin has verified a general solution (*Laws of Thought*, p. 362).

data, and, in effect, limit the problem. Every general solution, however, admits of a number of particular verifications by necessary consequence from the theorems established in this paper.

3rdly. It has been seen that a calculated probability is not necessarily a definite numerical value. It may be of the form $A + cC$, in which $c$ is an arbitrary positive fraction. Here it is implied that the probability admits of any value between $A$ and $A + C$. If, further, $A = 0$ and $C = 1$, it is implied that the probability may have any value between 0 and 1,—is therefore quite indefinite. This would really arise if we applied the method to a case in which the event of which the probability is sought had absolutely no connexion with those of which the probabilities are given.

Hence in the present theory, the numerical expression for the probability of an event about which we are totally ignorant is not $\frac{1}{2}$, but $c$.* Hence also, when all the probabilities given are measured by $\frac{1}{2}$, it is not to be concluded (upon the ground of ex nihilo nihil) that the probability sought will also be $\frac{1}{2}$.

4thly. While extending the real power of the theory of probabilities, the method tends in some cases to diminish the apparent value of its results. For all problems in which the data admit of logical expression can be solved by it; but the resulting solutions, founded upon the bare data, may be of an indeterminate character, in place of the determinate results to which ordinary methods, aided by hypotheses not really involved in the data, lead.

This is the case with the problem of the combination of different grounds of belief or opinion. The general solution is indefinite. In two limiting cases, however, it assumes a definite form; one of these, which agrees with the formula generally accepted, representing the extreme cumulative force of testimonies, the other the mean weight of judgments. Both these, however, occur as limiting cases, and they can only be applied with confidence under extreme circumstances,

---

* See on this subject a paper by Bishop Terrot, Edinburgh Transactions, vol. xxi, part 3.

such as probably never occur in human affairs.   (Edinburgh Memoir, pp. 630–645.)*

5thly. I have, in effect, remarked that there is reason to suppose that all questions in the theory of probabilities can ultimately be reduced to questions in which the immediate subjects of probability are *logical*, i.e. involve no other essential relations than those of genus and species, whole and part.   This is a question of theoretical, rather than of practical interest.   For instance, whether the formula of the arithmetical mean, which is the basis of the theory of astronomical observations, is self-evident, or whether it rests upon an ultimate logical basis, or whether, as I am inclined to believe, it may lawfully be regarded in either of these distinct but not conflicting lights, the super-structure remains the same.

* [See above, pp. 355–374.]

# APPENDIX A

## GEORGE BOOLE, F.R.S.

### [By the Rev. Robert Harley].*

(1) Various Papers on Linear Transformations, Differential Equations, the Theory of Probabilities, and other Branches of the Higher Mathematics. By GEORGE BOOLE.

(2) The Mathematical Analysis of Logic. By the Same. Cambridge. 1847.

(3) An Investigation of the Laws of Thought. By the Same. London : Walton & Maberly. 1854.

(4) A Treatise on Differential Equations. By the Same. Cambridge. 1859. Second Edition, Revised by I. Todhunter. Macmillan & Co. 1865.

(5) A Treatise on the Calculus of Finite Differences. By the Same. Cambridge : Macmillan & Co. 1860.

(6) A Treatise on Differential Equations. Supplementary Volume. By the late GEORGE BOOLE, F.R.S., Professor of Mathematics in the Queen's University, Ireland, etc. Edited by I. Todhunter, F.R.S. Cambridge : Macmillan & Co. 1865.

WE believe that to the great body of the reading public the name of George Boole first became known, if indeed it has yet become known, through the announcement of his death ; the announcement being accompanied in a few of the papers by a brief sketch of his life and works. Boole's researches were not of a nature to be appreciated by the multitude, and he never condescended to those arts by which less gifted men have won for themselves while living a more splendid reputation. When a great politician dies, or any man who has filled a large space in the public mind, and made a noise in the world, the newspapers long ring with

* [The *British Quarterly Review*, July, 1866. The article is simply signed " R. H."]

the event.   But it is otherwise with the great thinker, the mathematician or the philosopher, who has laboured silently and in comparative seclusion, to extend the boundaries of human knowledge.   When such a man is removed by death there are public journals, even among those professedly devoted to literature and science, which can dismiss the event with a few faint and cold remarks.*   But time rectifies all that.   It is found sooner or later that no reputation, however brilliant, is permanent or durable which does not rest on useful discoveries and real contributions to our knowledge. The names that live in the annals of philosophy are not those of men who achieved immediate fame; they are rather the names of men who, not thinking of fame, betook themselves to the arduous path of original investigation, and succeeded in adding new truths to the existing stock. Their presence was perhaps unobserved by the throng, and comparatively few even heard of their genius, but their works live when they are gone, and their influence and fame are real and abiding.   We propose to devote a few pages to an account of the life and writings of the remarkable man, a list of whose principal contributions to science we have placed at the head of this article.

George Boole was born in the city of Lincoln on the 2nd of November, 1815; he died at Ballintemple, near Cork, on the 8th of December, 1864.   The facts of his personal history are few and simple, but they serve to illustrate how a man of humble origin, with very slender aids from without, may, by the force of genius and the labour of research, rise to a position of great eminence.   We give the facts from documents in our possession, and other sources of information on which we can rely.

The life of Boole may be divided into two distinct periods, the leading events and features of which are soon described. The first, extending over four and thirty years, was, excepting

---

* The *Athenæum* for December 17, 1864, after noticing the death of an American writer, says, ' Nearer home, science has suffered some loss in the demise of Professor Boole, of Queen's College, Cork, in which institution he filled the mathematical chair.   The Professor's principal works were. " An Investigation into the Laws of Thought", and "Differential Equations ", books which sought a very limited audience, and we believe, found it.   He died on Friday (Thursday) last week.'

only a short interval, spent wholly in his native county, and for the most part in his native city.   This was the period in which he laid the foundation of his future greatness; his mind became furnished with rich and varied stores of information, and he acquired a mastery over processes of thought and methods of mathematical investigation that yielded the most valuable and important results in after years.   The second and shorter period commenced with his appointment to the professorship of mathematics in the Queen's College, Cork, the duties of which he entered upon at the opening of that institution in the year 1849, and continued to discharge until his premature and unexpected death.   It was during this latter period that he gave to the world those works on which his fame as a philosophical mathematician will principally rest.   His father was a tradesman of very limited means, but held in high esteem by those who knew him.   Having nothing to support his family but his daily toil, it was not to be expected that he could expend much on the education of his children; yet they were not neglected.   Being himself a man of thoughtful and studious habits, possessed of an active and ingenious mind, and attached to the pursuit of science, particularly of mathematics, he sought to imbue his children with a love of learning, and employed his leisure hours in imparting to them the elements of education.   The estimation in which his abilities were held by his wife will be learnt from the following little incident, which was told to the writer of this article some years ago by an eminent mathematician, the present Chief Justice of Queensland.   Our friend was then a barrister on the Midland circuit, and having read with deep interest some of Boole's earliest mathematical papers, he desired to make his acquaintance, and being in Lincoln, called at his residence.   He was not at home at the time; but meeting with his mother our friend entered into a conversation with her, in the course of which he took occasion to congratulate her on having so talented a son.   ' Yes ', she said, ' I dare say George is clever—very clever; but did you know his father, sir? '   ' No,' replied he, ' I had not the pleasure.'   ' Ah,' said the old lady with evident emotion,

' he was a philosopher ! ' And no doubt she thought there was not his equal in the world.

George received an ordinary school education, the best which the limited means of his parents could afford. He is described by an old fellow-pupil as being at this period of a shy and retiring disposition, a character which he retained to the end of his life, and as being fond of his books, but not averse to athletic sports. ' He was not of my class,' says our informant, ' or indeed of any class ; for we had no boy in the school equal to him, and perhaps the master was not, though he professed to teach him. This George Boole was a sort of prodigy among us, and we looked up to him as a star of the first magnitude.' All which we can quite believe. It was from his father, for whose memory he ever cherished a most affectionate and reverential regard, that he received his principal, if not his only, instruction in the rudiments of that science to which he afterwards made such large and important contributions. From him also he inherited a taste for the construction and adaptation of optical instruments. ' It was not, however,' writes one who knew his history well, ' until a comparatively late period of his earlier studies that his special aptitude for mathematical investigations developed itself. His earlier ambition seems to have pointed to the attainment of proficiency in the ancient classical languages ; but his father being unable to assist him in overcoming the first difficulties of this course of study, he was indebted to a neighbour for instruction in the elements of Latin grammar. This good neighbour was Mr. William Brooke, bookseller, a man of mental culture and an accomplished antiquary, with whom he kept up an uninterrupted correspondence throughout life, and who survives to mourn the loss of his friend and pupil. To the study of Latin he added that of Greek, we believe without any external assistance, and for some years he devoured every Greek and Latin author that came within his reach. At the age of fourteen he was the subject of a small literary controversy in his native town. He had produced a metrical version of an Ode to Spring, from the Greek of Meleager, which his father in the pride of his heart, had inserted in a local journal, stating the age of the translator. This drew forth a letter from a neighbouring schoolmaster, denying, from internal evidence, that the version could have been the work of one so young, and the result was a newspaper war of some continuance. Afterwards accident discovered to Boole certain defects in his method of classical study, inseparable from the want of proper early training; and it cost him two years of incessant labour to correct them. At the age of seventeen he first applied himself to the study of the higher mathematics, and simply with the aid of such books as he could procure. Without other assistance or guide he worked his way onward, and it was his own opinion that he had lost five years of educational progress by his imperfect method of study, and the want of a helping hand to get him over difficulties. This opinion may be doubted, as it does not take into account the invigorating effect on his mental powers of the successful struggles to surmount certain difficulties without external aid. And it is a fact that in his efforts to clear up points on which his books failed to satisfy him, he often lighted upon methods which afterwards proved to be original discoveries.'

The profession which he chose, that of a teacher of youth, was one for which he was eminently qualified, both by his character and attainments. When about sixteen years of age he sought and obtained an appointment as an assistant master in an education establishment at Doncaster. Here, besides prosecuting his studies in the ancient classics and the higher mathematics, he cultivated an acquaintance with the best English authors, and began to read the German, French, and Italian languages, in all of which he ultimately attained singular proficiency. We next find him occupying a similar post in a boarding school at Waddington, a village about four miles from Lincoln. Mr. Hall, the proprietor of this establishment, was highly popular with the substantial farmers of the neighbourhood, and seems to have attached great value to the services of his assistant. The connexion, however, was not of long continuance, for the age, growing infirmities, and straitened circumstances of his parents made Boole anxious to improve his position, so that he might be

better able to discharge the duties of filial piety. He therefore seized the first favourable opportunity, to open on his
own account, a day-school for the youth of both sexes in his
native city. A fair measure of success attended his efforts,
and the experience which he gained in this humble sphere
was no doubt of great advantage to him afterwards. On
the death of Mr. Hall, his old employer, he returned to
Waddington, accompanied by his parents and other members
of his family, and succeeded to the school there, which he
carried on for several years.

In this obscure place he commenced his career as a mathematical writer, and it is interesting to know that his earliest
papers, written, as he himself incidentally mentions, towards
the close of the year 1838, were prepared during his perusal
of the *Mecanique Analytique*, in the form of ' Notes on
Lagrange.' From these notes in the following year he made
selections, and wrote out what appears to have been his
first paper (though not the first published), entitled ' On
Certain Theorems in the Calculus of Variations,' wherein
he proposed various improvements on methods of investigation employed by the illustrious French analyst. About the
same time his attention was attracted to the transformation
of homogeneous functions by linear substitutions, a problem
which occupies a very conspicuous place in the *Mecanique
Analytique* of Lagrange, and which had also employed the
powers of Laplace, Lebesgue, Jacobi, and other distinguished
Continental mathematicians. The manner in which Boole
dealt with this important problem showed him at once to be
a man of most original and independent thought, and in
the course of his investigations he was led to discoveries
which may be regarded as the foundation of what Dr. Salmon
calls the Modern Higher Algebra. His first published paper
relates to this subject; and although he afterwards greatly
improved and extended his method of analysis, yet his
original memoir, entitled ' Researches on the Theory of
Analytical Transformations, with a Special application to
the Reduction of the General Equation of the Second Order,'
is interesting as showing how the subject first struck his
mind. This memoir he communicated in the year 1839 to

the *Cambridge Mathematical Journal*. In choosing that journal as the medium for the publication of his researches, he was singularly fortunate. It had not then been in existence for more than two years, and yet it already numbered among its contributors nearly all the leading Cambridge mathematicians. The object of its originators was set forth in their preface to the first number, which appeared in October, 1837. They had felt it to be matter of regret that no proper channel existed, either in Cambridge or elsewhere in the kingdom, for the publication of papers on mathematical subjects which might not be deemed of sufficient importance to be inserted in the transactions of any of the learned societies. ' In this place in particular,' said they, meaning of course Cambridge, ' where the mathematics are so generally cultivated, it might be expected that there would be an opening for a work exclusively devoted to that science which does not command much interest in the world at large. We think that there can be no doubt that there are many persons here who are both able and willing to communicate much valuable matter to a mathematical periodical, while the very existence of such a work is likely to draw out others, and make them direct their attention in some degree to original research.' These expectations were fully realised. It is impossible to glance through the contents of the First Series without being struck with the richness and variety of its articles, most of which were supplied by Cambridge men,— D. F. Gregory, R. Leslie Ellis, A. De Morgan, W. Walton, S. S. Greatheed, A. Smith, W. Thomson, A. Cayley, J. J. Sylvester, G. G. Stokes, J. Cockle, and others scarcely less distinguished. The Second Series, called *The Cambridge and Dublin Mathematical Journal*, also abounds with most valuable matter. Among its contributors we find, in addition to most of the Cambridge men above-mentioned, some of the ablest Oxford and Dublin mathematicians, with others who, like Boole, belonged to no University; W. F. Donkin, W. Spottiswoode, Sir W. Rowan Hamilton, G. Salmon, R. Townsend, S. Hawton, T. P. Kirkman, T. S. Davies, T. Weddle, &c.

To this journal, so originated and so sustained, Boole sent

his paper on Analytical Transformations, but it was not immediately inserted. A delay of some weeks occurred before it was even acknowledged, and perhaps the Waddington schoolmaster began to wonder what had become of it. At length he received a letter from the editor, Mr. D. F. Gregory, apologising for the delay, and explaining that he had been anxious to make himself thoroughly master of the contents of the paper before pronouncing an opinion upon it. He had now read it, was much pleased with it, and should be happy to give it a place in his journal; but before doing so he desired his correspondent to clear up one or two points which seemed to him to require elucidation. The corrections related chiefly to obscurities of style and expression, such as might naturally be expected in the first compositions of one not accustomed to write for the press. ' You spoke,' adds Mr. Gregory (we quote from a MS. letter dated from Trinity College, Cambridge, Nov. 4, 1839) ' when I saw you here of some investigations in the Calculus of Variations, which you were inclined to publish. If you still desire to do so I shall be happy to give them a place in the journal.' From this it appears that our author had been to Cambridge some time before, probably to consult Mr. Gregory respecting the publication of his mathematical researches. The corrections so kindly suggested were made, and the paper was published in the number for February 1840. In the following number, issued three months later, his paper on the Calculus of Variations occupies the place of honour, and a third paper from his pen, entitled ' On the Integration of Linear Differential Equations, with Constant Co-efficients,' is also inserted. Meanwhile he writes to a friend, ' You will feel interested to know the fate of my mathematical speculations in Cambridge. One of the papers is already printed in the *Mathematical Journal*. Another, which I sent a short time ago, has been very favourably received, and will shortly be printed together with one I had previously sent.' Altogether he contributed to that journal no fewer than twenty-four separate articles—namely, twelve to each series—some of them of very considerable length, and all of them dealing with questions of greater or less difficulty in mathematical analysis.

Of these articles and of his other writings we shall give some account hereafter.

Mr. Boole derived great advantage in conducting his earlier researches from his correspondence with Mr. Gregory, and we have no doubt that the advantage was reciprocal. The Cambridge editor and his Waddington correspondent often compared their respective views on various points in analysis, particularly with reference to the symbolical solution of Differential Equations, a subject with the early history and development of which, the names of Gregory and Boole will be for ever associated. That the former, if he had lived,* would have achieved as much for science as did the latter, may perhaps be doubted; but there can be on question that he was a man of most varied attainments and of remarkable ability, and that what he did achieve is quite enough to entitle his name to a prominent place among the mathematicians of the present century. The interest which he showed, up to the period of his death, in Mr. Boole's researches, and the encouragement and aid which he afforded him in his earlier efforts, ought not to be passed over un-

* Duncan Farquharson Gregory (who is not to be confounded with Olinthus Gregory, of Woolwich) died in his thirty-first year. R. Leslie Ellis, who succeeded him as editor of the *Cambridge Mathematical Journal*, has given a brief but interesting memoir of him in the fourth volume of that work, pages 145–152. This memoir, along with Gregory's mathematical writings, has recently been republished, under the editorship of Mr. W. Walton. From these and other sources we collect the following facts and particulars.

D. F. Gregory was born at Edinburgh, in April, 1813. He was the youngest son of Dr. James Gregory, the distinguished Professor of Medicine, and was thus of the same family as the two celebrated mathematicians, James and David Gregory. After studying at the Edinburgh Academy, at a private school in Geneva, and at the University of Edinburgh, his name was entered in 1833 at Trinity College, Cambridge, and shortly afterwards he went to reside there. In 1837 he proceeded to the degree of B.A., and came out fifth wrangler of his year. 'More, however', says Ellis, 'might, we may believe, have been effected in this respect, had his activity of mind permitted him to devote himself more exclusively to the prescribed course of study.' In 1840 he was elected Fellow of Trinity College; in the following year he became Master of Arts, and was appointed to the office of moderator, that is, of principal mathematical examiner. About the close of the year 1841 he produced his Collection of Examples of the Processes of the Differential and Integral Calculus. He also wrote a Treatise on the Application of Analysis to Solid Geometry, which has been published since his death. Late in the autumn of 1842 he had an attack of illness, which was succeeded by others, and in the spring of the following year he left Cambridge, never to return again. He died on the 23rd Feb., 1844.

E E

noticed. Even his occasional hints and suggestions proved a useful excitement to our author, who often and warmly acknowledged his great indebtedness to Mr. Gregory. The following letter, which we select from among several not less valuable, will be read with interest by mathematicians, and it will serve to convey, even to the non-mathematical reader, a general notion of the kind of assistance which Mr. Boole at this period received.

### *Mr. Gregory to Mr. Boole*

'Trinity College, Feb. 16, 1840.

' DEAR SIR,—Your method of simplifying the solution of Linear Differential Equations with constant co-efficients is exceedingly ingenious, and, I think, reduces the problem to the greatest degree of simplicity of which it admits. Every part of the process is now dependent solely on the ordinary theory of Algebra except the Theorem.

$$\left(\frac{d}{dx} - a\right)^n = \epsilon^{ax}\left(\frac{d}{dx}\right)^n \epsilon - ax.$$

This is all that can be desired, and I conceive that no farther improvement is likely to be made. I do not think that the non-insertion of your paper in the *Phil. Mag.* was due to any other cause than this : that the editor is ignorant of mathematics, and is very unwilling to risk the publication of any mathematical communication, unless a previous knowledge of the author gives him some security for the correctness of the paper. I shall be very happy to get your article inserted in the journal, but I have some doubts whether the paper, as you have sent it to me, is in the best form. You appear to me not to express sufficiently distinctly the points in which you have introduced the improvements, and I think that you have also sometimes made too great difficulty in points which would be very readily admitted by those who would read your paper. I allude, for instance, to your investigation of the form of the numerators for an equation of the third order, when the general method may be proved at once by the theory of the separation of the symbols combined with that of the decomposition of rational fractions. If it be agreeable to you I will draw up the paper in the way which I think is best fitted for publication, and will transmit [it] to you for your inspection.* I shall be glad to hear that you have made progress in the solution of equations, with variable co-efficients. The question is a very difficult one, and of the highest importance, as it is in that direction that we must look for some extension of our means of analysis.

'I remain, your obedient servant,

'D. F. GREGORY.'

Mr. Boole was now twenty-four years of age, and, considering the great power and capacity which he had shown, especially since he began the study of the higher mathematics, it is not to be wondered at that his friends should have urged him, as many of them at this period did, to enter himself at the University of Cambridge. There, no doubt, he would have taken a very high degree, and would have risen to distinctions which are wholly inaccessible to non-academic students; but, meanwhile, as Mr. Gregory explained to him, he must abandon everything in the shape of original research, and limit himself, like others, to the prescribed course of study. This to a man of his originality and genius

---

* This proposal, which of course was gratefully accepted, serves to illustrate the generous character of the man. In an article in the first number of his journal, he had applied the method of the separation of symbols to the problem above referred to; and that he should now so heartily welcome a paper setting forth processes which, on account of their greater simplicity and directness, were evidently destined to supersede his own, and that, moreover, he should actually offer to rewrite the paper, and present it to the mathematical world in a more attractive form, are facts which reflect on Mr. Gregory's character the highest honour. His biographer might well say of him that he was 'singularly free from the least tinge of jealous or personal feeling. That which another had done or was about to do, seemed to give him as much pleasure as if he himself had been the author of it, and this even when it related to some subject which his own researches might seem to have appropriated.' We ought to add that Mr. Boole, in his work on Differential Equations (p. 381, 1st Ed.; p. 391, 2nd Ed.) has distinctly recorded his obligations to Mr. Gregory on this matter. On reproducing the theorem which forms the principal feature of his method as distinguished from Gregory's, he there says, 'This theorem was first published in the *Cambridge Mathematical Journal* (1st series, vol. ii. p. 114) in a memoir written by the late D. F. Gregory, then editor of the journal, from notes furnished by the author of this work, whose name the memoir bears. The illustrations were supplied by Mr. Gregory. In mentioning these circumstances the author recalls to memory a brief but valued friendship.'

would have proved, we imagine, excessively irksome, and it is doubtful if the result would have rewarded the sacrifice. There was also the question of ways and means. Expenses at Cambridge were at that time enormous. Added to which, his aged parents were now largely dependent on him for their support, and he could not reconcile it with his duty to them to give up his school and so to cut off his only source of income. These considerations, and especially the last, decided his course; he did not go to Cambridge. We admire the way in which Mr. Gregory put the case before him.

### *Mr. Gregory to Mr. Boole*

' DEAR SIR,—I have considered what you say in your last letter about your intention of coming up here—I suppose with the intention of reading for a fellowship, and do not see any objection to your doing so from your age. A very considerable number of men who have taken high degrees of late years must have entered the University quite as late in life. I may mention Earnshaw, Kelland, Green, Potter. If you do determine on entering the University with the intention of reading for a Fellowship, you must be prepared to undergo a great deal of mental discipline, which is not agreeable to a man who is accustomed to think for himself. A high degree here is due quite as much to diligent labour in certain appointed paths as to mathematical capacity. If a person cannot bring himself to devote his whole energies to the training for the degree examination, he is likely to find himself much thrown out at the end of the course. I mention this particularly, because when a person takes such an important step at a more advanced time of life—involving a sacrifice of three or four years—he should be fully prepared to submit to all that his younger rivals endure, otherwise he has little chance of success, and it is in this I think that such men are apt to fail. From what I have seen of your mathematical acquirements, I should certainly say that you might turn them to good account by trying your fortune : at the same time you must know that success here is a little like a lottery, and it is not always the best plan to stake everything on a single throw of the die. The expense of an

University education depends almost entirely on the personal habits of the student, and it is a difficult thing to fix any precise amount for it. As far as my own experience goes few pensioners, even of those who live economically spend one way or another less than £250 a year, and I doubt whether any keep within £200. If a person come up as a Sizar, or receive assistance from the College as Scholar, of course his expenses will be less—how much so I could not well say. In this matter, however, I cannot pretend to be a very sure guide, as I know nothing of the habits of men in the other Colleges. In some at least I think the expenses must be considerably less than Trinity, as for instance in the rent of rooms. You mention nothing as to the College which you thought of belonging to. Trinity offers great advantages to one who has talents and ambition, and for many reasons is the one which I would always recommend; at the same time you must be aware that it is much easier to get a fellowship at a small College than here, and that in them the degree is all that is required, whereas here you have to undergo another examination. If, however, you will specify the points on which you desire information, I shall be glad to give you as much as lies in my power. If you have any more communications for the journal we shall be glad to see them as soon as you find it convenient to prepare them. We like to have communications sent early, as we are then better able to judge how the number is to be made up.

'I remain, yours truly,

'D. F. GREGORY.'

'Trin. Col. March 29, 1840.'

In a letter written a few weeks later, Mr. Gregory repeated his offer to Mr. Boole to supply him with any further information he might desire, but the subject does not appear to have come up again in any future correspondence. Mr. Boole's decision not to go to Cambridge may have been reached reluctantly, but it was maintained resolutely. By that decision science, we believe, suffered no loss : it probably gained much.

In the summer of the year 1840, Mr. Boole removed his boarding school from Waddington to Lincoln, taking with him his aged parents. The next nine years were years of unwearied industry in the prosecution of his mathematical researches; and yet all accounts agree in representing him as a most diligent, pains-taking, and conscientious teacher. He did not abstract time from his school for his favourite pursuits, but gave his best energies to promote the advancement of his pupils; and we learn from private sources that he was accustomed on the half holidays to take his boys out into the country for long and healthful rambles. We are interested to learn also, that while avoiding the agitations of political and public life, he was concerned for the welfare of his fellow-citizens, and gave valuable assistance to various philanthropic and benevolent institutions. His intense devotion to the exact sciences did not contract the affections of his heart, or damp the ardours of his devout and generous soul; the *man* was not lost in the *mathematician*.

In one of those wonderfully impassioned addresses with which the youthful and eloquent Chalmers was wont to stir up the enthusiasm of his mathematical class at St. Andrews, he attacks the notion that the effect of the study of mathematics is to divest the student of all that is human, and to congeal the fervours of a pious and benevolent heart. ' Dr. Johnson,' says he, ' who possessed the power of genius without its liberality, and who appears to have cherished an immovable contempt for mathematics, has directed all the powers of his ridicule against the ludicrous peculiarities which he is pleased to ascribe to mathematicians. He conceives a fire raging in a neighbourhood, and spreading destruction among many families; while all the noise and consternation is unable to disturb the immovable composure of a mathematician, who sits engrossed with his diagrams, deaf to all the sounds of alarm and of distress. His servants rush into his room, and tell him that the fire is spreading all around the neighbourhood. He observes simply, that it is very natural, for fire always acts in a circle,—and resumes his speculations.' To show that the study of mathematics begets no such insensibility, Chalmers points his pupils to the example of the illustrious Newton, who, 'amid the splendours of his discoveries and the proud elevation of his fame, rejoiced in all the endearments of friendship,' and who, 'in the spirit of a mild and gentle benevolence, maintained an inviolable serenity.' But a case still more to the point is supplied in the example before us. If Dr. Johnson's theory on this subject were true, we should expect that a man so devoted to the pursuit of mathematics as was George Boole during his life at Lincoln, would be wholly insensible to the great world around him with its ever-burning fires of trial and distress. Yet it was far otherwise. Step for a few moments into this Mechanics' Hall; there is a meeting here of young men, members of 'an association for obtaining an abridgment of the hours of business in all trades, with a view to the physical, mental, and moral improvement of those engaged therein'. They have just achieved the immediate object of their association, and are now assembled to listen to a lecture from a fellow-citizen, who has chosen as his topic—a most appropriate topic truly—*The Right Use of Leisure*. We have come in late : the lecturer, a man of middle-stature, light complexioned, slenderly built with a countenance in which both genius and benignity are expressed, and a manner gentle and modest, almost to womanliness, has held the attention of his youthful auditors for upwards of an hour, while he has discoursed in a clear and forcible style, on the different ways in which they may advantageously employ the limited portion of leisure allotted to them. He has spoken of 'that wise arrangement of Providence, by which there exist at once so great a diversity in the human mind, and so wide a variety of objects, in which it may innocently seek for gratification.' He has vindicated athletic sports and games as not merely conducive to health and recreation, but also as assisting to produce a vigorous and manly character of mind,' and to encourage 'a free, generous, and open disposition.' The education to be derived from books, from communion with nature, and from other sources, has been eloquently expatiated upon ; and now the lecturer concludes with these weighty words :—

' The last subject to which I am desirous to direct your attention as to a means of self-improvement, is that of philanthropic exertion for the good of others. I allude here more particularly to the efforts which you may be able to make for the benefit of those whose social position is inferior to your own. It is my deliberate conviction, founded on long and anxious consideration of the subject, that not only might great positive good be effected by an association of earnest young men, working together under judicious arrangements for this common end, but that its reflected advantages would overpay the toil of effort, and more than indemnify the cost of personal sacrifice. And how wide a field is now open before you ! It would be unjust to pass over unnoticed the shining examples of virtues, that are found among the poor and indigent. There are dwellings so consecrated by patience, by self-denial, by filial piety, that it is not in the power of any physical deprivation to render them otherwise than happy. But sometimes in close contiguity with these, what a deep contrast of guilt and woe ! On the darker features of the prospect we would not dwell, and that they are less prominent here than in larger cities we would with gratitude acknowledge ; but we cannot shut our eyes to their existence. We cannot put out of sight that improvidence that never looks beyond the present hour ; that insensibility that deadens the heart to the claims of duty and affection ; or that recklessness which in the pursuit of some short-lived gratification, sets all regard for consequences aside. Evils such as these, although they may present themselves in any class of society, and under every variety of circumstances, are undoubtedly fostered by that ignorance to which the condition of poverty is most exposed ; and of which it has been truly said, that it is the night of the spirit,—and a night without moon and without stars. It is to associated efforts for its removal, and for the raising of the physical condition of its subjects, that philanthropy must henceforth direct her regards. And is not such an object great ? Are not such efforts personally elevating and ennobling ? Would that some part of the youthful energy of this present assembly might thus expend itself in labours of benevolence ! Would that we could all feel the deep weight and truth of the Divine sentiment that " No man liveth to himself, and no man dieth to himself." '

The man who spoke thus was surely no misanthrope; yet he was a mathematician, and one who moved amid the most recondite paths of mathematical research. It was George Boole. When we think of the daily demands upon his time at this period in connexion with his school, and the absorbing nature of his mental pursuits, we are certainly amazed to find how abundant were his labours in behalf of philanthropic movements, particularly of the Mechanics' Institute. He was one of its directors; he helped to form its library and museum; he afforded gratuitous instruction to the members in classics and mathematics; and he gave in its hall occasional lectures, always of a solid and instructive character, two of which were published at the time,—one, ' On the Genius and Discoveries of Sir Isaac Newton,' * called forth by the presentation of a marble bust of that philosopher by the Right Honourable Lord (afterwards Earl) Yarborough; and one, from which we have given an extract above ' On the Right Use of Leisure.' He was also a vice-president of the Early Closing Association, and a trustee of the Female Penitents' Home, an institution in the establishment and success of which he felt a deep interest.

All this time he was busily engaged in extending his mathematical researches. Paper after paper, in rapid succession, proceeded from his pen, and appeared in the pages of the *Cambridge Mathematical Journal*, each succeeding paper serving to raise still higher the reputation of its

---

* Since the above was written we have discovered that the lecture on Newton, a copy of which now lies before us, was delivered on the 5th of February, 1835. Boole was then only nineteen years of age; he had not yet left Waddington, but was still an assistant-master there. His father, however, was at this time the curator, and he himself a member of the institution in which the lecture was delivered. We learn from the printed copy which has come into our possession, that the noble donor of the bust presided on the occasion. The address is dedicated to him in the following terms :—' To the right honourable Lord Yarborough, as a testimony of esteem for his active and enlightened philanthropy, this address, the chief recommendation of which is the event with which it was associated, is, by permission, most respectively inscribed by the author.' Considered as the production of one so young, and whose educational advantages had been so limited, it is a very remarkable address. We regret that we cannot afford space for some extracts from it.

author. Some of these communications run to a great length. We may mention one of them in particular; it is entitled, 'Exposition of a General Theory of Linear Transformations.' This Paper, as originally prepared, threatened to occupy a whole number of the Journal, and it became necessary, therefore, to have it divided and published in separate parts. The editor always endeavoured to keep the articles within the limits of eight pages, so as to secure as much variety as possible in each number. But both parts of Mr. Boole's paper greatly exceed these limits : the first extends over no fewer than twenty (octavo) pages, while the second, which the author condensed by omitting demonstrations and confining himself chiefly to an exhibition of results, fills thirteen pages, that is, more than one-third of the number.

In following out his researches on differential equations, Mr. Boole was led to the discovery of a *general method in analysis*. The work was too elaborate and weighty for the *Mathematical Journal*; and he seems at first to have hesitated whether he should print it separately, at his own expense, or send it to the Royal Society, with a view to its publication in the 'Transactions' of that learned body. On writing to his friend, Mr. Gregory, for advice on the subject, he received the following reply :—

### *Mr. Gregory to Mr. Boole*

' 5 Manchester Sq., London, June 19, 1843.

' DEAR SIR,—I have been prevented from answering your letter by a severe attack of illness, from which I have not yet recovered. My advice certainly is, that you should endeavour to get your paper printed by the Royal Society, both because you will thereby avoid a considerable expense, and, because a paper in the " Philosophical Transactions " is more likely to be known and read than one printed separately. If you know any member of the Society, you may ask him to communicate it to the Society, but in the event of your not knowing any such person, I can ask Mr. Airy to do so. Of course he cannot be in any way answerable for getting it printed; that must depend on the report of those to whom the paper will be referred. I may just remark that a paper for the " Transactions " ought to contain fewer illustrations and examples than one which you might print yourself. My own solution of the equation of differences in my problem paper is much simpler than that which you propose : but I am not in a fit state to enter on the subject at present.

' Yours truly,

' D. F. GREGORY.'

This seems to have been the last letter which Mr. Gregory wrote to Mr. Boole. The advice which it contains was acted upon; the paper was drawn up in proper form, and in January 1844 it was communicated to the Royal Society by S. Hunter Christie Esq., one of the secretaries. According to the usual rule, the Council referred the paper to two of the Fellows of the Society, to report upon its merits. One of them, it is said, reported unfavourably; he could see in the paper nothing worthy of note, and he therefore recommended its rejection. But fortunately for the interests of science, the other referee was a more competent judge, and his opinion had greater weight with the members of the Council, who, influenced by his strong representations of the value of the paper, ordered it to be printed in the ' Transactions '.* Nor was this all : they resolved to bestow on it a special mark of approbation. Some time before, they had announced their intention to give one of the Society's gold

* Another version of the story is, that the Council of the Royal Society, consisting of fifteen Fellows, had nearly rejected the paper without examination, but that one of their number stood up and maintained that the fact of the author being poor and unknown, was no reason why the paper should be so summarily dismissed; it might contain valuable matter, and in any case it ought to be referred to competent judges, just as if it were the production of a known man. He had some difficulty in carrying his point, but at last the paper was referred, and with the result stated in the text. Whichever version be adopted, the essential part of the story remains, that Boole's first communication to the Royal Society, and that for which he shortly afterwards received the Royal Medal, had nearly been denied insertion in the ' Philosophical Transactions '. The circumstance has not been without its influence; and no man, however obscure, who now sends a really valuable communication to the Royal Society, need fear that it will receive other than fair and honourable treatment.

medals in the year 1844, for the most important unpublished paper in Mathematics that should be communicated to the Society for insertion in their ' Transactions,' after termination of the session in June 1841, and prior to the termination of the session in June 1844. Mr. Boole's paper was now selected for this distinguished honour; and in setting forth the grounds of the award, the Council describe it as a paper ' containing matter as useful as it is original and classifying, and comprehending analytical operations.' And they add, ' anticipating that Mr. Boole's method will find a permanent place in the science, the Council have not hesitated to award to him a Royal Medal.' Accordingly, at the anniversary meeting of the Society in November 1844, the Marquis of Northampton, President, in the chair, Mr. Boole received the Royal Medal in the department of Mathematics, for ' his important paper on the General Method in Analysis.'

In the course of these speculations, and others of a like nature which grew out of them, Mr. Boole was led to consider the possibility of constructing a calculus of deductive reasoning. The severe discipline of his efforts to extend the powers of the analysis had given him not only a complete mastery over its mechanical processes, but also, what was of far greater advantage, a profound insight into its logical principles. In tracing out those principles he discovered that they admitted of an application to other objects of thought than number and quantity; he found, in fact, that logical symbols in general conform to the same fundamental laws which govern the symbols of algebra in particular, while they are subject also to a certain special law. This discovery suggested a variety of inquiries which he seems at different periods to have pursued, but without any intention of publishing his views on the subject. In the spring of the year 1847, however, his attention was drawn to the question then moved between Sir W. Hamilton and Professor De Morgan, and he ' was induced by the interest which it inspired, to resume the almost-forgotten thread of former inquiries.' It appeared to him that, ' although logic might be viewed with reference to the idea of quantity, it had also another and a deeper system of relations. If it was lawful to regard it from *without*, as connecting itself through the medium of number with intuitions of space and time, it was lawful also to regard it from *within*, as based upon facts of another order, which have their abode in the constitution of the mind '. The results of this view, and of the inquiries which it suggested, he embodied in a remarkable essay, entitled, ' The Mathematical Analysis of Logic '. This Essay, in the autumn of the year was put on sale in Cambridge and London, and by a curious coincidence it made its appearance in the same month, if not on the same day, as Professor De Morgan's ' Formal Logic.' * Early in the following year (1848) Mr. Boole communicated to the *Cambridge and Dublin Mathematical Journal*, a Paper entitled, ' The Calculus of Logic,' in which, after premising the notation and the fundamental position of his Essay, he gives some further developments of his system, especially that portion of it relating to categorical propositions.

From this time forward he applied himself diligently to a course of study and reflexion on psychological subjects, with a view to the production of a much more elaborate and exhaustive work than either of those above named. He felt that the inquiry on which he had entered was worthy of his best powers; and that in seeking to perfect his theory of deductive reasoning, he was rendering an important service to science. He meditated deeply on the nature and constitution of the human intellect. The most eminent authorities, both ancient and modern, were consulted; opinions differing widely from each other, and often wholly opposed to his own, were carefully considered; and whatever was likely to help him in the great work which he had undertaken, was eagerly sought. Mental science became his study; mathematics were his recreation. So we have heard him say; and yet it is a remarkable fact, and one which serves to show the great power and genius of the man, that his most valuable and important mathematical works were produced after he had commenced his psychological investigations.

During the years 1847 and 1848 (that is, while he was

* De Morgan's preface is dated Oct. 14; Boole's Oct. 29, 1847.

engaged on his earliest logical essays), Mr. Boole wrote a series of short but suggestive articles on Differential Equations, and some Notes on Quaternions, which were printed in the *Philosophical Magazine*. He contributed also two profound Papers, one on Discontinuous Functions, and another on Definite Integrals, to the Transactions of the Royal Irish Academy. Other Papers from his pen appeared at this period, in the *Cambridge and Dublin Mathematical Journal*. One of these, ' On a General Transformation of any Quantitative Function,' is deserving of special notice ; for therein the author announces and demonstrates a theorem, of which the celebrated theorems of Lagrange and Laplace are only particular forms.

In the year 1849, Mr. Boole was selected from among several candidates to fill the office of professor of mathematics in the newly-formed Queen's College, in Cork. The emolument connected with the office was not large, and the number of pupils was, for some time, very limited ; yet, in this new and honourable sphere, he found occupations more worthy of his powers, and greater leisure for the prosecution of original research, than he had hitherto enjoyed. His father was now dead, and his aged mother, for whom he always evinced the greatest tenderness and respect, could not be prevailed upon to cross the Irish channel. He, therefore, made provision for her maintenance and comfort during the remainder of her days. On leaving Lincoln he received many tokens of the high esteem in which he was held by his fellow-citizens. At a public supper, over which Dr. Snow, the chief magistrate of the city, presided, he was presented with a handsome silver inkstand, and a valuable collection of books. The members of the Mechanics' Institute also, anxious to show their appreciation of his services, raised a subscription, with a view to a testimonial. On hearing of this, the Professor, with his characteristic generosity, attempted to have the gift applied for the good of the Institute ; he proposed that they should either add to their apparatus a larger astronomical telescope, or enrich their library with a complete copy of Newton's works. Finding, however, that they were inflexible in their purpose, he, at length, accepted their contribution in the form of Johnston's Atlas of Physical Geography, a work which is one of the most costly and valuable of its kind. These testimonials, and others less publicly presented, were as honourable to those who gave them, as they were grateful to the feelings of him by whom they were received.

For some months after his settlement at Cork, Professor Boole was much occupied in arranging his classes, receiving students, and attending to other preparatory work, which is always most heavy at the commencement of a new institution. It was a principle with him, throughout life, to do well whatever he undertook to do at all. He permitted no side pursuits to divert his strength from the performance of present duty. The way in which he applied himself to his new avocation, and the rare abilities which he brought to his task, soon made it evident that, though not a university man, he was yet eminently fitted for the post to which he had been appointed. His teaching in the class-room was thorough and efficient. He possessed, in a remarkable degree, the power of communicating knowledge; he condescended to the meanest capacity, waiting even on dulness, and adapting his instructions to the average intellect of his pupils. The affectionate interest which he showed in their welfare, endeared him to their hearts, and in a very short time, he had become an immense favourite among them. By his colleagues also he was esteemed and beloved; they recognised his merits, and felt that he was a man with whom it was an honour to be associated.

At the opening of the third session of the College, it fell to his lot, as Dean of the Faculty of Sciences, to deliver the Introductory Lecture. He chose for this theme ' The Claims of Science, especially as founded in its relations to Human Nature.' This subject, it will be observed, was at once appropriate to the occasion, and in accordance with a congenial train of thought, on which his attention had been long employed. He first examines the sources, both external and internal, from which scientific knowledge is derived. He next considers the conclusion, with reference to the constitution of the material universe to which the generalisations of science point; after discussing which he enters on the inquiry with which the main body of his discourse is occupied, viz. ' Does the dominion of science terminate with the world of matter, or is there held out to us the promise of something like exact acquaintance, however less in extent, with the interior and nobler province of the mind? ' In pursuing this inquiry, he first establishes the position that the mind is a proper object of science, and then discusses the nature of the relation which the mind sustains to the scientific laws of its constitution. As confirmatory of his views of the claims of science, the Professor, towards the close of his lecture, makes a felicitous reference to the testimonies and indications, bearing upon the subject, which have been left by antiquity.* . . .

Notwithstanding the length of the preceding extract, we cannot refrain from presenting to our readers a portion of the Note which Professor Boole appended to his Essay. It will be found to contain not only a vindication of his views, with reference to the relation of the logical or pre-inductive stage of science to ' the science that was yet to appear,' but also a clear statement of the most general conclusions to which his logical investigations had already conducted him, some of which are hinted at in the closing sentences of the above passage.† . . .

Throughout the whole of the year 1851, the year in which this Lecture was produced, Professor Boole's pen was actively employed. In the *Cambridge and Dublin Mathematical Journal*, the *Philosophical Magazine*, and other periodicals for that year, we find numerous papers bearing his name. One of these relates to the theory of linear transformations, a branch of analysis which had begun to attract much attention among both English and Continental mathematicians. The theory had been greatly extended, both by his own labours and by those of others, more particularly by the researches of Messrs. Cayley and Sylvester, two men of high analytical power and of transcendent

---

* [There follows a quotation from the text printed on pp. 202–204 of this volume, from " The instinctive thirst for knowledge . . ." to " . . . can scarcely be valued too highly."]

† [See pp. 207–209 of this volume.]

genius. He deemed it desirable, therefore, to pause in the prosecution of the subject, and ' endeavour to take a connected view of the methods and results already attained '; he considered that such a retrospect would ' serve both to afford an estimate of its actual state of progress, and to indicate the direction in which future effort might be most usefully engaged '. With a view to the accomplishment of this important object, as well as to supply some additions to the theory, he drew up the elaborate memoir which we have cited above, and which will be found in the sixth volume of the second series of the *Mathematical Journal*. Dr. Salmon, in his admirable work on the Higher Algebra, states that it was from this memoir that he derived his ' first clear ideas of the nature and objects of the theory of linear transformations '; and we believe there are other mathematicians who look back to their first perusal of that paper with equal interest for similar reasons.

Mitchell's problem of the distribution of the fixed stars * was at this time creating considerable discussion among mathematicians and astronomers. Professor Boole felt much interest in it, both because of its intrinsic importance, and because of its close connexion with a class of speculations in the pursuit of which he had long been engaged. His views on the theory of probabilities seem to have been first publicly announced in a paper on this problem which was printed in the *Philosophical Magazine* for June 1851. Two months later he communicated to the same periodical some ' further observations ' on the subject. The original and comprehensive manner in which he treated the question may be inferred from what the author says towards the close of his second paper. ' The theory of probabilities has, in the view which I have been led to take of it, two distinct but accordant sources. From whichever of these it may be derived, it will be found to involve the idea of numerical magnitude; but in the one case that idea will have reference simply to the relative frequency of the

---

* ' An Inquiry into the probable Magnitude and Parallax of the Fixed Stars, from the quantity of light which they afford to us, and the particular circumstances of their situation.' By the Rev. J. Mitchell, Philosophical Transactions for 1767.

F F

occurrence of events, being in fact the received ground of the theory; in the other, to the persistency of certain forms of thought, which are manifested equally in the operations of the science of number, and in the reasonings and discourses of common life. Setting out from either of these grounds, we may, I conceive, without difficulty attain to a knowledge of the other. Now, it appears to me to be perfectly in accordance with the nature of probability that this should be the case; for its relation to number is not more essential than its relation to the manner in which events are combined. But while the expression of the former relation belongs to arithmetic, or more generally to algebra, that of the latter belongs to logic.' These views he afterwards developed more fully in his great work on the ' Laws of Thought ', which was now rapidly approaching completion.

In February 1852, the University of Dublin conferred on Professor Boole the honorary title of LL.D., in consideration of ' his eminent services in the advancement of mathematical science '. Great credit is due to that distinguished body for having so early after his appointment to the chair at Cork, recognised his high scientific merits.

Late in the year 1853, our author brought to its close a labour on which he had bestowed a vast amount of profound and patient thought. His ' Mathematical Analysis of Logic ' was written hastily, and on this account he afterwards regretted its publication; but the work which he now gave to the world must be regarded as the most carefully matured of all his productions. It is entitled, ' An Investigation of the Laws of Thought, on which are founded the Mathematical Theories of Logic and Probabilities '. The principle on which the investigation proceeds is essentially the same as that enunciated by the author in his earlier logical essays; but, as he himself remarks, ' its methods are more general, and its range of applications far wider '. We shall speak of this work again, and endeavour to give some account (brief and imperfect it must necessarily be) of the system of fundamental laws on which it is based.

Among other institutions in the city of Cork with which Dr. Boole became connected was the Cuvierian Society.

This society, as its name indicates, was originally established for the prosecution of the study of natural history, but its field of inquiry was subsequently enlarged so as to embrace various departments of art, science, and antiquity. Dr. Boole, besides attending its meetings, and taking a prominent part in its discussions, read before the members several papers relating chiefly to archæological subjects. In the year 1854, he was chosen president, and on the occasion of a soirée, held at the close of the session in the Cork Athenæum he delivered an address, which was afterwards published, on 'The Social Aspect of Intellectual Culture'. This is an admirable specimen of what such an address should be; it is full of fine genial feeling, and shows its author to have been in thorough sympathy with those who desired to devote to mirth and friendship a brief season 'snatched from the dust and toil of life, from studies and cares and political anxieties'. It is pitched, indeed, in a very elevated strain, but then, it is to be remembered that, though spoken on a convivial occasion, it was addressed to the ear of the educated and the refined. Many of the topics touched upon are of enduring interest. This is especially the case in the latter portion of the address, where the author ascends from the particular circumstances of the hour to the general principle on which such meetings rest, viz:—'That within proper limits, and under proper conditions, intellectual tastes are not only compatible with social enjoyment, but tend to refine and enlarge that enjoyment; that an interest in the progress of the arts and sciences, and in the researches of the antiquary and the scholar is calculated not to destroy but to deepen our interest in humanity'. After intimating his dissent from the opinion entertained by some that there is nothing higher and greater than humanity, he proceeds thus :—

'Perhaps it is in the thought that there does exist an Intelligence and Will superior to our own—that the evolution of the destinies of our species is not solely the product either of human waywardness or of human wisdom; perhaps, I say, it is in this thought, that the conception of humanity attains its truest dignity. When, therefore, I use this term,

I would be understood to mean by it the human race, viewed in that mutual connexion and dependence which has been established, as I firmly believe, for the accomplishment of a purpose of the Divine mind. . . . One eminent instance of that connexion and dependence to which I have referred, is to be seen in the progression of the arts and sciences. Each generation as it passes away bequeaths to its successor not only its material works in stone and marble, in brass and iron, but also the truths which it has won, and the ideas which it has learned to conceive; its art, literature, science, and, to some extent, its spirit and morality. This perpetual transmission of the light of knowledge and civilisation has been compared to those torch-races of antiquity in which a lighted brand was transmitted from one runner to another until it reached the final goal. Thus, it has been said, do generations succeed each other, borrowing and conveying light, receiving the principles of knowledge, testing their truth, enlarging their application, adding to their number, and then transmitting them forward to coming generations—

' Et quasi cursores vitai lampada tradunt '.

' Now, this connexion between intellectual discovery and the progressive history of our race, gives to every stage of the former a deep human interest. Each new revelation, whether of the laws of the physical universe, of the principles of art, or of the great truths of morals and of politics, is a step not only in the progress of knowledge, but also in the history of our species.'

This short extract will serve to show that when the nature of the subject admitted of such treatment, our author could adorn his thoughts with all the higher graces of composition. We have seldom met with a more beautiful illustration, or one more aptly introduced, than that which is here drawn from Lucretius.

In 1855, Dr. Boole was married to Miss Mary Everest, daughter of the late Rev. T. R. Everest, rector of Wickwar in the County of Gloucester, and niece of Colonel Everest,*

* Mount Everest, the highest peak of the Himalayas, was named after this distinguished officer.

of the Indian Survey, as also of Dr. Ryall, the vice-president and professor of Greek in Queen's College, Cork. In her he found a true helpmeet, a woman who, by high mental culture and natural endowments, was well qualified to sympathise with him in his pursuits. It is in our own knowledge that Mrs. Boole rendered essential service to her husband by copying papers, correcting sheets for the press, and doing other similar work, which a thoroughly educated woman knows so well how to execute. Five daughters were the fruit of this happy union.

The Keith Prize, consisting of a gold medal and from £40 to £50 in money, is awarded once in every two years by the Royal Society in Edinburgh, ' for the best communication on a scientific subject, communicated, in the first instance to the Society '. Preference is given to a paper containing an original discovery. The prize is not awarded unless a paper of sufficient merit has been received within the biennial period. Now, it so happened that Professor Boole, early in the year 1857, communicated to the Edinburgh Society a paper entitled, ' On the Application of the Theory of Probabilities to the Question of the Combination of Testimonies or Judgments '. This paper was read in his absence by the Right Rev. Bishop Terrot, who himself, a short time before, had communicated to the Society a memoir * on a similar subject. The merits of the paper were at once perceived, and it was ordered to be printed in the ' Transactions '. It is a very elaborate investigation, occupying 56 quarto pages. For this paper the Keith medal (biennial period 1855–1857), the highest honour in the shape of prize which the Edinburgh Society has at its disposal, was awarded to Dr. Boole. The formal presentation took place on the 1st March 1858, Professor Kelland, V.P.R.S.E., in the chair, when Bishop Terrot was requested by the Council to take charge of the prize for Professor Boole, and to express to him their ' wishes for his future success in the career to which he had devoted himself '. Professor

* Bishop Terrot ' On the Possibility of combining two or more Probabilities of the same Event, so as to form one Definite Probability ', Transactions of the Royal Society of Edinburgh. Vol. xxi. part 1, 1856. [See Appendix C of this volume.]

Kelland's address on the occasion will be found in the Society's ' Proceedings ', vol. iv., 1857–1862, p. 84. The first part of this address is devoted to an account of Professor Boole's personal history. The sketch is brief and not wholly accurate ; but it states one fact which deserves to be generally known. It appears that Boole's paper ' On a General Method in Analysis ', for which he received the royal medal in the department of Mathematics in 1844, was referred by the Council of the Royal Society to Professor Kelland, and that it was he (Professor Kelland) who recommended that the paper should be printed, and that some special mark of approbation should be bestowed on its author. The remaining portion of Professor Kelland's address is occupied with an account of the paper for which the Keith prize was then being awarded.

At a meeting of the Royal Society in June 1857, Dr. Boole was elected a Fellow of that distinguished body. We wonder that he was not elected earlier ; but probably the expense had hitherto hindered him from applying. There are cases in which such a hindrance should not be permitted to exist, and this was certainly one of them. A few months before his election, he had communicated to the Society a memoir entitled, ' On the comparison of Transcendants, with certain applications to the theory of Definite Integrals ', which was afterwards printed in the ' Philosophical Transactions '. This memoir, it will be observed, though written in the same year as his paper on probabilities, for which he received the Keith prize, relates to an entirely distinct class of speculations. Dr. Boole seems to have always had two or three principal subjects before him, so that by turning from one to another, he might diversify his intellectual life. But when once he had taken hold of a problem. and satisfied himself that its solution was practicable, though he might often have to lay it aside, yet he never wholly abandoned it ; on the contrary, he returned to it again and again, constantly varying the form of attack, until he had completely mastered the difficulties that encircled it. Thus it was with the method which he had proposed for the solution of questions in the theory of probabilities. The application of that

method to particular problems he had illustrated in his
treatise on the 'Laws of Thought'; and yet more fully in
his Edinburgh memoir. Some observations too, on the
general character of the solutions to which the method leads,
founded upon induction from particular cases, were contained
in the original treatise, and the outlines, still in some measure
conjectural, of their general theory, were given in an appendix
to the 'Memoir'. But the development of that theory was
still incomplete, and so long as this was the case, he could
not think of leaving it where it was. At length, after years
of persistent effort, he succeeded in overcoming the analytical
difficulties of the question, and in obtaining what he considered a complete development of the theory. The results
of this protracted investigation he embodied in a memoir,
'On the Theory of Probabilities', and forwarded along with
a paper on a question in pure analysis, to the Royal Society.
Both these memoirs were 'read' on the same day on which
they were 'received', June 19th, 1862, and were printed
forthwith in the Society's 'Transactions'. The latter
memoir is entitled, 'On Simultaneous Differential Equations
of the First Order in which the Number of the Variables
exceeds by more than one the Number of the Equations'.
To this paper, a few months later, he wrote a sequel entitled,
'On the Differential Equations of Dynamics', which was
published in the 'Philosophical Transactions' for the
following year. His last communication * to the Royal
Society was being printed in the 'Transactions' at the time
of his death, and it is an interesting fact that it contains a
generalisation of an important theorem established in his
first communication to the same Society just twenty years
before.

Early in the year 1858, Professor Boole was elected an
Honorary Member of the Cambridge Philosophical Society.
At the Oxford Commemoration in the following year, he
received the honorary degree of D.C.L. Among the distinguished men who were associated with him on the latter

---

* The title of this paper is, 'On the Differential Equations which
determine the form of the Roots of Algebraic Equations'—*Philosophical
Transactions* for 1864.

occasion were Sir John Lawrence, the present Governor-General of India, Sir A. Wilson, and Colonel Greathead. The three Indian heroes were received by the Undergraduates with great cheering.

> ' Their names shone bright through blood and pain,
>   Their swords flashed back their praise again.'

But a different reception was awarded to the man who wielded only the ' calm sceptre of his pen ', and who, in the face of poverty and great external disadvantages, had fought his way up to a commanding position in the scientific world. The Undergraduates knew nothing whatever of Boole, and indeed, how could it be otherwise? His works had in them none of that kind of demonstrativeness which is so fascinating to the youthful mind.

When the Queen's Colleges of Belfast, Galway and Cork were united so as to form the Queen's University of Ireland, Professor Boole was appointed one of the public examiners for degrees. This office he filled with the highest reputation. In 1859, he produced his ' Differential Equations ', and in the following year his ' Finite Differences ',—two works which display a vast amount of original research as well as an extensive acquaintance with the mathematical writings of others. These have become class-books at Cambridge. The circumstance is worthy of special notice; it is, we believe, unexampled, that works written by a self-taught man should attain to such a position in a university distinguished in the particular department of science to which they relate.

In the *Bulletin de l'Academie Impériale des Sciences de St. Pétersbourg*, Vol. IV., 1862, there is an article entitled, ' Considérations sur la recherche des integrales premières des équations differéntielles partielles du second ordre, par G. Boldt (Lu le 7 Juin, 1861).' Respecting this article, Mr. Todhunter remarks : ' Although the name does not quite correspond, I consider that to be a misprint, and I attribute the article to Professor Boole, partly from the nature of the contents, and partly because it is known by his friends that he was engaged at a time corresponding to the date here given in the preparation of a mathematical article in French '.* He also wrote about the same time, a mathematical memoir in German; it is entitled, ' Ueber die partielle Differentialgleichung zweiter Ordnung $Rr +$ $Ss + Tt + U(s^2 - rt) = V$,' and will be found in volume 61 of ' Crelle's Journal '. These seem to have been the only papers which he contributed to Continental Journals.

Soon after the publication of his Treatise on Differential Equations, Professor Boole resolved that if a new edition of the work should be called for he would reconstruct it on a more extended scale. For several succeeding years his studies and researches were largely inspired and directed by this object, which however, he did not live to accomplish. The Treatise had been for some time out of print, and he was engaged on preparing a new and enlarged edition when he was suddenly struck by the hand of death. About three weeks before this sad event, the writer received from him a letter, written in evident haste, in the close of which he thus refers to his projected work :—

' I have been working, not hard, but pretty steadily (and at times hard), at my ' Differential Equations ', not yet in the press, since I last saw you. In the early summer I went to London to consult the great original memoirs on the subject (Lagrange, Euler, Legendre, &c., &c.) in the Library of the Royal Society, and remained in London nearly two months. I cannot be too thankful that I did this. When the work will actually go to the press I cannot say, I hope before long; but I have now delayed so long that it seems to me best to aim at making it as perfect as I can, regardless of time. But whether, indeed, it is a disposition to procrastinate, or a desire for an ideal excellence, or something of both, that make me so slow in the accomplishment of what I undertake, I cannot tell. I have almost ceased to be ashamed of my neglects, and that is not good. Give my very kind regards to Mrs. ——, and remember me to the little ones.'

This letter bears date Nov. 14, 1864. Ten or twelve days later he walked from his residence at Ballintemple to the

* See p. 143 of ' Boole's Differential Equations '. Supplementary volume. Edited by I. Todhunter, M.A., F.R.S., Fellow and Principal Mathematical Lecturer of St. John's College, Cambridge.

College in Cork, a distance of little more than two miles, in a drenching rain, and lectured in his wet clothes. The result was a feverish cold, which soon fell upon his lungs and terminated fatally. Thus passed away, in the full maturity of his faculties and in the midst of intellectual labours, the fruits of which were looked forward to by scientific men with interest and expectancy, one of the deepest thinkers which this age has produced.

Dr. Boole was a man of great goodness of heart. By those who knew him intimately, he was regarded with a feeling ' akin to reverence '. ' Apart from his intellectual superiority ', says one of his colleagues, ' there was shed around him an atmosphere of purity and moral elevation, which was felt by all who were admitted within its influence. And over all his gifts and graces there was thrown the charm of a true humility, and an apparent total unconsciousness of his own worth and wisdom. His intercourse with his pupils was of the most affectionate character. It was his delight to assemble those of whose conduct he approved in his own house and in association with his family; and this valuable privilege was accorded not to those who exhibited remarkable ability, but rather to those whose moral qualities had won his regard. He visited them in sickness, and where their means were limited, supplied them with those little luxuries which their cases required, but which their own resources failed to supply. The hold he had obtained on their affection was apparent in their demeanour as they followed his remains to the grave. It was evident to those friends who were admitted to his closer intimacy that higher interests than the claims of human science were gradually asserting their supremacy over his inner life. This deepening tone of religious thought and feeling did not manifest itself in any neglect of those claims; but it could not fail to be observed that the desire of earthly fame, which may have stimulated his earlier efforts, had lost its hold upon him and that he continued his labours from a solemn sense of duty and the simple love of truth. Nor did it lead to any disregard of the common interests of life, but rather to an enlarged sympathy in the joys and sorrows of others, to a tenderness to their faults and a ready recognition of any redeeming quality in the very worst of them. You could see by the expression of his countenance that it was absolutely painful to him to hear the shortcomings of others dwelt upon in his presence.' *

Like many other great men, Dr. Boole was very fond of children. His playfulness with them, and his readiness to enter into their little world of thought and action, brought out very beautifully the simplicity and tenderness of his nature. In closing his letters to the writer, most of which related almost exclusively to mathematical investigations, he never failed to say, ' Remember me to the little ones '; and the little ones loved to remember him and to be remembered by him. There was no relaxation in which he so much delighted as a romp with young people; and an invitation which he once received from a party of them to come out of his study and ' roar ' for them, for that he would make a ' capital lion ' (!), was accepted by him as a great compliment. He thoroughly believed in the cultivation of the child element in the heart of the grown man.

In his family and among his immediate friends, he was looked up to as a religious teacher and guide rather than as an author and a man of science. His piety was warm and devotional, while it was at the farthest remove from superstition and fanaticism. In short, what Mr. Lewis in his ' History of Philosophy ' says of George Berkeley, Bishop of Cloyne, may be affirmed with equal truth of George Boole, Professor at Cork—' There are few men of whom England has better reason to be proud, for to extraordinary merits as a writer and thinker, he united the most exquisite purity and generosity of character; and it is still a moot point,' among his friends, ' whether he was greater in head or heart.'

The foregoing sketch is far from being complete. When the biography of Boole is written, the materials of which we are glad to learn are being collected, many illustrations will doubtless be given of the versatility of his talent, his love of

---

* From an article accompanying a portrait of Professor Boole, in the *Illustrated London News* for January 21, 1865. We are permitted to mention that the article was written by Dr. Ryall, of Queen's College, Cork.

poetry and music, his fine appreciation of the beauties of
external nature, his profound reverence for truth, especially
religious truth,* and many other qualities of his intellect
and heart which we have not so much as touched upon.

Boole's mathematical researches have exercised a very
considerable influence upon the study of the higher branches
of the analysis, especially in this country. They have
stimulated and directed the efforts of other investigators to
an extent that is not, we think, generally known. Out of
his theory of linear transformations, has grown the more
general theory of co-variants,† with all its important geometrical and other applications. By his invention of an
algebra of non-commutative symbols, a great impulse has
been given to the cultivation of the calculus of operations.
His general method in analysis is the most powerful instrument which we possess for the integration of differential
equations, whether total or partial. To Sir John Herschel is
due the high praise of having first applied the method of

* A few short passages, which we extract from letters written by Boole
when he was in London in June and July, 1864, will throw some light on his
theological leanings, and on one or two other related questions :—' Heard
your friend in Vere Street twice yesterday. The morning sermon, such
as he only of living men can preach. . . . I had a little discussion with —
this morning about preaching. He said preaching was all the same thing
over again—that there was no new knowledge to be got, only different
ways of stating what was known or thought before. I remarked that the
same words, preached with equal sincerity of conviction and feeling by two
different persons, would produce very different effects; that the personal
element—the wonderful influence of man over man, must be taken into
account—that it always existed, and always would exist. But though
he admitted, or rather did not openly dissent from this, he seemed to think,
" more the pity that it is so ". He would have everything like Euclid.
. . . I have just returned from hearing Maurice. To say that I was
pleased is to say nothing, or what is better left unsaid. To say that I
was deeply impressed is only what you would expect. But I should not
express my real feeling if I said less than that I listened to him with a sense
of awe. The congregation was small, but it seemed to me as if this was
the feeling among them. I sat almost immediately under the pulpit, and
lost no single word. We shall, I have no doubt, sometime read the sermon.
The text was, " Grieve not the Holy Spirit of God ". I should exceedingly
like to read the sermon carefully. The idea even crossed my mind of
applying anonymously for it, but I felt that I had no right to take up the
time of a man who works not for us, but for a generation, and as I think for
generations to come. . . . I feel with you that I should not like to leave
the Church while Maurice is in it.'

† The theory of co-variants is due to Professor Cayley. Dr. Salmon's
' Lessons introductory to the Modern Higher Algebra', is a useful
elementary guide to this important branch of mathematics. The reader
will find in the preface to Dr. Salmon's work a brief historical sketch of the
progress of the theory.

the separation of symbols to the solution of linear differential equations with constant co-efficients.*  But it was reserved for Gregory and Boole to set the logical principles of that method in a clear and satisfactory light ; and to Boole alone belongs the honour of having extended the theory to the solution of equations with variable coefficients.  His principal discoveries in this department will be found in his ' Differential Equations ', and the Supplementary Volume,† works which, though primarily intended for elementary instruction, may be read with advantage by the advanced mathematical student.  Other original investigations will be found in the same volumes, and more especially in those parts which relate to Riccati's equation, to integrating factors, to singular solutions, to the inverse problems of geometry and optics, to partial differential equations, and to the projection of a surface on a plane.

The calculus of logic, upon the invention of which Boole's fame may be permitted to rest, is most fully developed in his ' Investigation of the Laws of Thought '.  The design of this work is—to use the author's own words—' to investigate the fundamental laws of those operations of the mind by which reasoning is performed ; to give expression to them in the symbolical language of a calculus, and upon this foundation, to establish the science of logic, and construct its method ; to make that method itself, the basis of a general method for the application of the mathematical doctrine of probabilities ; and, finally, to collect from the various elements of truth, brought to light in the course of these inquiries, some probable intimations concerning the nature and constitution of the human mind '.  Accordingly, in Boole's system, the fundamental laws of thought are deduced, not as has sometimes been represented, from the science of Number, but from the nature of the subject itself.  Those laws are indeed expressed by the aid of algebraical symbols, but the several forms of expression are determined on other grounds than

---

* *Philosophical Transactions* for 1814.  ' Consideration of various Points in Analysis '.   See § iv. ' On Equations of the First Degree '.

† This volume contains all the unpublished matter relating to differential equations which was found among Professor Boole's papers after his death. Mr. Todhunter has executed his task as editor with great skill and ability.

those which fix the rules of arithmetic, or, more generally, of algebra; they are determined in fact, by a consideration of those intellectual operations which are implied in the strict use of language as an instrument of reasoning. The interpretation of the symbols, and of the laws, is not mathematical, but logical.

In algebra, letters of the alphabet are used to represent numbers, and signs connecting those letters, represent either the fundamental operations of addition, subtraction, multiplication, &c., or (as in the case of the sign of equality) a relation among the numbers involved in the inquiry. In Boole's calculus of logic, literal symbols are used to represent things as subjects of the faculty of conception, and other symbols are used to represent the operations of that faculty, the laws of the latter being the expressed laws of the operations signified. The canonical forms of the Aristotelian syllogism are really symbolical; but the symbols are less perfect of their kind, than those which are employed by Boole. His adoption of algebraical signs of operation, as well as of literal symbols, and the mathematical sign of equality, enables him to give a complete expression to the fundamental laws of reasoning, and to construct a logical method, which is by far the most complete and comprehensive of any hitherto proposed.

In borrowing the notation of algebra, Boole does not assume that, in its new application, the laws by which its use is governed, will remain unchanged; such an assumption would be ' mere hypothesis '. He shows, indeed, that the ultimate laws of logic can be expressed in the symbolical language of mathematics, and that, moreover, ' those laws are such as to suggest this mode of expression, and to give it a peculiar and exclusive fitness for the ends in view '. But logic is never identified or confounded with mathematics; the two systems of thought are kept perfectly distinct, each being subject to its own laws and conditions. The symbols are the same for both systems, but they have not the same interpretation; they represent in the one, objects of thought and operations of the mind, which are wholly different from the objects and operations represented by them in the other.

Each set of symbols has a definite interpretation, and is subject to laws founded upon that interpretation alone. That there is, to some extent, a formal agreement between the laws in the two cases, is a discovery made *a posteriori* by actual comparison. But it is simply a mistake to regard Boole's calculus as an attempt to reduce the ideas of logic under the dominion of number.*

There are three laws to which all the symbols of algebra, which represent numbers,† are subject, viz., *the law of commutation*, expressed by $x \times y = y \times x$, or more simply $xy = yx$; *the law of the convertibility of terms*, expressed by $x + y = y + x$, $x - y = -y + x$; and *the law of distribution*, expressed by $x(y + z) = xy + xz$, $x(y - z) = xy - xz$. In these equations, the letters $x$, $y$, $z$, represent any numbers whatever, the sign $=$ indicates the relation of equality, and the signs $+$, $-$, $\times$, stand for the respective operations of addition, subtraction, multiplication. These laws are fundamental; the science of algebra is built upon them. And they are axiomatic; we do not derive them by induction from many instances, but they become apparent in all their generality the moment we clearly apprehend a single instance. Thus to exemplify the first law, let it be required to multiply together the numbers 4 and 5. Anyone can see that whether we multiply 4 by 5 or 5 by 4, the result will be the same : 4 times 5 equals 5 times 4. So, in like manner, if we take any two numbers and call them 1st No. and 2nd No., we shall have 1st No. $\times$ 2nd No. $=$ 2nd No. $\times$ 1st No., which makes evident the law of commutation. And the other laws may be exemplified in a similar manner.

* This is the error which pervades the strictures on Boole's method contained in the article on Logic, *Encyclopædia Britannica*, eighth edition, p. 578. The *Investigation of the Laws of Thought* is there characterised as an ' exceedingly subtle and able work ', but the critic does not seem to have read the book with any degree of care or attention. Certainly nothing can be more unfair than his representation of Boole's calculus as an attempt ' to incorporate into the universal theory of thought a special and systematic development of relations of number and quantity '. If there be those who, as this writer says, ' endeavour to theorise all thinking by examining thought only as exerted on one kind of objects ', and who ' allege, as bearing on thought universally, laws which rule it only in certain cases ', Boole must not be classed among them.

† In the higher branches of the analysis literal symbols are often used to represent not numbers, but operations, as for instance, *differentiation*. In these cases the symbols do not always obey the laws indicated in the text.

Now let the notion of number be dismissed from the mind, and let the literal symbols, $x, y$, &c., each represent a class of individuals to which a particular name or description is applicable. Further, let the combination $xy$ represent that class of things to which the names or descriptions, denoted by $x$ and $y$, are simultaneously applicable. For instance, if $x$ alone stand for ' all men ', or the class 'men', and $y$ stand for the adjective ' good ', or what, for logical purposes is equivalent, all things to which the description ' good ' is applicable, then, according to the proposed notation, $xy$ will stand for ' men that are good ', or 'all good men'. The order in which the symbols are written, is indifferent; for $xy$ and $yx$ equally represent that class of things to the several members of which the names or descriptions $x$ and $y$ are together applicable. Hence we have $xy = yx$, a law which ' may be characterised by saying that the literal symbols, $x, y, z$, are *commutative, like the symbols of algebra* '. ' In saying this ', remarks Boole, ' it is not affirmed that the process of multiplication in algebra, of which the fundamental law is expressed by the equation $xy = yx$, possesses in itself any analogy with that process of logical combination which $xy$ has been made to represent above; but only that if the arithmetical and the logical process are expressed in the same manner, their symbolical expressions will be subject to the same formal law.   The evidence of that subjection is in the two cases quite distinct '.*

Again, let $x + y$ represent the aggregation of the classes $x$ and $y$, and let $x - y$ represent what is left, when from the class $x$, the class $y$ is withdrawn.   For instance, if $x$ stand for ' men ', and $y$ for ' women ', $x + y$ will stand for ' men and women '.   If $x$ represent ' all forms of government ', and $y$ ' republican ', $x - y$ will represent ' all forms of government except republican '.   This notation being premised, it is at once seen that in logic, as in algebra, $x + y = y + x$, $x - y = -y + x$.   That is to say, *the terms are convertible*.

In the same way, it may be shown that logical symbols are *distributive*.   Let $x$ stand for the adjective ' good ', $y$ for the class ' boys ' and $x$ for the class ' girls '; then, since it is in

* [*Laws of Thought*, p. (31) 34.]

effect the same thing to apply the adjective ' good ' to
' boys and girls ', both, as to say ' good boys and good girls ',
we have $x(y + z) = xy + xz$. In like manner, to apply
the adjective ' tame ' to such a group of animals as is
expressed by the phrase ' All quadrupeds except tame dogs '.
So that, writing $x$ for ' tame ', $y$ for ' quadrupeds ', and $z$
for ' dogs ', we have $x(y - z) = xy - xz$.

So far forth the laws of logic are seen to be identical in
form with the laws which govern the general symbols of
algebra.   But Boole has brought to light another law of
thought, and it is one to which the symbols of quantity, as
such, are not subject.   The combination $xy$ represents ' the
whole of the class of objects to which the names or qualities
represented by $x$ and $y$, are together applicable '.   It
follows, therefore, that if the two symbols have exactly the
same signification, their combination will express no more
than either of them taken alone would do.   Hence, $xx = x$,
$yy = y$; or, adopting the notation of algebra $x^2 = x$,
$y^2 = y$. ' This law ', remarks Boole, ' is practically exemplified in language.   To say, " good, good " in relation to
any subject, though a cumbrous and useless pleonasm, is the
same as to say " good ".   Thus, " good, good " men is
equivalent to " good " men.   Such repetitions of words
are, indeed, sometimes employed to heighten a quality or
strengthen an affirmation.   But this effect is merely secondary and conventional; it is not founded in the intrinsic
relations of language and thought.' *

Now, there are only two numbers which conform to the
law $x^2 = x$, viz., 0 and 1; $0^2 = 0$, and $1^2 = 1$.   Instead,
therefore, of seeking to determine ' the measure of formal
agreement of the symbols of logic with those of number
generally ', Boole compares them with the symbols of quantity, admitting only of the values 0 and 1.   He virtually
constructs an algebra in which the symbols $x, y, z$, &c., admit
indifferently of these particular values, and of these alone;
and he shows that ' the laws, the axioms, and the processes
of such an algebra are identical in their whole extent with
the laws, the axioms, and the processes of an algebra of

* [*Laws of Thought*, p. (32) 35.]

G G

logic '. Difference of interpretation alone divides them. Upon this principle his logical method is founded.

The preceding general laws, deduced immediately from the constitution of language, which is ' the instrument and product of thought ', are confirmed by the study of those intellectual operations by which the mind combines or modifies the ideas or qualities of things. Thus, in illustration of the law $xy = yx$, Boole says,—' Let us suppose that the universe of our discourse is the actual universe, so that words are to be used in the full extent of their meaning, and let us consider the two mental operations implied by the words " white " and " men ". The word " men ", implies the operation of selecting in thought from its subject, the universe, all men; and the resulting conception " men " becomes the subject of the next operation. The operation implied by the word " white " is that of selecting from its subject, " men ", all of that class which are " white ". The final resulting conception is that of " white men ". Now it is perfectly apparent that if the operations above described had been performed in a converse order, the result would have been the same. Whether we begin by forming the conception of " men ", and then by a second intellectual act limit that conception to " white men ", or whether we begin by forming the conception of " white objects ", and then limit it to such of that class as are " men ", is perfectly indifferent, so far as the result is concerned. It is obvious that the order of the mental processes would be equally indifferent if for the words " white " and " men ", we substituted any other descriptive or appellative terms whatever, provided only that their meaning was fixed and absolute. And thus the indifference of the order of two successive acts of the faculty of conception, the one of which furnishes the subject upon which the other is supposed to operate, is a general condition of the exercise of that faculty. It is a law of the mind, and it is the real origin of that law of the literal symbols of logic which constitute its formal expression,' * $xy = yx$. The other laws admit of being illustrated in a similar manner.

In reasoning by the aid of symbols, we may put out of

* [*Laws of Thought*, pp. (44–45) 49.]

thought the meaning of the symbols, and attend only to the laws of their combination. So long as those laws are not transgressed, we are at liberty to combine the symbols anyhow that may serve our purpose, without regard to the meaning of the symbols, or even to the question of the interpretability of intermediate results. The final result must, of course, be in an interpretable form, otherwise we should fail to attain the end for which we reason, ' the knowledge of some intelligible fact or truth '. Little progress would have been made in the higher departments of mathematical analysis if this principle had not been distinctly recognised and fearlessly applied. We owe to it our knowledge of some of the most important theorems in the Differential Calculus and in Finite Differences. Boole's application of this principle to Formal Logic was bold and original in the highest degree. Having shown that any system of propositions may be represented by equations involving symbols, $x$, $y$, &c., which, whenever interpretation is possible, are subject to laws identical in form with the laws of a system of quantitative symbols, susceptible only of the values 0 and 1, he proceeds :—

' But as the formal processes of reasoning depend only upon the laws of the symbols, and not upon the nature of their interpretation, we are permitted to treat the above symbols, $x$, $y$, $z$, as if they were quantitative symbols of the kind above described. *We may, in fact, lay aside the logical interpretation of the symbols in the given equation ; convert them into quantitative symbols, susceptible only of the values 0 and 1 ; perform upon them, as such, all the requisite processes of solution ; and, finally, restore to them their logical interpretation.* [And this is the mode of procedure which Boole actually adopts.] The processes to which the symbols $x$, $y$, $z$, regarded as quantitative, and of the species above described, are subject, are not limited by those conditions of thought to which they would, if performed upon purely logical symbols, be subject, and a freedom of operation is given to us in the use of them without which the inquiry after a general method in logic would be a hopeless quest.' *

* [*Laws of Thought*, pp. (69–70) 76.]

Numerous applications of his method are given by Boole in the ' Laws of Thought '. That method ' has for its object the determination of any element in any proposition, however complex, as a logical function of the remaining elements. Instead of confining our attention to the " subject ", and " predicate ", regarded as simple terms, we can take any element, or any combination of elements entering into either of them; make that element, or that combination, the " subject " of a new proposition; and determine what its " predicate " shall be, in accordance with the data afforded to us '. In this way also, any system of equations whatever, by which propositions or combinations of propositions, can be represented, may be analysed, and all the " conclusion " which those propositions involve, be deduced from them. In the light of this method, Boole examines the Aristotelian logic and some of its modern extensions. He shows that conversion, syllogism, &c., are not the ultimate processes of logic, but themselves rest upon and are resolvable into, ulterior and more elementary processes. And the conclusion at which he arrives with respect to the nature and extent of the scholastic logic is, ' that it is not a science, but a collection of scientific truths, too incomplete to form a system of themselves, and not sufficiently fundamental to serve as the foundation upon which a perfect system may rest '.

It ought perhaps to be distinctly stated here that Boole did not propose his calculus of 0 and 1 as a substitute for common reasoning. He was well aware that any, the most perfect, system of formal logic must possess a theoretical rather than a practical importance. ' The perfection of the method of logic ', he says, ' may be chiefly valuable as an evidence of the speculative truth of its principles. To supersede the employment of common reasoning, or to subject it to the rigour of technical forms, would be the last desire of one who knows the value of that intellectual toil and warfare which imparts to the mind an athletic vigour, and teaches it to contend with difficulties, and to rely upon itself in emergencies. Nevertheless ', he adds, ' cases may arise in which the value of a scientific procedure even in those things which fall confessedly under the ordinary dominion of the reason, may be felt and acknowledged '.

The power of the method is most strikingly exemplified in its application to the theory of probabilities, but that is a branch of the subject on which it is impossible here to enter. We could not exhibit the formulæ for the expansion, elimination, &c., of logical functions, or show how such formulæ may be applied to the analysis of propositions, without covering our pages with symbols that would render them as unintelligible and uninviting to the general reader as a work written in Arabic. We must, therefore, content ourselves with having briefly stated the axiomatic laws on which Boole's system is based, and pointed out their formal connexion with the fundamental laws of Algebra. ' Mr. Boole's generalisation of the forms of Logic ', says Professor De Morgan, ' cannot be separated from mathematics, since it not only demands Algebra, but such taste for thought about the notation of Algebra as is rarely acquired without much and deep practice. When the ideas thrown out by Mr. Boole shall have borne their full fruit, Algebra, although only founded on ideas of number in the first instance, will appear like a sectional model of the whole form of thought. Its forms considered apart from their matter, will be seen to contain all the forms of thought in general. The anti-mathematical logician says that it makes thought a branch of Algebra, instead of Algebra a branch of thought. It *makes* nothing, it *finds*; and it finds the laws of thought symbolised in the forms of Algebra.'—*English Cyclopædia, Art. Logic.*

In a very ingenious little work entitled, ' Pure Logic, or the Logic of Quality apart from Quantity ', Mr. W. Stanley Jevons has lately developed a system of deductive reasoning closely analogous to, and in some respects identical with, that given by Boole. Of the merits or defects of Mr. Jevons's system, we shall not now speak, but we cannot close this article without saying a word or two touching his objections to Boole's method. Those objections are entitled to attention if for no other reason than this, that they evidently proceed from one who has made a careful study of

the work which he undertakes to criticise. Yet we are far
from being satisfied that they are well founded. His first
objection is, that ' Boole's symbols are essentially different
from the names or symbols of common discourse '. Here
the question turns wholly upon the office assigned in the
*Laws of Thought* to the symbol $+$, which is there used to
connect terms which are mutually exclusive. It is objected
that in common discourse the conjunctions ' and ', ' or ',
are not invariably so used. This, however, is distinctly
admitted by Boole (chap. IV., § 6), who nevertheless, vin-
dicates his mode of using the symbol $+$, and as it appears to
us, upon good and sufficient grounds. Mr. Jevons's second
objection, viz., that ' there are no such operations as addition
and subtraction in pure logic ', is founded upon a misapprehension. The mental operation indicated in Boole's
system by the sign $+$, is that by which from the conception
of two distinct classes of things, we form the conception of
that group or collection of things which those classes taken
together compose. Now this, as a mental operation, is
wholly different from that process of the mind by which
we pass from the arithmetical notion of one object to that
of two, three, or more of the same. In like manner, logical
subtraction expressed by the sign $-$, and which is the
opposite or negative of logical addition, is entirely distinct
as a mental operation from arithmetical subtraction. Yet
Mr. Jevons enters into a somewhat elaborate argument to
prove that arithmetical addition and subtraction have no
place in pure logic ! Another objection, viz., that Boole's
system is ' inconsistent with the self-evident law of thought,
the law of unity $(A + A = A)$,' is equally unfounded. Mr.
Jevons attaches his own meaning to the symbol $+$, and this
is essentially distinct and different from that assigned to the
symbol $+$ by Boole. These, therefore, in the two systems
are not one and the same symbol; they are two, and any
argument built upon their assumed identity must of course
be fallacious. In Boole's system, the expression $A + A$, is
not equivalent to A, neither does this expression in general
admit of interpretation. We cannot conceive of the addition
of a Class A to itself. Mr. Jevons's fourth and last objection

relates to Boole's interpretations of the numerical symbols 0, 1, &c. Those interpretations are necessitated by the nature of the notation adopted. In every symbolical system there are concessions which must be made to notation.

Mr. Jevons rejects the calculus of 0 and 1, and proposes in its place a method which he thinks is equally powerful, and at the same time more simple, intelligible, and purely logical. His little book may be read with advantage in connexion with the *Laws of Thought*. In his general estimate of Boole's system we entirely concur. 'It is not to be denied', he says, 'that Boole's system is complete and perfect within itself. It is, perhaps, one of the most marvellous and admirable pieces of reasoning ever put together. Indeed, if Professor Ferrier, in his "Institutes of Metaphysics", is right in holding that the chief excellence of a system is in being reasoned and consistent within itself, then Professor Boole's is nearly or quite the most perfect system ever struck out by a single writer.'

We understand that Boole has left behind him a considerable quantity of logical manuscripts, and that these are to be published either in a separate form, or in a new edition of the *Laws of Thought*. His works are his noblest monument, but his friends and admirers are raising other memorials. Of these we may mention in particular, a memorial window in the cathedral at Lincoln, and another in the College Hall at Cork, the glass alone of the latter window is to cost £350. His widow has placed a mural tablet to his memory in the church of Ballintemple, the inscription on which is as follows :—' To the memory of George Boole, D.C.L., F.R.S., First Professor of Mathematics in the Queen's College, Cork, in whom the highest order of Intellect, cultivated by unwearied Industry, produced the Fruits of deep Humility and Child-like Trust. He was born in Lincoln, on the 2nd November 1815. And died at Ballintemple on the 8th December, 1864. "For ever, O Lord, thy Word is settled in Heaven".'

There are some men whose office gives them celebrity; there are other men who give celebrity to their office. Boole was one of the latter. The Chair of Mathematics which

he filled at Cork would not have made his name illustrious;
but that chair has, through the genius and labours of its
first occupant, acquired a reputation which only powers
of the highest order in his successors can sustain and
perpetuate.

R. H.

# APPENDIX B

## ON THE THEORY OF CHANCES DEVELOPED IN PROFESSOR BOOLE'S " LAWS OF THOUGHT "

By Henry Wilbraham, M.A., Fellow of Trinity
College, Cambridge *

SOME communications having already within the last few months appeared in the Philosophical Magazine, by Mr. Cayley and Professor Boole, relating to the subjects treated in the work lately published by the latter on the Laws of Thought, it may be considered not out of place to publish in the pages of the same Magazine the following observations on the theory of chances developed in that work.

The object of this paper is to show that Professor Boole does in the greater number of questions relating to chances solvable by his method (or at least in those which are most difficult to treat by other methods), tacitly assume certain conditions expressed by the data of the problem, and to show how these assumed conditions may be algebraically expressed.

When no condition among the chances of the simple events, but only the absolute chances of those several simple events are given, the reasoning of Chapter XVII. of Prof. Boole's book shows that it is assumed that the events are independent, i.e. that the event A is as likely to happen in one state of circumstances as regards the remaining events as in another; for instance, that A is as likely to happen if B happen and C do not, as it is if B and C both happen or both fail; and this assumption is implicitly introduced in the logical method of working the problem. It is an assumption easily expressed by an algebraical equation or system of equations. For instance, take the most simple case,—there are two events,

* [*The Philosophical Magazine*, Supplement to vol. vii, Series 4, June 1854.]

A and B, the chance of A happening is $a$, of B, $b$; what is the chance of A and B both happening? There are four possible cases; viz. (1) both happening, (2) B happening without A, (3) A without B, (4) both failing. Let the chances of these four contingencies be respectively $\theta$, $\lambda$, $\mu$, $\phi$. To determine these we have the equations

$$\theta + \lambda + \mu + \phi = 1, \ \theta + \mu = a, \ \theta + \lambda = b.$$

Another equation is given in Professor Boole's assumption that A is as likely to happen if B happen as it is if B fail, viz.

$$\frac{\theta}{\theta + \lambda} = \frac{\mu}{\mu + \phi} \text{ or } \frac{\theta}{\mu} = \frac{\lambda}{\phi}.$$

The same equation is given by the condition that B is as likely to happen as if it fail. These four equations determine the values of $\theta$, $\lambda$, $\mu$, $\phi$. Again, suppose three simple events, A, B, C, the chances of which are $a$, $b$, $c$. There are here eight possible cases, ($\theta$) A, B, C all happening, ($\lambda$) B and C but not A, ($\mu$) A and C not B, ($\nu$) A and B not C, ($\rho$) A not B or C, ($\sigma$) B not A or C, ($\tau$) C not A or B, ($\phi$) all failing. Denoting the chances of these several contingencies by the Greek letters prefixed to them, we have the equations

$$\theta + \lambda + \mu + \nu + \rho + \sigma + \tau + \phi = 1$$
$$\theta + \mu + \nu + \rho = a$$
$$\theta + \lambda + \nu + \sigma = b$$
$$\theta + \lambda + \mu + \tau = c.$$

Professor Boole's assumption of the independence of the simple events completes the system of equations necessary to determine the unknown quantities. It gives the equations

$$\frac{\theta}{\lambda} = \frac{\mu}{\tau} = \frac{\nu}{\sigma} = \frac{\rho}{\phi}, \ \frac{\theta}{\mu} = \frac{\lambda}{\tau} = \frac{\nu}{\rho} = \frac{\sigma}{\phi}, \ \frac{\theta}{\nu} = \frac{\lambda}{\sigma} = \frac{\mu}{\rho} = \frac{\tau}{\phi},$$

which comprise, in fact, four independent equations, from which, together with the first four, the unknown quantities may be determined algebraically.

That Professor Boole's method does in such cases as the two just mentioned tacitly make the assumptions stated, is evident as well *à posteriori* as *à priori*. For, in the first case, if we seek to find by the Professor's logical equations the chance of A and B both occurring, we find it to be $ab$, that of B and not A $(1 - a)b$, and so on, which necessarily imply the condition I have stated to be assumed. So in the second case, we should find the chance of A, B, C all happening to be $abc$, that of B and C but not A $(1 - a)bc$, and so on, which imply the four additional assumed conditions.

Now let us pass to the cases where certain conditions among the chances of the several events are given. In the first question which I have stated, where there are only two simple events A and B, suppose there to be another given relation among the chances besides the absolute chances of the simple events A and B. The new *given* condition appears now to supersede and take the place of the previously *assumed* condition; and with this new condition combined with the three former equations among $\theta$, $\lambda$, $\mu$, $\phi$, the problem is easily solvable by algebra. In the second question, where there are three simple events A, B and C, suppose there to be one other given relation among the chances. This new condition does certainly to some extent supersede those previously assumed; and it appears to me that Professor Boole's reasoning would lead one to suppose that the former assumptions are entirely banished from the problem, and no others except the said newly given condition assumed in their stead. The fact, however, is that in this case certain additional assumptions are made, otherwise the problem would be indeterminate. The nature of these assumptions, which are different from the assumptions made when no condition besides the absolute chances of the simple events is given, will perhaps, be better seen from the following discussion of an example than from any general reasoning. I shall adopt in it the same assumptions as are made in Professor Boole's method, but work it out without the aid of his logical equations. Any question which can be solved by the logical method may also be treated in this manner.

The chances of three events, A, B, and C, are $a$, $b$, $c$, respectively, and the chance of all three happening together is $m$; what is the chance of A occurring without B?

Suppose A, B, and C, and a further event S, to be four

simple events mutually independent, the absolute chances of which are respectively $x$, $y$, $z$, and $s$. We suppose for the present no connexion to exist between the original simple events A, B, and C, and the subsidiary event S. There will be altogether sixteen possible mutually exclusive compound events, the chances of which (since the simple events are independent) are as follows :—

| | | | |
|---|---|---|---|
| ($\delta$) | $xyzs$, | ($\bar{\omega}$) | $x(1-y)(1-z)s$, |
| ($\epsilon$) | $(1-x)yzs$, | ($\rho$) | $x(1-y)z(1-s)$, |
| ($\theta$) | $x(1-y)zs$, | ($\tau$) | $xy(1-z)(1-s)$, |
| ($\iota$) | $xy(1-z)s$, | ($\upsilon$) | $x(1-y)(1-z)(1-s)$, |
| ($\kappa$) | $xyz(1-s)$, | ($\phi$) | $(1-x)y(1-z)(1-s)$, |
| ($\lambda$) | $(1-x)(1-y)zs$, | ($\chi$) | $(1-x)(1-y)z(1-s)$, |
| ($\mu$) | $(1-x)y(1-z)s$, | ($\psi$) | $(1-x)(1-y)(1-z)s$, |
| ($\nu$) | $(1-x)yz(1-s)$, | ($\omega$) | $(1-x)(1-y)(1-z)(1-s)$. |

Let us now make an assumption with respect to the subsidiary event S, viz. that it is never observed except in conjunction with the three other events, and is always observed to happen if they concur. Consequently, those of the above sixteen compound events which represent S occurring while any one or more of the other three events do not occur, and which represent A, B, C, all to occur without S occurring, must be considered as beyond the range of our observation. This does not contradict the former assumption of the mutual independence of the four simple events; for we do not by this last supposition say that such compound events are impossible, nor do we make any new assumption as to the probability of their occurrence, but only that, as they are beyond the limits of our observation, we have nothing to do with them. The events therefore, which come within our circle of observation are those marked respectively $\delta, \nu, \rho, \tau, \upsilon, \phi, \chi, \omega$; and the absolute chance that any event which may occur is an event within the range of our observation is

$$xyzs + (1-x)yz(1-s) + x(1-y)z(1-s)$$
$$+ xy(1-z)(1-s)$$
$$+ x(1-y)(1-z)(1-s) + (1-x)y(1-z)(1-s)$$
$$+ (1-x)(1-y)z(1-s) + (1-x)(1-y)(1-z)(1-s),$$

which is similar to the quantity called V in Professor Boole's book.

I must here observe that $x$, $y$, and $z$ are not the same as the given quantities $a$, $b$, and $c$; for the latter represent the chances of A, B, and C respectively occurring, provided that the event is one which comes within our range of observation, whereas $x$, $y$, and $z$ represent the absolute chances of the same events whether the event be or be not within that range.

Of the eight events $\delta$, $\nu$, $\rho$, $\tau$, $\upsilon$, $\phi$, $\chi$, $\omega$, which compose V, four, viz. $\delta$, $\rho$, $\tau$, and $\upsilon$, imply the occurrence of A. Consequently, the chance that if the event be within our range of observation A will occur, is the sum of the chances of these last four events divided by the sum of the chances of the eight. This will be equal to the given chance $a$. Hence

$$\frac{xyzs + \{(1-y)z + y(1-z) + (1-y)(1-z)\}x(1-s)}{V} = a.$$

So also

$$\frac{xyzs + \{(1-x)2 + x(1-z) + (1-x)(1-z)\}y(1-s)}{V} = b.$$

$$\frac{xyzs + \{(1-y)z + y(1-z) + (1-y)(1-z)\}z(1-s)}{V} = c.$$

Also as the event S always in cases within our range of observation occurs conjointly with A, B, and C, the chance of S occurring and that of A, B, and C all occurring are the same, and equal to $m$. Therefore

$$\frac{xyzs}{V} = m.$$

Out of the events represented by V there are two, $\hat{\omega}$ and $\upsilon$, which imply that A occurs but not B; consequently, the chance of A occurring but not B, which is the required chance and may be called $u$, $= \dfrac{x(1-y)(1-s)}{V}$. From these five equations $x$, $y$, $z$, $s$, may be eliminated, and there remains an equation which gives $u$. Or the values of $x$, $y$, $z$, and $s$ may be found from the first four equations, and thence the value of any function of them is known.

This method of solution is almost identical with Professor Boole's. The assumptions are the same in both, and they differ separately. Representing the chances of the sixteen separate compound events by the Greek letters prefixed to them, the condition that the four events A, B, C, and S are mutually independent is equivalent to the following relations among $\delta$, $\epsilon$, &c.

$$\frac{\delta}{\epsilon} = \frac{\theta}{\lambda} = \frac{\iota}{\mu} = \frac{\kappa}{\nu} = \frac{\hat{\omega}}{\psi} = \frac{\rho}{\chi} = \frac{\tau}{\phi} = \frac{\upsilon}{\omega},$$

$$\frac{\delta}{\theta} = \frac{\epsilon}{\lambda} = \frac{\iota}{\hat{\omega}} = \frac{\kappa}{\rho} = \frac{\mu}{\psi} = \frac{\nu}{\chi} = \frac{\tau}{\upsilon} = \frac{\phi}{\omega},$$

$$\frac{\delta}{\iota} = \frac{\epsilon}{\mu} = \frac{\theta}{\hat{\omega}} = \frac{\kappa}{\tau} = \frac{\lambda}{\psi} = \frac{\nu}{\phi} = \frac{\rho}{\upsilon} = \frac{\chi}{\omega},$$

$$\frac{\delta}{\kappa} = \frac{\epsilon}{\nu} = \frac{\theta}{\rho} = \frac{\iota}{\tau} = \frac{\lambda}{\chi} = \frac{\mu}{\phi} = \frac{\hat{\omega}}{\upsilon} = \frac{\psi}{\omega}.$$

These are reducible to eleven independent equations, viz. the seven in the first line and $\frac{\delta}{\theta} = \frac{\iota}{\hat{\omega}} = \frac{\kappa}{\rho} = \frac{\tau}{\upsilon}$ and $\frac{\delta}{\iota} = \frac{\kappa}{\tau}$. The statement that the four simple events are independent is only a concise way of stating that these eleven equations are assumed to hold good. The assumption of these eleven is equivalent to saying that $\delta$, $\epsilon$, &c. are proportional to $xyzs$, $(1 - x)yzs$, &c.

We have taken S to represent a simple event of which the absolute chance is $s$, not to represent the concurrence of A, B, and C; and when eight of the sixteen compound events were struck out as implying the concurrence of the events which we know to be incompatible, we did not make S identical with A, B, and C concurring, but we only say that the cases in which S is accompanied with the absence of A, B, and C, or of any of them, are beyond our universe of observation. The truth of the eleven assumed equations is supposed throughout the problem; for if at any point we were to discard or deny them, all conclusions based on them would fall to the ground.

It may naturally be asked, how comes it that when there were given only the chances of the events A, B, and C, we assumed the independence of only *three* events, which is equivalent to assuming *four* equations; and when an additional datum was given, viz. the chance *m* of the concurrence of A, B, and C, we assumed the independence of *four* events A, B, C, and S, which implies *eleven* equations, whereas we might have expected that one assumed equation less than before would have been requisite? The answer is, that though all the eleven equations have been stated to be assumed only some of them are in the actual working of the problem necessary assumptions. It is sufficient that the eleven equations should be true so far as they affect the relations among the eight contingencies in the compound event represented by V. It will be found that three only out of the eleven give such relations; and upon the assumptions comprised in these last three equations rests the truth of the solution. The three equations are $\dfrac{v}{\omega} = \dfrac{\tau}{\phi} = \dfrac{\rho}{\chi}$, and $\dfrac{\phi}{\omega} = \dfrac{v}{\chi}$. The other eight equations, though not contradictory to the data, are not essential to the solution, and need not have been assumed. If these three conditions had been inserted in the data of the problem, it might have been solved by a simple algebraical process without introducing the subsidiary event S.

This assumption of the independence of the simple events made directly in the solution I have given of the last question is, as I have said, tacitly made in the logical solutions of the questions given in Professor Boole's book. In Proposition I. of Chapter XVII. the events represented by $x$, $y$, &c. are by hypothesis independent. In other words, the equations of condition implied by that independence (in number, 1 if there be 2 events $x$, $y$, 4 if there be 3 events, $2^n - n - 1$ if there be $n$ events) are assumed to subsist among the compound events, which are combinations of the simple events $x$, $y$, &c. The theorem is proved and proveable only on this assumption. This proposition is assumed in Prop. II., and forms the basis of the application of the logical equations to questions of chances. In Prop. II., p. 261, the question is of this nature; given that, whenever it be known that the event which will happen will belong to a certain group of events represented by V, the chance of $x$ happening is $p$, of $y$, $q$, &c.; required the absolute probabilities of $x$, $y$, ... when we have no such previous knowledge. As in the solution in the book, Prop. I. is in the outset assumed with regard to $x$, $y$, ...$m$ the conditions of Prop. 1 are assumed, and one of these is that $x$, $y$, ... are " simple unconditioned events ", which (page 258) implies that they are independent. Consequently, $x$, $y$, ... are in Prop. II. assumed to be independent. How this can be reconciled with Professor Boole's statement with regard to a particular example of the proposition that his reasoning " does not require that the drawings of a white and marble ball should be independent in virtue of the physical constitution of the balls; that the assumption of their independence is indeed involved in the solution, but does not rest upon any prior assumption as to the nature of the balls, and their relations or freedom from relations, of form, colour, structure, &c." (page 262), I am at a loss to understand. It would appear that its being involved in the solution proves that it must rest on a prior assumption, and that the prior assumption in this case is that the simple events are subject to the results of Prop. I.

When additional conditions, that the chance of a combination of events $\phi_1(x, y, ...)$ is $m$, that of $\phi_2(x, y, ...)$ is $n$, and so on, are given, and consequently subsidiary events $s$, $t$, are introduced, the question becomes this :—given that $x$, $y$, ...$s$, $t$, ... are independent events, and that if it be known that the event which will happen will belong to a certain group of events selected out of the whole number of possible combinations, in which $s$ does not happen except in conjunction with $\phi_1(x, y, ...)$, nor $\phi_1(x, y, ...)$ except in conjunction with $s$, and so on with respect to $t$ and $\phi_2(x, y, ...)$, &c., the chances of $x$, $y$, ... are $p$, $q$, ... and of $s$, $t$, ... are $m$, $n$, ... ; required the absolute probabilities of $x$, $y$, ... when we have no such previous knowledge; or more usually, required the probability that out of the same group of events as before the event will be some definite combination of $x$, $y$, ....

The independence of the events $x$, $y$, ... $s$, $t$, ... is, as before, assumed in the assumption of the results of Prop. I. Nevertheless, Professor Boole says (page 264) that the events denoted by *s, t,* &c. whose probabilities are given, have such probabilities not as *independent events*, but as events subject to a certain condition V. He seems throughout to consider V as a condition which does always obtain, and consequently that the chance of any event inconsistent with it is 0, and therefore he ignores the previously assumed independence of the simple events which is inconsistent with such a supposition, instead of considering V as a condition which, if it obtain, the chances of $x, y, \ldots$ are as given in the data of the problem.

I will now take the first problem of Chap. XX., p. 321, which is the question treated of by Mr. Cayley in a paper in the Philosophical Magazine of last October, which elicited an answer from Professor Boole in a succeeding Number of the same Magazine, and work it out in the same manner as I have done a former question on Professor Boole's assumptions. The question is,—the probabilities of two causes $A_1$ and $A_2$ are $c_1$ and $c_2$ respectively; the probability that if $A_1$ happen E will happen is $p_1$, that if $A_2$ happen E will happen is $p_2$. E cannot happen if neither $A_1$ nor $A_2$ happen. Required the probability of E.

I will first, however, examine what result can be arrived at without making any assumption. Let $\xi$ be the chance of $A_1$ and $A_2$ both happening and being followed by E, $\xi'$ that of their both happening but not followed by E, $\eta$ and $\eta'$ the chances of $A_2$ happening without $A_1$, according as it is followed and not followed by E, $\zeta$ and $\zeta'$ those of $A_1$ happening without $A_2$ according as it is followed or not by E, and $\sigma'$ the chance of neither $A_1$ nor $A_2$ happening, and E of course not happening. The data of the problem give the equations

$$\xi + \xi' + \eta + \eta' + \zeta + \zeta' + \sigma' = 1,$$
$$\xi + \xi' + \zeta + \zeta' = c_1,$$
$$\xi + \xi' + \eta + \eta' = c_2,$$
$$\xi + \zeta = c_1 p_1,$$
$$\xi + \eta = c_2 p_2,$$

the chance ($u$) of E happening $= \xi + \eta + \zeta = c_1 p_1 + c_2 p_2 - \xi,$

H H

where $\xi$ is necessarily less than either $c_1 p_1$ or $c_2 p_2$. We can get no further in the solution without further assumptions or data, having only six equations from which to eliminate seven unknown quantities. Without such the question is indeterminate.

Now, to adopt Professor Boole's assumptions, let $x$, $y$, $z$ be the chances of $A_1$, $A_2$, and $E$ respectively, and $s$, $t$, those of two subsidiary events; $x, y, s, t$, are assumed to be mutually independent events; consequently, the chances of the sixteen mutually exclusive contingencies formed by combinations of these four simple events will be

| | | | |
|---|---|---|---|
| $(\delta)$ | $xyst$, | $(\hat{\omega})$ | $x(1-y)(1-s)t$, |
| $(\epsilon)$ | $(1-x)yst$, | $(\rho)$ | $x(1-y)s(1-t)$, |
| $(\theta)$ | $x(1-y)st$, | $(\tau)$ | $xy(1-s)(1-t)$, |
| $(\iota)$ | $xy(1-s)t$, | $(\upsilon)$ | $x(1-y)(1-s)(1-t)$, |
| $(\kappa)$ | $xys(1-t)$, | $(\phi)$ | $(1-x)y(1-s)(1-t)$, |
| $(\lambda)$ | $(1-x)(1-y)st$, | $(\chi)$ | $(1-x)(1-y)s(1-t)$, |
| $(\mu)$ | $(1-x)y(1-s)t$, | $(\psi)$ | $(1-x)(1-y)(1-s)t$, |
| $(\nu)$ | $(1-x)ys(1-t)$, | $(\omega)$ | $(1-x)(1-y)(1-s)(1-t)$. |

The relations among these sixteen events implied by the independence of the four simple events are, as before, eleven in number. As the events represented by $s$ and $t$ in all cases within our range of observation are concomitant with the concurrence of $A_1$ and $E$, and of $A_2$ and $E$ respectively, the events represented by $\epsilon, \theta, \iota, \kappa, \lambda, \nu, \chi, \hat{\omega}, \psi$, must be struck out, being inconsistent with such concomitance, and consequently the aggregate event V comprises only the events $\delta, \mu, \rho, \tau, \upsilon, \phi, \omega$. Of the eleven equations given by the independence of the simple events, only two involve merely terms comprised in V, and consequently those two are the only necessary assumptions. The truth of the remaining nine is immaterial to the questions. The two which affect the terms in V only are

$$\frac{\delta}{\mu} = \frac{\rho}{\omega} \text{ and } \frac{\tau}{\upsilon} = \frac{\phi}{\omega}.$$

As the events represented by $s$ and $xz$ are concomitant, and also those represented by $t$ and $yz$, the event $\delta$ is equivalent to $A_1$, $A_2$ and $E$ all happening, $\mu$ to $A_2$ and $E$ not $A_1$, $\rho$ to $A_1$

E not $A_2$, $\tau$ to $A_1$ $A_2$ not E, $v$ to $A_1$ not $A_2$ or E, $\phi$ to $A_2$ not $A_1$ or E, $\omega$ to neither $A_1$ $A_2$ nor E. Consequently, the two equations assumed by Professor Boole in virtue of the method he employs are

$$\frac{\text{Prob. of } A_1, A_2, \text{ and E all happening}}{\text{Prob. not } A_1, A_2, E} = \frac{\text{Prob. } A_1, \text{ not } A_2, E}{\text{Prob. not } A_1, \text{ not } A_2, \text{ not E,}},$$

and

$$\frac{\text{Prob. } A_1, A_2, \text{ not E}}{\text{Prob. not } A_1, A_2, \text{ not E}} = \frac{\text{Prob. } A_1, \text{ not } A_2, \text{ not E}}{\text{Prob. not } A_1, \text{ not } A_2, \text{ not E}}.$$

These two conditions being assumed, it is easy by common algebra to determine the question; for, besides the six equations given, as I said before, in the data, we have the two

$$\frac{\xi}{\eta} = \frac{\zeta}{\sigma}, \text{ and } \frac{\xi'}{\eta'} = \frac{\zeta'}{\sigma'}.$$

From the first five and these last two it is easy to eliminate $\xi'$, $\eta$, $\eta'$, $\zeta$, $\zeta'$, and $\sigma'$, leaving a quadratic in $\xi$; and in this the value $c_1 p_1 + c_2 p_2 - u$ must be substituted for $\xi$, giving a quadratic to determine $u$ similar to that found by Professor Boole.

The second of these two assumed equations, though perfectly arbitrary, is perhaps not an unreasonable one. It asserts that in those cases in which E does not occur, the relation of independence subsists between $A_1$ and $A_2$; that is, that provided E do not occur, $A_1$ is as likely to happen if $A_2$ happen as if $A_2$ fail. I do not see, however, that is a more reasonable or probable hypothesis than others that might be framed; for instance, than those assumed by Mr. Cayley in his memoir in this Magazine. But the first of these equations appears to me not only arbitrary but eminently anomalous. In the form in which it stands as a relation among the chances of $A_1$, $A_2$ and E, no one, I should think, can contend that it is either deduced from the data of the problem or that the mind by the operation of any law of thought recognizes it as a necessary or most reasonable assumption. Neither can it be said that the mutual inde-

H H 2

pendence of the events $A_1$, $A_2$, and the other two represented by $s$ and $t$ (from which assumed independence the two equations are derived), is either a datum of the problem or a condition necessarily recognized by the mind; the absurdity of this is shown enough by the fact that the latter two are purely imaginary events.

Mr. Cayley's solution is, in fact, as follows : he introduces the subsidiary quantities $\lambda_1$, $\lambda_2$ determined by the equations

$$p_1 = \lambda_1 + (1 - \lambda_1)\lambda_2 c_2$$
$$p_2 = \lambda_2 + (1 - \lambda_2)\lambda_1 c_1,$$

and finds $u$ by the equation

$$u = \lambda_1 c_1 + \lambda_2 c_2 - \lambda_1 \lambda_2 c_1 c_2.$$

In the preceding notation, and according to the meaning which Mr. Cayley attaches to the subsidiary quantities $\lambda_1 \lambda_2$, we have

$$\xi = c_1 c_2 (\lambda_1 + \lambda_2 - \lambda_1 \lambda_2),$$
$$\xi' = c_1 c_2 (1 - \lambda_1)(1 - \lambda_2),$$
$$\eta = c_2 (1 - c_1)\lambda_2,$$
$$\eta' = c_2 (1 - c_1)(1 - \lambda_2),$$
$$\zeta = c_1 (1 - c_2)\lambda_1,$$
$$\zeta' = c_1 (1 - c_2)(1 - \lambda_1),$$
$$\sigma' = (1 - c_1)(1 - c_2);$$

values which, combined with the equations for the determination of $\lambda_1$, $\lambda_2$, satisfy, as they should do, the fundamental system of relations between $\xi$, $\xi'$, $\eta$, $\eta'$, $\zeta$, $\zeta'$, $\sigma'$. But the equations last written down give also

$$\sigma'\xi' = \eta'\zeta'$$
$$\sigma'(\xi + \xi') = (\eta + \eta')(\zeta + \zeta');$$

or, as they may also be written,

$$\frac{\xi'}{\eta'} = \frac{\zeta'}{\sigma'}$$

$$\frac{\xi + \xi'}{\eta + \eta'} = \frac{\zeta + \zeta'}{\sigma'};$$

i.e.,

$$\frac{\text{Prob. } A_1, A_2, \text{ not } E}{\text{Prob. not } A_1, A_2, \text{ not } E} = \frac{\text{Prob. } A_1, \text{ not } A_2, \text{ not } E}{\text{Prob. not } A_1, \text{ not } A_2, \text{ not } E}$$

and

$$\frac{\text{Prob. A}_1, \text{A}_2}{\text{Prob. not A}_1, \text{A}_2} = \frac{\text{Prob. A}_1, \text{not A}_2}{\text{Prob. not A}_1, \text{not A}_2},$$

which are the assumptions made in Mr. Cayley's solution; it is clear that they amount to this, viz. that the events $A_1$, $A_2$ are treated as independent; first, in the case in which E does *not* happen; secondly, in the case where it is not observed whether E does or does not happen.

Though the data of the problem, together with the equations derived from the assumed independence of the simple events, are always enough to determine the unknown quantities $x$, $y$, &c., and consequently, to determine the chances of the compound events represented above by the Greek letters $\delta$, $\epsilon$, &c., there are cases in which the required chance cannot be exactly expressed in a series of the terms $\delta$, $\epsilon$, &c. In these cases, the problem remains indeterminate, notwithstanding the assumptions. Of this nature are Examples 1, 4, 7 of Chapter XVIII. In Ex. 1, for instance, the absolute chances of the four events there represented by $ux$, $u(1-x)$, $(1-u)x$, $(1-u)(1-x)$ may be found, but the chance of the required event cannot be expressed in a series of these chances, for it comprises all cases which come under the event $ux$, but only part, an unknown part, of those which come under $(1-u)(1-x)$.

What, now, is the practical value of Professor Boole's logical method as applied to the theory of chances? In cases determinable by ordinary algebraical processes, his book gives a systematic and uniform method of solving the questions, though very commonly a longer one than we should otherwise use; at least it appears to me that the really determinate problems solved in the book, as 2 and 3 of Chap. XVIII., might be more shortly solved without the logical equations. In these cases the originally assumed independence of the simple events is unnecessary, none of the equations implied thereby consisting wholly of terms comprised in V. The disadvantage of Professor Boole's method in such cases is, that it does not show us whether the problem is really determinate or requires further assumptions,—whether, in fact, the assumptions made are necessary or not. On the other hand, in cases not determinable by ordinary algebra, his system is this; he takes a general indeterminate problem, applies to it particular assumptions not definitely stated in his book, but which may be shown, as I have done, to be implied in his method, and with these assumptions solves it; that is to say, he solves a particular determinate case of an indeterminate problem, while his book may mislead the reader by making him suppose that it is the general problem which is being treated of. The question arises, Is the particular case thus solved a peculiarly valuable one, or one more worthy than any other of being solved? It is clearly not an assumption which must in all cases be true; nor is it one which, without knowing the connexion among the simple events, we can suppose more likely than any other to represent that connexion; for if we examined the assumptions as applied to any particular problem (as has been done with reference to the problem last discussed), we should find them to be such as do not strike us as particularly applicable, as was the case with that problem. If, being in ignorance what system of assumptions ought to be made to render the problem determinate, we were to wish to give a definite answer to the problem, it might be in the following form : ascertain the chance of the required event happening on any one system of assumptions, and the chance of that system representing the true connexion among the simple events, and multiply the values of these chances together; the sum of a series of these products comprising every possible system of assumptions would be the true chance of the event. But Professor Boole's method evidently does not attempt to solve any question of this nature. It would seem that though Professor Boole gives a uniform and eminently elegant method of solving a class of cases of such indeterminate problems, that class is not one of much practical application.

# APPENDIX C

## ON THE POSSIBILITY OF COMBINING TWO OR MORE PROBABILITIES OF THE SAME EVENT, SO AS TO FORM ONE DEFINITE PROBABILITY*

### By the Right Rev. Bishop Terrot

#### (Read 17th March 1856)

(1) The inquiry which, with its results, I propose to lay before the Society, was suggested by the following passage in the very popular Treatise on Logic by Dr. Whately, now Archbishop of Dublin.

" As in the case of two probable premises, the conclusion is not established except upon the supposition of their being *both* true, so in the case of two (and the like holds good for any number) distinct and independent indications of the truth of some proposition, unless *both* of them *fail*, the proposition must be true : we therefore multiply together the fractions indicating the probability of the failure of each —the chances against it—and the result being the total chances against the establishment of the conclusion by these arguments, this fraction being deducted from unity, the remainder gives the probability *for* it.

" *E.g.* A certain book is conjectured to be by such and such an author, partly, 1*st*, from its resemblance in style to his known works; partly, 2*nd*, from its being attributed to him by someone likely to be pretty well informed. Let the probability of the conclusion, as deduced from these arguments by itself, be supposed $\frac{2}{5}$, and in the other case $\frac{3}{7}$; then the *opposite* probabilities will be respectively $\frac{3}{5}$ and $\frac{4}{7}$, which multiplied together give $\frac{12}{35}$ as the probability against the conclusion; *i.e.* the chance that the work may *not* be his, notwithstanding the reasons for believing that it is; and, consequently, the probability in *favour* of the conclusion will be $\frac{23}{35}$, or nearly $\frac{2}{3}$ " (Whately's *Logic*, 8th Ed., p. 211).

* [*Transactions of the Royal Society of Edinburgh*, vol. xxi, 1857.]

(2) Now, this reasoning appears to me erroneous, because it can be so applied as to bring out two inconsistent conclusions. It must be observed, that there is no such generic difference between the chances *for* and *against* the truth of a proposition, as can require or justify any difference in the laws and methods applied to them. A negative can always be turned into an affirmative by a change of verbal expression, without any change of meaning. Thus the chance of not hitting a mark is the same as the chance of missing it. The chance of a life not failing before sixty, is the chance of its continuance up to sixty. The chance that A was not the author of the book, is the chance that someone else was the author.

Let us then take as the proposition whose probability is to be found, the negative—he did not write it—the partial probabilities *for* which are by the data $\frac{3}{5}$ and $\frac{4}{7}$. The opposite probabilities are now $\frac{2}{5}$ and $\frac{3}{7}$, and their product is $\frac{6}{35}$, the probability *against* the conclusion whose probability we are now seeking. Consequently, $1 - \frac{6}{35} = \frac{29}{35}$ is the probability *for* our conclusion, namely, that he did not write the book. But by the former calculation, the probability of the same conclusion was found to be $\frac{12}{35}$: and, as these incompatible results follow from the same principle and method, the principle and method must be erroneous.

(3) The only mathematical attempt at the solution of this problem which I have met with, is in section 15 of the Article Probability, in the *Encyclopaedia Metropolitana*.* It is given there as follows :—

" It is an even chance that A is B, and the same that B is C; and, therefore, 1 to 3 on these grounds alone, that A is C. But other considerations of themselves give an even chance that A is C. What is the resulting degree of evidence (or the probability) that A is C ? " There is a previous solution which I omit, and then the passage proceeds as follows :—" Let us now treat the preceding question as having two contingencies, the compound argument 1 to 3 *for*, and the independent evidence an even chance. We have, therefore, four possible cases.

* [By De Morgan.]

Prob. A is C.

" Argument and Evidence both true   .   $\frac{1}{4} \times \frac{1}{2} = \frac{1}{8}$

Argument false, Evidence true   .     $\frac{3}{4} \times \frac{1}{2} = \frac{3}{8}$

Argument true, Evidence false   .     $\frac{1}{4} \times \frac{1}{2} = \frac{1}{8}$

Argument and Evidence both false     .       $= 0$

" The sum of these is $\frac{5}{8}$ as before (for the resulting probability that A is C). The above generalized is as follows :— Let $a$ and $(1 - a)$ be the probabilities for and against the argument (conclusion from the argument) ; and $\epsilon$ and $(1 - \epsilon)$ be the probabilities from any other source. Then the chance that both are wrong is $(1 - a) \cdot (1 - \epsilon)$, and of the contradictory, namely, that (A is C) follows from the one or the other, is $1 - (1 - a) \cdot (1 - \epsilon) = a + \epsilon - a\epsilon.$"

This is the formula adopted by Whately; and it is open to the same objection, namely, that by applying it we can arrive at two contradictory conclusions. But, further than this, what is the meaning of *Argument true, Evidence true*? The argument and the evidence are here treated as two independent events having respectively the probabilities of $\frac{1}{4}$ and $\frac{1}{2}$; and their coincidence is represented by $\frac{1}{8}$. But nothing corresponding to this goes forward in the mind. The argument merely affords the information, that for every reason for believing that A is C, there are three equivalent reasons for believing that A is not C. This information we are supposed to believe absolutely; there is no question as to the probability of its truth or the probability of its falsehood. The only matter in question is whether A is C, or is not C.

The falsity of the expression $a + \epsilon - a\epsilon$ will be evident, if we give to $a$ and $\epsilon$ the values $\frac{2}{7}$ and $\frac{3}{7}$. Then $a + \epsilon - a\epsilon = \frac{2}{7} + \frac{3}{7} - \frac{6}{49} = \frac{1}{2} + \frac{10}{49}.$ That is to say, while each of the independent probabilities is less than $\frac{1}{2}$, and, therefore in favour of the negative, their compound force is much above $\frac{1}{2}$; and, therefore, in favour of the affirmative. If then we found from internal evidence and external evidence severally, that the chances were against the truth of the proposition that A is C, we ought to conclude from their united force, that the chances are in favour of the proposition. But the human mind is incapable of coming to such a conclusion.

It may be well to notice in passing, that the problem under consideration is altogether different from that of finding the compound force of two identical assertions made by two witnesses, whose veracity, that is, the probability of their speaking the truth, is expressed by $a$ and $\epsilon$. In that problem, we possess among the data the fact, that each witness *makes the same assertion.* But in the problem we have been considering, there is no such *assertion.* Neither the argument nor the evidence assert or deny that A is C. What they give as data, is merely that the reasons for believing that A is C, are in a given ratio to those for believing that A is not C. And as the data of the two problems are of totally different character, the methods to be applied must of course be different. I have mentioned this, because some good mathematicians whom I have consulted, were at first disposed to consider $\dfrac{a\epsilon}{a\epsilon + 1 - a \cdot 1 - \epsilon}$ as the proper expression for the conjoined force of the argument and the evidence.

(4) Let us now consider the Problem under the following form. A, *whose veracity is undoubted, states that, from his knowledge of the facts of the case, the probability of the event* E *is* $\dfrac{p}{q}$. B, *under the same conditions, states, that it is* $\dfrac{r}{s}$. *Supposing the facts known by each to be altogether distinct, what is the proper measure of the expectation formed in a third mind by these two statements ?*

(5) Before attempting to show how a solution of the problem ought to be sought, it may be well to observe, that the mind cannot admit two probabilities of the same event as co-existent probabilities. Thus, if A tells me that the probability of rain tomorrow is $\frac{2}{5}$, and B that it is $\frac{4}{7}$, I cannot admit both of these as probabilities; for that would be equivalent to believing on the authority of A, that it is *less* likely to rain than not, and at the same time to believe on the authority of B, that it is *more* likely to rain than not.

What really takes place is this. The two fractions are received as indications of the effects reasonably produced upon the minds of the informants, by the knowledge of certain facts which they have not communicated to us. The fractions which they give are admitted as true exponents of the results of their respective partial knowledge, no doubt resting either upon their veracity, or upon the accuracy of their inferences. We admit, that each states the probability as he ought, under *his* circumstances : and the question is, how ought we to state it under *our* circumstances, knowing as we do something *more*, and also something *less* than either of our informants.

(6) In attempting to answer this question, I shall have recourse to the ordinary illustration of an urn and balls. Let us suppose that A has seen $p$ white and $q - p$ black balls introduced into an urn, which he believes to have been previously empty. He properly infers that the probability of drawing a white is $\frac{p}{q}$. B, under the same circumstances, has seen $r$ white and $s - r$ black balls introduced, and infers that the probability of drawing a white is $\frac{r}{s}$. If they communicate to each other only their *inferences*, there is an apparent contradiction, and no combination or agreement can take place. But if they communicate the *facts* from which the inferences were deduced, then each knows that the urn contains $p + r$ white, and $q + s - p - r$ black balls, and agree in making the probability of drawing a white $\frac{p + r}{q + s}$. If the number of balls whose introduction has been seen by the two observers be equal, then $\frac{p + r}{q + s} = \frac{p + r}{2q} = \frac{1}{2}\left(\frac{p}{q} + \frac{r}{q}\right) = \frac{1}{2}$, the sum of the several probabilities.

It may be observed that $\frac{p + r}{q + s}$, as the expression of the combined probabilities $\frac{p}{r}$ and $\frac{q}{s}$, is not exposed to the objection of admitting contradictory results, for, if we take the negative as the conclusion whose probability is to be found, then A gives for the probability of the conclusion $1 - \frac{p}{q} = \frac{q - p}{q}$, while B gives $1 - \frac{r}{s} = \frac{s - r}{s}$, therefore the combined probability against the event is $\dfrac{q-p+s-r}{q+s}$.

But the combined probability for the event was $\dfrac{p+r}{q+s}$,

and $\dfrac{p+r}{q+s} + \dfrac{q-p+s-r}{q+s} = \dfrac{q+s}{q+s} = 1$, as it ought to be.

(7) But what we have to consider, is the impression made upon the mind of a third person, who is informed by A that, from his observation, the probability of drawing a white is $\dfrac{p}{q}$, and by B that, from his observation, it is $\dfrac{r}{s}$, and to whom no further information is given, except that the observations were totally distinct. Now as these data give only the ratio of white to black balls at each introduction, there may have been in the first, $p$ white and $q-p$ black, or there may have been $np$ white and $nq - np$ black, where $n$ is any whole number from one to infinity. In like manner, the second may have consisted of $nr$ white and $ns - nr$ black, where $n$ is any number from one to infinity. And one assumed state of the first introduction may have co-existed with any assumed state of the second; and thus assuming that the first contained $p$ white and $q-p$ black, we have the infinite series of probabilities,

$$\frac{p+r}{q+s-p-r}, \frac{p+2r}{q+2s-p-2r}, \cdots \frac{p+nr}{q+ns-p-nr}.$$

Again, assuming that the first contained $2p$ white and $2q - 2p$ black, we have

$$\frac{2p+r}{2q+s-2p-r}, \frac{2p+2r}{2q+2s-2p-2r}, \cdots \frac{2p+nr}{2q+ns-2p-nr},$$

and so on *ad infinitum*.

This infinite series of infinite series I cannot sum. If they can be summed, then their sum divided by the infinite of the second order $n^2$, is the probability required.

In no case, except when $\dfrac{p}{q} = \dfrac{r}{s}$, so far as I can see, can the sum of their sums, or the whole probability, be determinately expressed. When $\dfrac{p}{q} = \dfrac{r}{s}$, the fractions being in their lowest terms, $p = r$ and $q = s$. The two pieces of information are then identical; the same information is given by both observers; and the information, unaffected by the repetition, is absolutely received by the third party; and this is the result, if, in the foregoing series we substitute $p$ for $r$ and $q$ for $s$.

(8) If we revert to the expression (3) given in the *Encyclopaedia Metropolitana*, where the separate probabilities are $a$ and $\epsilon$, and their conjoint force is stated to be $a + \epsilon - a\epsilon$, it would follow that the effect produced by two observers making the same statement as to the probability of an event should be twice the asserted probability *minus* its square. Now in the case of a repetition of the same probability by two observers, it must, I think, be allowed that my result is conformable to that of which we are all conscious. If, for example, the Northampton and the Carlisle Tables both give $\frac{1}{2}$ as the probability that a man of thirty will live to the age of fifty, and are both implicitly believed, we believe that there is an even chance of his living to fifty, and not, as would follow from the expression given in the Encyclopaedia, that the chances are three to one in his favour.

(9) It perhaps deserves to be noticed, that when a second series of observations or experiments is added to one previously admitted, the probability is not increased by the mere preponderance of favourable over unfavourable cases in the second series. To increase the probability, the ratio of favourable to unfavourable cases must be greater in the second series than in the first. For the first received probability is $\dfrac{p}{q}$, and the composite is $\dfrac{p+r}{q+s}$. (6)

Now $\dfrac{p+r}{q+s} > \dfrac{p}{q}$, when $rq > sp$, or $rq - rp > sp - rp$,

or $r(q - p) > p \cdot (s - r)$, or $\dfrac{r}{s-r} > \dfrac{p}{q-p}$.

When the ratios only are given, any conceivable case of the grounds upon which the probabilities are given may be represented by $mp$, $mq$, $nr$, and $ns$. Hence the original probability is $\dfrac{mp}{mq}$, the composite is $\dfrac{mp+nr}{mq+ns}$, and this is greater than $\dfrac{mp}{mq}$, when

$$m^2pq + mnqr > m^2pq + mnps$$
$$\text{or } rq > ps, \text{ as before.}$$

(10) Valid objections may, I think, be made to the last paragraph of the section in the Encyclopaedia already referred to. As this is not long, I quote it entire. " The following theorem will be readily admitted on its own evidence. If any assertion appear neither likely nor unlikely in itself, then any logical argument in its favour, however weak the premises, makes it in some degree more likely than not. In the manner in which writers on Logic apply the calculus of probabilities, this is never the consequence of their suppositions. For what we have called $a$ is their resulting probability of the argument. Suppose, for instance, a writer on logic presumed that the argument from analogy gave $\frac{3}{10}$ to the probability that there is vegetation on the planets, which must be regarded as a thing neither likely nor unlikely in regard of evidence from any other source, he would take $\frac{3}{10}$ to be the probability of this result, that is, *less after an argument in its favour than it was before*. We substitute $\frac{1}{2} + \frac{1}{2} \cdot \frac{3}{10} = \frac{13}{20}$."

This numerical equation is the value of the expression $(a + \epsilon - a\epsilon)$, when $a = \frac{1}{2}$, $\epsilon = \frac{3}{10}$. I have already shown that this expression does not truly represent the composite force of the two probabilities $a$ and $\epsilon$. But farther than this, the argument from analogy, giving $\frac{3}{10}$ as the probability of the affirmative, is an argument, not *in favour of*, but *against* the proposition that there is vegetation in the planets. It implies that for every three reasons for believing that there *is*, there are seven for believing that there *is not*; and, consequently, the effect of the argument ought to be to diminish our disposition to believe the proposition, or, in other words, to diminish its probability.

(11) But it may be worth while to examine whether the fraction $\frac{1}{2}$ be, after all, a true available expression for the probability of an event, which is neither likely nor unlikely to happen, or to have happened, there being no evidence, no reasons for belief, either for or against it.

Probability, as Mr Boole, in his *Laws of Thought*, properly defines it, is " expectation founded upon partial knowledge ". Events, therefore, of which we possess *complete* knowledge, and events of which we possess *no* knowledge, are equally, by the terms of the definition, excluded from the class of probable events, that is to say, of events to which the calculus of probabilities can be applied. If we are *certain* that an event has happened, we totally neglect and are unaffected by any subsequent information, which, but for that certainty, would have given to the event a definite probability expressed by a proper fraction; and never think of looking for a form by which to combine such fraction with the unit expressing the certainty. If, again, we derive from experience or observation a definite probability of any event, such, for example, as the probability for drawing a white ball from an urn, whose contents are given; namely, the fraction whose numerator is the number of white balls, and its denominator the total number of balls contained, we never think of combining this with the $\frac{1}{2}$ which is assumed as the probability when nothing whatever was known, except that the ball drawn must be either black or white. *Complete* knowledge comprehends all previous partial knowledge; and, therefore, all fractional expressions for probability derived from the latter, are virtually contained in the unit, which is the expression adopted for the certainty produced by the former. On the other hand, *partial* knowledge destroys total ignorance, and any inference that may be drawn from it. It comprehends the hypothesis that the event may, and that it may not happen, with a definite probability to each, which do not supplement but supersede the probabilities of $\frac{1}{2}$ previously assumed for each. I cannot conclude without suggesting a doubt, whether $\frac{1}{2}$ be at any time the proper expression for the probability of an event which is " neither likely nor unlikely in regard of evidence ".

It seems more analogous with the practice in other cases to express such probability by the indefinite fraction $\frac{0}{0}$. If this expression be applied to either of the probabilities constituting the compound probability $\dfrac{p+r}{q+s}$, the compound probability will be reduced to the remaining simple probability, for $\dfrac{0+r}{0+s} = \dfrac{r}{s}$. And this agrees with the necessary action of the mind, which takes no note of its original ignorance, after it has arrived at a definite probability from partial knowledge.

(12) Hitherto, I have been speaking of the combined result of two probabilities of the same event, derived from distinct sources of partial knowledge; and I have shown that to obtain a definite result, the mere ratio in such case is insufficient, and that the actual number of favourable and unfavourable cases in each of the data is requisite.

But when the given probabilities are of different events, and the quaesitum is the probability of their joint occurrence, the ratio alone is sufficient, because as factors $\dfrac{mp}{mq}$ and $\dfrac{np}{nq}$ give the same results.

(13) To sum up the propositions proved in the foregoing paper :—

1. If the *ratio only* of equally probable cases, in two or more probabilities for the same event be given, no definite probability can be derived from their composition. (7)

2. If the two given probabilities $\dfrac{p}{q}$, $\dfrac{r}{s}$, indicate not merely the *ratio*, but also the *actual number* of favourable and unfavourable hypotheses or cases, their conjoined force is properly expressed by $\dfrac{p+r}{q+s}$. (6)

3. Under both of these conditions, the second given probability increases or diminishes the force of the first, according as the fraction expressing the second is greater or less than that expressing the first. When the ratios only are given, then the extent of increase or diminution is indefinite. When the actual numbers are given, it is definite. (9)

4. The *à priori* probability derived from absolute ignorance has no effect upon the force of a subsequently admitted probability. (11, 12)

# INDEX